Canadian Nurses and the Law

Second Edition

J.J. Morris, B.A., M.A., LL.B.
Margot J. Ferguson, B.A., M.A., LL.B.
Mary Jane Dykeman, B.A., LL.B.

 Butterworths
Toronto and Vancouver

Canadian Nurses and the Law, Second Edition
© 1999 Butterworths Canada Ltd.
March 1999

The Butterworth Group of Companies

Canada:
75 Clegg Road, MARKHAM, Ontario L6G 1A1
and
1721-808 Nelson St., Box 12148, VANCOUVER, B.C. V6Z 2H2
Australia:
Butterworths Pty Ltd., SYDNEY
Ireland:
Butterworth (Ireland) Ltd., DUBLIN
Malaysia:
Malayan Law Journal Sdn Bhd, KUALA LUMPUR
New Zealand:
Butterworths of New Zealand Ltd., WELLINGTON
Singapore:
Butterworths Asia, SINGAPORE
South Africa:
Butterworth Publishers (Pty.) Ltd., DURBAN
United Kingdom:
Butterworth & Co. (Publishers) Ltd., LONDON
United States:
Michie, CHARLOTTESVILLE, Virginia

Canadian Cataloguing in Publication Data

Morris, John J. (John Joseph), 1952–
    Canadian nurses and the law

2nd ed.
Includes index.
ISBN 0-433-41609-2

1. Nursing — Law and legislation — Canada. I. Ferguson, Margot.
II. Dykeman, Mary Jane. III. Title.

KE2714.N8M67 1999   344.71'0414   C99-930151-9
KF2915.N8M67 1999

Printed and bound in Canada

Cover image supplied by Corel Corporation.

Preface

This second edition of *Canadian Nurses and the Law* represents an acknowledgement that neither the law, nor nursing practice, stays frozen in time. Since the first edition was published in 1991, changes in the Canadian health care system have led nurses into new professional territory. Legal guidelines have been clarified in some areas, but they are more obscure in others. We have attempted to retain the general structure of the first edition, but you will notice that significant updating has been done to reflect the current state of the law.

This edition also represents a collaboration between the original author of the first edition, John Morris, and two new co-authors, Margot Ferguson and Mary Jane Dykeman. Revising your own successful work is a difficult task, let alone helping to revise another writer's successful work, and the new co-authors wish to thank John for graciously encouraging them to participate freely in rewriting his 1991 text. Additionally, Margot and Mary Jane have been the best of friends since their New Brunswick childhood, and they report that this collaboration proved to be an enjoyable experience, despite its inherent potential for tension and hard feelings.

We wish to thank the many people who assisted in the production of this edition. Mary Anne Logan, our product development editor at Butterworths Canada Ltd., was an unfailing source of support and humour through times of frustration. It is safe to say that we would never have seen this project completed without her persistence (and frequent inspirational e-mails). John's colleagues at Borden & Elliot provided ongoing support to the development of this publication; his legal assistant, Julie Ong, has outdone herself in facilitating his busy law practice. Three law students who summered at Borden & Elliot provided the excellent research evident in this book: Jasmine Ghosn, Kristin Taylor and Jill Magazine. Their contribution transformed this book from a good general overview into a valuable technical resource for lawyers as well as nurses.

Each of the authors in turn would like to thank their families for the patience and encouragement that has been essential in getting us through this process. John's wife, Julie Wang-Morris (a publisher in her own right), and his four children (Darcy, Deirdre, Nathan and Peter) have seen him through several publications, and so deserve extra credit for their abiding support. They each demonstrated their love and faith. Margot's husband, Steven Parker, has provided her with exactly the right mixture of humour and level-headed advice, and her daughter, Ellen, has provided the relief of a four-year-old's perspective on life at times when deadlines were closing in. Mary Jane's husband, Peter MacLauchlan, monitored the progress of the book with unfailing good cheer, and even willingly endured constructive exile during the final phases of the revision. We owe our thanks to all of you.

Finally, we would like to acknowledge the many challenges faced by nurses as they balance patient care with the ongoing upheaval in the health sector. Health is a matter that affects every individual, and the contribution and dedication of the nursing profession is without parallel. Based on the numerous changes of designation within the profession, we have used the generic term "nurse" throughout the book, which is intended to capture RNs, RPNs, RNAs and any other titles used in various jurisdictions. We also recognize that the designation "patient" will not please each and every reader (who might favour client, customer, citizen, consumer/survivor, *etc.*). However, we have opted to preserve it, while recognizing that today's patient is no longer a passive recipient of health care.

John J. Morris
Toronto, Ontario
Margot Ferguson
Kingston, Ontario
Mary Jane Dykeman
Toronto, Ontario

March, 1999

Table of Contents

Chapter 3: Professional Status of Nurses

Chapter 9: Nursing Malpractice

Table of Cases

CHAPTER 1

Canadian Health Care Facilities

SYNOPSIS

This chapter sets out the provincial regulation of hospitals and other health care facilities. It discusses the role of hospital boards, by-laws and medical advisory committees, and the necessity of quality assurance programs and accreditation of facilities.

INTRODUCTION

Hospitals provide care to more patients and employ more nurses than any other type of health care facility in Canada. However, recent developments, like the trend toward home-based care, mean that nurses play an increasingly instrumental role in all sectors of health care, including home care, physicians' private offices, community health clinics, public health offices and other facilities.

Nurses occupy a central role in the hospital, both in their numbers and in their functions. Part-time nurses, student nurses and registered nursing assistants further increase the contingent of nurses. Practising nurses, who gain a multitude of experiences within the hospital, often become members of the administrative staff of a hospital and, in some instances, members of the board of directors.

Hospitals are a relatively recent addition to the history of health care in Canada. In the nineteenth century, patients suffering from symptoms that required medical attention received treatment in their homes. Medical treatment tended to be less invasive and more palliative; therefore, the home was in many ways the most appropriate environment for the type of treatment provided. Medicine had not advanced technologically to the extent it has since then, and there was little in the way of large equipment used for the diagnosis and treatment of patients. Family members or an attendant paid directly by the patient provided nursing services in the patient's own home. Hospitals usually consisted of small units that formed a part of a charitable or religious organization and

provided accommodation for patients who were without homes or who
were too poor to afford a private physician.[1]

Patients were also reluctant to be admitted to hospitals, where they
believed that the conditions they would be subjected to and the treatment
they would receive were a poor alternative to the consolation of dying in
their own homes.

> In those days (1867) it was with the greatest difficulty patients could be in-
> duced to go into a hospital. It was the popular belief that if they went in
> they would never come out alive. No records were kept. The clinical ther-
> mometer had not come into use; the patients had to look after themselves;
> fresh air was not thought necessary. Armies of rats disported themselves
> about the wards, instruments were looked after by a man who assisted in
> the operating room and at post-mortems in the dead house. Nothing was
> known of sepsis or antisepsis. Surgeons operated with dirty instruments
> and septic hands and wore coats which had been for years baptized with
> the blood of victims.[2]

Since these hospitals were privately run either by charitable organizations or by religious institutions, there was no regulation by any outside
supervising authority, governmental or otherwise, to ensure reasonable
standards of care and treatment were achieved.

Today, the hospital is at the forefront of modern health care. While
many hospitals continue to have a strong link to their philanthropic and
historical roots, provincial governments are heavily involved in finances
and supervision. This is true of all hospitals whether public or private,
religious or lay. Every hospital must be licensed and approved by a particular government body before it can provide health services.

The hospital community in Canada now consists of a variety of types
of institutions. Statistics Canada draws a distinction between general and
special hospitals.[3] General hospitals provide care to people of all ages
and genders and for all types of diseases. Special hospitals specialize in
the care they provide. Thus there are paediatric hospitals, maternity
hospitals, rehabilitation hospitals and chronic care hospitals. Psychiatric
hospitals and tuberculosis hospitals are in special categories of their own.

Another distinction is that between private and public hospitals.
Private hospitals, also known as proprietary hospitals, are owned by
individuals or private organizations. Although such hospitals are
strongly linked to provincial governments from a supervisory point of

---

[1] See G.H. Agnew, *Canadian Hospitals, 1920 to 1970 — A Dramatic Half Century, passim*
(Toronto: University of Toronto Press, 1974) Ch. 1, "Hospitals of the 1920's".
[2] Dr. F.J. Sheperd, quoted by Agnew, *ibid.*, p. 3.
[3] Statistics Canada, *Hospital Statistics, Preliminary Annual Report 1990-91* (Ottawa: Statistics Canada, 1993).

view, they are not so linked to government from a financial point of view. Only two per cent of Canada's hospital beds are contained in proprietary hospitals.[4]

Public hospitals are non-profit institutions. They range in size from small hospitals of fewer than fifty beds to large, general, teaching hospitals, such as the Manitoba Health Sciences Centre. Most public hospitals, whether small or large, and whether operated by lay, religious or government bodies, are corporations. Most public hospitals are also general hospitals. All public hospitals are heavily dependent on government funding.

The size and nature of hospitals in Canada has prompted the enactment of many laws for their regulation and supervision. Although some of these laws apply only to proprietary hospitals, most of them are directed toward the public general hospital.

PROVINCIAL REGULATION

Provincial governments received the responsibility for the "establishment, maintenance and management of hospitals" when the *British North America Act* (now the *Constitution Act*) came into force in 1867.[5]

The provincial governments spend vast sums of money for the operation of hospitals. In order to oversee their investment, provinces have enacted legislation that sets out certain standards and requirements for the operation of public hospitals.[6] These statutes may provide for grants and loans to approved hospitals. Since the public hospital is normally a non-profit corporation, the legislation requires the appointment of a board of directors and gives it the overall responsibility for administering the hospital. The legislation may provide for the mandatory acceptance of a patient by a hospital where a physician has admitted that patient, even if that patient is unable to pay.[7] It may stipulate that hospitals provide certain conditions for the training of health practitioners, including "student nurses".[8] It may provide for a limitation period after which no

---

[4] *Ibid.*

[5] *Constitution Act*, 1867 (U.K.), c. 3, s. 91(7).

[6] Alberta: *Hospitals Act*, R.S.A. 1980, c. H.11; British Columbia: *Hospital Act*, R.S.B.C. 1996, c. 200; Manitoba: *The Hospitals Act*, R.S.M. 1987, c. H.120; New Brunswick: *Public Hospitals Act*, R.S.N.B. 1973, c. P-23; Newfoundland: *The Hospitals Act* R.S.N. 1990, c. H.9; Nova Scotia: *Hospitals Act*, R.S.N.S. 1989, c. 208; Ontario: *Public Hospitals Act*, R.S.O. 1990, c. P.40; Prince Edward Island: *Hospitals Act*, R.S.P.E.I. 1988, c. H.10; Quebec: *Health Services and Social Services Act*, R.S.Q. 1977, c. S-5; Saskatchewan: *The Hospital Standards Act*, R.S.S. 1978, c. H.10.

[7] For example, *Public Hospitals Act*, R.S.O. 1990, c. P.40, s. 20.

[8] For example, *The Hospital Standards Regulations, 1980*, Sask. Reg. 331/79, ss. 93-96.

lawsuit can be started against the hospital or any of its servants or agents.[9] Physicians may be appointed to the staff of a hospital, or removed, according to procedures set out in the legislation and may be provided with further rights of appeal to a provincial tribunal and to the courts.

Regulations have been passed in every province which relate to such matters as the management and administration of the hospitals, funding for capital, and operating expenses, classification of hospitals and the establishment of hospital districts and areas.

REGIONAL HEALTH AUTHORITIES (RHAs)

The much publicized decline in federal funding for health care has resulted in provincial initiatives to reform the health system. Some provinces have moved toward regionalization: the transfer of responsibility for planning and allocating health care resources from a central government to a smaller local body.[10] Regionalization aims to effectively implement primary health care, to ensure essential health services are available to all residents, to respond to local needs related to the delivery of health care services, and to improve the management and redistribution of health care resources.[11] Several provinces (*e.g.*, Alberta, British Columbia, New Brunswick, Nova Scotia, Prince Edward Island, Quebec, Saskatchewan) have established some form of Regional Health Authority to carry out those objectives.

Saskatchewan is often cited as being the province furthest along the path of regionalization. District health boards receive funding for some services (*e.g.*, supportive and non-primary acute care) based on a variety of characteristics in the population, ranging from age and gender to premature death rates and whether seniors are living alone or with their families and friends. District boards then distribute the funding to the services based on their community needs assessments.[12]

Nurses are numerically the largest group of health care providers, and therefore such reforms have a dramatic impact upon the profession. "RHAs [Regional Health Authorities] are being instructed to focus on reducing hospital care and developing more community services ... they may also look at ways to privatize services or introduce measures to increase competition between providers."[13] Almost every move that an

---

[9]   For example, *Public Hospitals Act*, R.S.O. 1990, c. P.40, s. 31.
[10] S. Vail, "The Move to Regionalization", (1995) 91 (No. 8) *The Canadian Nurse* 60, at 60.
[11] *Ibid.*
[12] S. Vail, "Moving to a Needs-Based System" (1996) 92 (No. 7) *The Canadian Nurse* 60.
[13] *Ibid.*

RHA makes is bound to have implications for the nurses in the region. See the "Current Issues" section at the end of this chapter for more on the implications of regionalization for nurses.

HOSPITAL BOARDS

A board of governors or trustees or a board of management usually holds the ultimate authority for the administration of a public hospital in instances where a regional authority does not exist. The board is composed of members of the community and, in some cases, members of the hospital staff who serve on a voluntary basis. For the most part, the members of the board are lay persons who have no medical training. The board is responsible for the actions of the hospital entity that, under public hospital legislation, is usually a non-profit corporation.

The notion of a board of directors of the corporation has its roots in the early formation of hospitals. Early hospital institutions were established as a result of humanitarian concern on the part of community leaders who raised funds for establishing and maintaining hospitals that functioned as charities for the poor.[14] In modern hospitals, the board has a wide array of legal duties and obligations that it must perform in order to comply with the governing legislation. Among the duties and obligations that a board may be required to carry out under provincial legislation are the following:

1.   To develop and implement an accident prevention policy within a hospital;
2.   To appoint an "administrator" responsible to the board and who is charged with administering the hospital in accordance with provincial legislation and the by-laws of the hospital;
3.   To pass by-laws for the internal administration and management of the hospital, including by-laws regulating the activities of the health care staff (*i.e.*, the doctors and nurses), and the review of these by-laws at regular intervals;
4.   To arrange regular meetings of medical staff;
5.   To assure that all orders for treatment are in writing and signed by the attending physician and that upon admission of the patient, proper records are prepared, maintained and kept confidential;
6.   To assure that written consents are obtained in respect of certain medical procedures;
7.   To install an accounting system;

---

[14]   G.H. Agnew, *supra*, note 1, p. 3.

8.   To designate hospital wards as standard, private and semi-private;
9.   To allocate "gift" revenues for the specific purposes for which the gifts were made and to apply other revenues to projects that increase the productivity of the establishment; and,
10.   To educate and train nurses and other hospital personnel.

In addition to duties imposed directly upon the board of the hospital, provincial legislation sometimes sets out a number of other duties which are designed to meet a minimum standard for the provision of hospital and medical services. As you will see in Chapter 9, "Nursing Malpractice", where minimum standards set out in the legislation are not met, and harm results to a patient, there is a risk that the hospital and any health care workers involved could be legally liable for the damage.

HOSPITAL BY-LAWS

A set of by-laws regulates the activities of the board of directors in governing the hospital. Provincial statutes regulating public hospitals may specifically require the board of the hospital to pass by-laws that govern the organization, management and operation of the hospital that it owns and operates.[15] These by-laws are supposed to conform with guidelines set by the Minister responsible for the operations of hospitals in the province or with general by-laws recommended by the Canadian Hospital Association or its provincial affiliate.

The by-laws passed by the board form the "constitution" of the hospital corporation. All activities by the board or by anyone employed by the corporation must conform to the by-laws in order to be valid. The by-laws usually state how the members of the board of directors are to be elected or appointed, what duties they will have, how these duties are to be carried out and when meetings will take place. The by-laws cover basic financial aspects of the corporation's activities such as its banking, the maintenance of books and records, the appointment of an auditor for the corporation and the appointment of a treasurer.

The by-laws usually also regulate the appointment and supervision of medical staff, classes of medical staff, organization of the medical staff, and the organization of various departments throughout the hospital. In doing so, they must conform to any other applicable legislation. By-laws will also provide for the establishment of such committees as the Medical Advisory Committee, Credentials Committee,

---

[15]   For example, *Hospitals Act*, R.S.A. 1980, c. H.11, s. 28 [am. 1996, c. 22, s. 1].

Medical Records Committee, Infection Control Committee, Medical Audit Committee and Utilization Committee.

Hospital by-laws must conform to any regulations prescribed under the public hospital legislation and they may also be subject to the approval of the Minister.[16]

MEDICAL ADVISORY COMMITTEE

Most provinces have legislation that provides for the establishment of a medical advisory committee in a hospital. Various titles for this body are used in each province: "Medical Advisory Committee", "Medical Staff Review Committee", "Hospital Standards Committee" or "Advisory Management Committee". The medical advisory committee is primarily composed of staff physicians. It is established by the board under the by-laws and it is charged with advising the board on medical issues. Since the majority of the board is often lay members, and since the board is in the position of making decisions that are often of a medical nature, the medical advisory committee plays an important role. In some instances, the board may authorize the medical advisory committee to reach and implement decisions of a medical nature without consultation with the board. In other instances, the board considers recommendations made by the medical advisory committee, but reaches the ultimate decision itself.

Provincial legislation may stipulate that the medical advisory committee can only make recommendations about certain subject matters (*e.g.*, the appointment of medical staff to the hospital) and that the ultimate decision must be left up to the board. In cases where the medical advisory committee has purported to decide an issue that must be decided by the board, the decision is invalid.[17] If a board relies too much upon the medical advisory committee and simply adopts a recommendation as if it were a decision, without considering the issue on its own merits, that

---

[16] For example, *Public Hospitals Act*, R.S.O. 1990, c. P.40, s. 9(1). In 1989, the Ontario government amended its hospital management regulation to require the participation of staff nurses and nurse managers in public hospital committees: O. Reg. 83/89. Following enactment of the regulation, the Ontario Nurses' Association brought an application to a judge for enforcement of nurses' rights at a particular hospital. The hospital had provided for the election of nurses to two budget committees, but not to a "fiscal advisory board"as required by the legislation. The court held that the nurses were entitled to be elected to a fiscal advisory committee which would have direct access to the board of the hospital: *O.N.A. v. Toronto Hospital* (1989), 70 O.R. (2d) 389 (H.C.).

[17] *Haber v. Wellesley Hospital* (1986), 54 O.R. (2d) 16, 12 O.A.C. 384, 10 C.C.E.L. 52, 25 D.L.R. (4th) 439 (Div. Ct.).

may render the decision of the board invalid as well.[18] The principle that cannot be compromised is that the board of a hospital bears the ultimate responsibility and authority for any activity carried out by the hospital through its medical staff and employees. Other committees or individuals within the hospital may have considerable influence in guiding the activities of a hospital, but no other entity within the hospital can supersede the authority of the board.

QUALITY ASSURANCE

Aside from its day-to-day management of the hospital, the board of a hospital is also legally responsible for ensuring that the medical care and treatment provided to patients in the hospital meets an acceptable standard. In many cases, health care professionals administering treatment will be responsible for delivering the appropriate standard of medical care. If they fail to provide the appropriate standard of treatment, it may result in disciplinary measures against the health care personnel. If the patient suffers harm, it may result in civil or criminal proceedings. The health care professional has the primary responsibility for providing acceptable care. Still, the board of the hospital can also bear direct responsibility if the hospital fails to make certain that safeguards are employed to ensure appropriate standards of treatment are provided. The responsibility of a hospital in these circumstances is discussed further in Chapter 9, "Nursing Malpractice".

In a number of provinces, the provincial legislation that governs the operation and management of hospitals within the province has set guidelines and minimum requirements concerning many aspects of care and treatment within a hospital. It is the responsibility of the board of a hospital, through management and health care personnel, to ensure that the hospital meets these requirements.

Where governments have enacted detailed legislation, the guidelines are mandatory and any departure from the requirements contained in the legislation may be grounds for civil liability against the hospital and any members of its staff who do not comply with the legislation.

Minimum standards and practices in respect of patient treatment may include requirements to:

---

[18] *Geddes v. Metropolitan Toronto (Municipality) Commrs. of Police*, [1973] 1 O.R. 199, 30 D.L.R. (3d) 547; affd. (1974), 1 O.R. (2d) 591n, 41 D.L.R, (3d) 175 (C.A.).

- admit and discharge patients in a hospital, determine which staff members have the power to admit and discharge patients, and the admission and discharge procedure which is to be followed.[19]
- prepare and maintain hospital records and determine the types of records to be compiled by whom, the time periods for retention of hospital records, the conditions for access to medical records and the considerations of confidentiality.[20]
- determine prerequisites for surgical care including the execution by the patient of a written consent, the provision of mandatory work-ups prior to surgery and the administration of anaesthesia, and determine the necessity of assistance and consultation in respect of certain surgical procedures.[21]
- perform pathological examinations on certain types of tissue removed during surgery.[22]
- perform autopsies, ensure notification of the Coroner, and provide for the storage and removal of corpses.[23]
- treat and isolate patients suffering from infectious diseases.[24]
- set guidelines and restrictions for the role of health care personnel in the hospital including physicians, nurses, dentists and radiologists.[25]

In some provinces, the quality and quantity of the nursing staff of the hospital has warranted special regulation. In Prince Edward Island, a hospital must have on duty:

> (a) during the period from midnight until eight o'clock in the forenoon, at least one registered nurse for each 50 patients or fraction thereof; and
> (b) during the period from eight o'clock in the forenoon until midnight, at least one registered nurse for *each* 35 patients or fraction thereof.[26]

This is a minimum requirement and does not relieve the hospital from the responsibility of always having sufficient nursing staff on duty to provide nursing care to every patient in the hospital as is required for the patients' proper care and treatment.[27]

---

[19] For example, *Operation of Approved Hospitals Regulation*, Alta. Reg. 247/90 (hereinafter, "Alta. Reg. 247/90").

[20] For example, N.B. Reg. 92-84, ss. 20-24.

[21] For example, R.R.P.E.I., c. H.10.

[22] For example, N.S. Reg. 16/79, s. 11.

[23] For example, Alta. Reg. 247/90.

[24] For example, *The Hospital Standards Regulations, 1980*, Sask. Reg. 331/79, ss. 60-64.

[25] *Ibid., passim.*

[26] *Hospital Management Regulations*, R.R.P.E.I., c. H.10.

[27] *Ibid.*, s. 16(1).

In Saskatchewan, a hospital must ensure that there is at least one registered nurse on duty on each shift and is required to employ, regardless of
the size of the hospital, at least three full-time registered nurses. One of
whom must be appointed the "Director of Nursing".[28]

In Alberta, the regulations passed following the provincial Hospitals
Act provide:

> The nurse in charge of an operating room shall be a graduate nurse with
> special training in operating room management or equivalent experience.[29]

If a nurse or a hospital fails to comply with minimum standards set
out in the legislation, it will result not only in a breach of the legislation,
but possibly in some form of legal liability if a patient suffers harm.

Most provincial legislation provides for inspections to be carried out
by inspectors appointed by the Minister responsible for hospitals within
the province. These inspectors are to ensure that the hospital is meeting
the requirements set out in the legislation and that the care and treatment
being provided by a hospital and its staff is otherwise satisfactory.

CANADIAN COUNCIL ON HOSPITAL ACCREDITATION (CCHA)

Traditionally, in Canada, the most intense scrutiny of the standards of
health care at hospitals has been carried out by a private agency called
the Canadian Council on Hospital Accreditation (CCHA). This organization represents five major health organizations: the Canadian Hospital
Association, the Canadian Medical Association, the Royal College of
Physicians and Surgeons of Canada, l'Association des Médecins de
Langue Française du Canada, and the Canadian Nurses Association.

The CCHA publishes, on an annual basis, standards for accreditation
of health care facilities in Canada. The vast majority of hospitals in Canada have been accredited. Non-accredited hospitals tend to be smaller
hospitals in rural and outlying areas.[30] Accreditation is voluntary. Although no province requires that a hospital be accredited, the accreditation process and any report on the hospital by the CCHA will carry considerable weight in a provincial government's own evaluation of a hospital's performance.

In Alberta, a regulation passed under the *Hospitals Act* specifically
provides that each hospital shall "strive to meet the standards for ac-

[28] *The Hospital Standards Regulations, 1980*, Sask. Reg. 331/79, s. 11(3).
[29] *Operation of Approved Hospitals Regulations*, Alta. Reg. 247/90.
[30] L. Soderstrom, *The Canadian Health System* (London: Croom Helm, 1983), p. 32.

creditation" established by the CCHA.[31] In Nova Scotia, the equivalent regulation stipulates that a hospital must forward any report prepared by the CCHA in relation to the hospital to the Minister.[32]

In order to meet the accreditation standards, hospitals are surveyed by "physician-surveyors" appointed by the CCHA. The physician-surveyor prepares a report, after which the CCHA notifies the hospital of deficiencies found and of its decision whether to confer accreditation on the hospital.[33] The CCHA revises its standards every year. The survey will result in an examination of all elements of the administration, care and treatment within the hospital. One of the areas examined is "nursing services". A hospital must meet certain standards in respect of the provision of nursing services, including goals and objectives, the organization and administration of the nursing staff, direction and staffing practices, facilities, equipment and supplies, policies and procedures, care program, education and quality assurance.[34]

OTHER HEALTH CARE INSTITUTIONS

Although the focus of this chapter is the hospital, in particular the public hospital, nurses play an increasingly instrumental role in all sectors of health care. Some health services are now being privatized while other services receive often-decreasing levels of funding from government and are now provided in a community or home-based setting. Nurses continue to play a pivotal role in doctors' offices and increasingly in our community health clinics. Some of these clinics provide primary medical services to individuals, such as alcoholism and drug abuse clinics, communicable disease control clinics, non-hospital rehabilitation centres, special cancer detection programs and community mental health programs. Others provide counselling and educational services, such as environmental health and occupational health services, and the counselling of expectant mothers or school children. At the centre of these services is the clinical or public health nurse. Nurses may also work for voluntary organizations such as the Canadian Paraplegic Association, the Canadian National Institute for the Blind or the Society for Crippled Children and Adults. Nurses also engage in home care nursing through such bodies as the Victorian Order of Nurses. Various provinces have enacted legislation that regulates the provision of health care in these areas.

---

[31] Alta. Reg. 247/90, s. 33.
[32] N.S. Reg. 16/79, s. 9.
[33] See L. Soderstrom, *supra*, note 30, p. 32.
[34] See *Standards for Accreditation of Canadian Health Care Facilities, 1985* (Toronto: Canadian Council on Hospital Accreditation, 1984).

One institution that deserves special mention is the nursing home. Most nursing homes are proprietary institutions with elderly residents. Although historically they were not closely controlled, many are now licensed or approved by a government body and are subject to special legislation.

Residents of nursing homes may require both personal care, (*e.g.* assistance in feeding, washing and clothing themselves), and the type of health care that can only be provided by a qualified professional such as a physician or nurse. More professional health care is provided in nursing homes than in homes for the aged, but not as much as is provided in chronic care hospitals.

It is obvious from the vantage point of the late 1990s that health care is going places never thought possible. The introduction of telemedicine holds promise,[35] but also requires that nurses and other health professionals adapt to new technology that may render old roles obsolete. The final report of the National Forum on Health[36] (established by the federal government in 1994) was released in 1997 and its recommendations may give a sense of some future trends in Canadian health care that are likely. The report recommends that home care and pharmaceuticals be made a fundamental part of the publically funded system, that a comprehensive home care system with a single point of entry be funded by reallocated savings from the reductions made in the institutional area, and that primary care be reformed in order to allow for a range of prevention and treatment services provided by a multidisciplinary team. It is clear from the report that while the first movements toward these objectives have only recently been made, the provision of health care has entered a new, uncharted realm.

CURRENT ISSUES: REGIONALIZATION

In all but Ontario, responsibility for health care planning has been transferred to regional health authorities (RHAs) and away from centralized provincial government. The reasoning behind this shift is that more effective planning and efficient delivery of health care can be achieved by local authorities than by a distant, bureaucratic regime. While it is still too early to tell whether this strategy will meet its objective, the implications for nurses are far-reaching. Nurses are the largest group of health care providers and

---

[35] See for example, "Telemedicine: Reengineering Health Care Access and Delivery in a Wired World", Discussion Paper, New Brunswick: Health and Community Services, January 1997.

[36] *Canada Health Action: Building on the Legacy* (Ottawa: Public Works and Government Service, 1997).

are, therefore, profoundly affected by any decision made by their RHA, but they are effectively excluded from RHA board membership in many jurisdictions. They are excluded because it is perceived that a conflict of interest might exist if the RHA board is ever called to make a decision in the interest of the RHA that might affect their employment or that of other nurses. Some advocates claim that a blanket exclusion of this type serves little purpose, and that the potential loss of knowledge and experience to the RHA that results from excluding health care providers could be avoided if RHAs were structured in a way that precluded issues from being decided by any member with a potential conflict of interest.

CURRENT ISSUES: MANAGED CARE

Managed care is a term frequently heard in the same sentence as "health reform". It is an idea that has not yet gained a strong foothold in Canada, but it is a common practice in the United States. At its most basic level, managed care refers to any arrangement where a purchaser (such as a government or an insurer) attempts to influence the price, volume and quality of health care supplied. It also involves the use of capitation payments, which give health providers a lump sum to provide all health services to the people who enroll with them.[37] Flood, in "Conflicts Between Professional Interests," identifies two main problems with capitation from the point of view of nurses: cream skimming (where facilities only accept the most desirable patients to be enrolled and desirability is defined as those patients least likely to require health care services) and provider moral hazard (where the quality of health services is cut below adequate levels in order to retain profitability). She cites the case of a U.S. Health Maintenance Organization that proposed a contract to nurses in Southern California that would pay them bonuses if the overall costs of their facilities fall. It is easy to see how this sort of incentive might lead to decreased health care standards, and, therefore it is important for nurses and other health care providers to insist upon clear, fair guidelines if the model of managed care becomes commonplace.

---

[37] C. Flood, "Conflicts Between Professional Interests, the Public Interest, and Patients' Interests in an Era of Reform: Nova Scotia Registered Nurses" (1997), 5 Health Law Journal 27.

Relevant Legislation

ALBERTA

Health Facilities Review Committee Act, R.S.A. 1980, c. H-4

Health Statutes Amendment Act, 1996, c. 22

Health Statutes Amendment Act, 1998, 2nd session, 24th Legislature, Bill 37, second reading April 6, 1998.

Hospitals Act, R.S.A. 1980, c. H-11
　Hospital Districts Regulations, Alta. Reg. 243/90
　Hospitalization Benefits Regulations, Alta. Reg. 244/90
　Operation of Approved Hospitals Regulations, Alta. Reg. 247/90

Nursing Homes Act, S.A. 1985, c. N-14.1 (substantially am. by S.A. 1996, c. 22)
　Nursing Homes General Regulation, Alta. Reg. 232/85
　Nursing Homes Operation Regulation, Alta. Reg. 258/85

Public Health Act, S.A. 1984, c. P-27.1 (and *Public Health Amendment Act, 1996*, C-31, not yet proclaimed in force)
　Co-ordinated Home Care Program Regulation, Alta. Reg. 239/85

BRITISH COLUMBIA

Community Care Facility Act, R.S.B.C. 1996, c. 60
　Adult Care Regulations, B.C. Reg. 536/80

Hospital Act, R.S.B.C. 1996, c. 200
　Hospital Act Regulations, B.C. Reg. 289/73

Hospital Districts Act, R.S.B.C. 1996, c. 202

MANITOBA

The Elderly and Infirm Persons' Housing Act, R.S.M. 1987, c. E20
　Application for Grants Regulation, Man. Reg. 311/88

The Health Services Act, R.S.M. 1987, c. H30
　Medical Nursing Unit Districts, Hospital Districts and Hospital Areas Regulation, Man. Reg. 455/88

The Hospitals Act, R.S.M. 1987, c. H120
  Hospital Standards Regulation, Man. Reg. 453/88

The Private Hospitals Act, R.S.M. 1987, c. P130
  Private Hospitals Regulation, Man. Reg. 58/93

NEW BRUNSWICK

Hospital Act, R.S.N.B. 1992, c. H-6.1
  General Regulation, N.B. Reg. 92-84.

Hospital Services Act, R.S.N.B. 1973, c. H-9
  General Regulation, N.B. Reg. 84-167

Nursing Homes Act, S.N.B. 1982, c. N-11
  General Regulation, N.B. Reg. 85-187

NEWFOUNDLAND

The Homes for Special Care Act, R.S.N. 1990, c. H-5

The Hospitals Act, R.S.N. 1990, c. H-9

NORTHWEST TERRITORIES

Medical Care Act, R.S.N.W.T. 1988, c. M-8

NOVA SCOTIA

Homes for Special Care Act, R.S.N.S. 1989, c. 203
  General Regulations, N.S. Reg. 127/77

Hospitals Act, R.S.N.S. 1989, c. 208
  General Regulations, N.S. Reg. 16/79

ONTARIO

Homes for the Aged and Rest Homes Act, R.S.O. 1990, c. H.13
  General Regulation, R.R.O. 1990, Reg. 637

Homes for Retarded Persons Act, R.S.O. 1990, c. H.11
  General Regulation, R.R.O. 1990, Reg. 635

Homes for Special Care Act, R.S.O. 1990, c. H.12
  General Regulation, R.R.O. 1990, Reg. 636

Nursing Homes Act, R.S.O. 1990, c. N.7
   General Regulation, R.R.O. 1990, Reg. 832

Private Hospitals Act, R.S.O. 1990, c. P.24
   General Regulation, R.R.O. 1990, Reg. 937
Public Hospitals Act, R.S.O. 1990, c. P.40
   Hospital Management Regulations, R.R.O. 1990, Reg. 965

PRINCE EDWARD ISLAND

Hospitals Act, R.S.P.E.I. 1988, c. H-10
   Hospital Management Regulations, R.R.P.E.I., c. H-10

QUEBEC

Health Services and Social Services Act, R.S.Q. 1977, c. S-4.2
   *Hospital Centres (Appointment and Remuneration of Directors of Profes-
   sional Services and Heads of Community Health Departments) Regulation*,
   O.C. 2351-84
   Organization and Management of Establishments Regulation, O.C. 1320-84

SASKATCHEWAN

The Hospital Standards Act, R.S.S. 1978, c. H-10
   The Hospital Standards Regulations, 1980, Sask. Reg. 331/79

The Housing and Special-care Homes Act, R.S.S. 1978, c. H-13
   The Housing and Special-care Homes Regulations, Sask. Reg. 34/66

YUKON

Health Act, S.Y. 1989-90, c. 36

Hospital Act, S.Y. 1989-90, c. 13

Hospital Insurance Services Act, R.S.Y. 1986, c. 85

CHAPTER 2

Canadian Health Insurance

SYNOPSIS

This chapter provides an historical overview of health insurance. It outlines the role of the federal government in providing transfer payments to the provinces, which have responsibility under the *Canadian Charter of Rights and Freedoms*[1] for health matters.

INTRODUCTION

Prior to the advent of health care insurance, most patients in Canada were responsible for the cost of their own health care. Broadly speaking, this involved the cost of medical services received from health professionals, the use of hospitals and other health care facilities and the expense of medication. To many patients, the cost of such medical treatment was not inconsiderable and, consequently, patients were burdened with substantial and often unexpected expenses for medical treatment at times when they were least able to afford it. For lower income groups in the population, even elementary health care was beyond their means; individuals would be forced to forego very basic treatment simply as a result of financial constraint. In some instances, physicians, institutions and other health care professionals would be put in the position of having to provide treatment to individuals without fair remuneration for their services.

An insurance mechanism established by law for the payment of services is especially appropriate in the field of health care. Collectively, it is possible for society to pay for services which individuals cannot afford. This is the theoretical basis for all insurance. Society is able to pool its resources in such a way that individuals who are ill will not be met suddenly with unexpected and substantial costs. Rather, it will participate in a system where each individual contributes to a fund that is available to him or her in time of need. As a contributor to the fund, each patient has

---

[1] Part I of the *Constitution Act, 1982*, being Schedule B to the *Canada Act, 1982* (U.K.), 1982, c. 11 (hereinafter "the *Charter*").

an entitlement to draw from the fund for the payment of health services as required. Certain individuals draw from the fund on a frequent basis, while others may never place any significant reliance on it. The essential benefit is the assurance to each individual that should health care services be required, the collective resources of other members of society will be available to underwrite the costs of that individual's care.

The introduction of government assistance and regulation in the funding of health care in Canada began in 1948, when the federal government introduced a program of National Health Grants which provided funding for a wide variety of provincial health services including health planning, public health measures, hospital construction and professional medical training.[2] These were areas in which, generally speaking, the provincial governments exercised constitutional authority for health care.[3] However, there was still no comprehensive, government-sponsored plan to assist individual patients in paying for the cost of health care services.

With the introduction of these grants to the provinces, several provinces began to establish government-sponsored hospital and medical insurance plans. Over time, the federal and provincial governments combined to form a health insurance scheme in Canada that is available to all residents in all provinces.

CANADA HEALTH ACT

Government health insurance in Canada is regulated by the federal *Canada Health Act* (hereinafter "CHA")[4] in conjunction with individual legislation from the various provinces. The preamble to the CHA specifically recognizes the following conditions and objects for the legislation:

- that Canadians, through their system of insured health services, have made outstanding progress in treating sickness and alleviating the consequences of disease and disability among all income groups;
- that Canadians can achieve further improvements in their well-being through combining individual lifestyles that emphasize fitness, prevention of disease and health promotion with collective action against the social, environmental and occupational causes of disease, and that they desire a system of health services that will

---

[2] T. G. Fain (ed.), "National Health Insurance" in *Public Documents Series* (New York: R.R. Bowker Co., 1977), p. 188.

[3] *Constitution Act*, 1867 (U.K.), c. 3, s, 91(7).

[4] *Canada Health Act*, R.S.C. 1985, c. C-6 (hereinafter "CHA").

promote such physical and mental health and protection against disease;
* that future improvements in health will require the co-operative partnership of governments, health professionals, voluntary organizations and individual Canadians;
* that continued access to quality health care without financial or other barriers will be critical to maintaining and improving the health and well-being of Canadians.

The CHA establishes a system to provide federal funding assistance to the provinces for the payment of insured services in the health care system.

In order to qualify for federal funding, provinces must meet certain conditions stipulated by the federal government. Under the federal legislation, the term "insured health services"is defined as:

> hospital services, physician services and surgical-dental services provided to insured persons, but does not include any health services that a person is entitled to and eligible for under any other Act of Parliament or under any Act of the legislature of a province that relates to workers' compensation.[5]

The legislation commits the federal government to sharing the cost of a variety of insured health services that the federal government does not otherwise fund and that are not otherwise funded by the province. For example, the federal government, as part of its constitutional responsibility, provides health care services to war veterans. Therefore, there is no need for a qualified war veteran to resort to the government-sponsored health care insurance system in the various provinces because the war veteran is entitled already to medical and hospital treatment funded directly by the federal government. Another exception where funding will not be provided under the CHA is health care services provided to victims of industrial accidents under provincial workers' compensation legislation.

In order to receive the federal contribution for insured services under the CHA, the provincial insurance scheme must meet certain guidelines outlined below.

1. Public Administration

It is a requirement that all provincial health care insurance plans be administered and operated on a non-profit basis by a public authority, ap-

---

[5]   *Ibid.*, s. 2.

pointed or designated by the government of the province.[6] The public authority's accounts and financial transactions are subject to audit in a manner similar to any branch of the provincial government.

2. Comprehensiveness

The health care plan of the province must insure all insured health services provided by hospitals, medical practitioners, and where applicable, similar or additional services rendered by other health care practitioners.[7] This is an area that, in recent years, has been subject to controversy. The cost of health care in Canada correlates directly to the comprehensiveness of service. Some provinces have "de-listed" treatments considered non-essential; these treatments are not covered by the provincial health insurance plan. Variation of coverage of treatment from province to province has an impact on universality, another principle of Canada's national health insurance. On the other hand, there are those who argue that there must be some limits on the types of services offered. They cite the experience of other jurisdictions in which controversial, experimental, highly expensive, or trivial treatments are not funded.[8] A "hospital" is defined in the CHA to include "any facility ... that provides hospital care, including acute, rehabilitative or chronic care".[9] However, it does not include hospitals or institutions "primarily for the mentally disordered" or facilities that provide nursing-home care, intermediate care, adult residential care or comparable services for children.

The term "hospital services" is defined in the legislation and designates a list of services to be provided to in-patients or out-patients of a hospital if the services are medically necessary for the purposes of maintaining health, preventing disease or diagnosing an injury, illness or disability. The listed services include accommodation and meals, nursing services, diagnostic procedures, medication, and the use of operating facilities and equipment, radiotherapy and physiotherapy facilities.[10]

---

[6]   *Ibid,.* s. 8.

[7]   *Ibid.,* s. 9.

[8]   See "Canadian Health Ministers are Preparing to Impose User Fees", *Toronto Star*, July 13, 1995, A17; this article cites the Oregon Experience in which, as a result of state-wide hearings, 565 procedures were listed for which the state government would pay. These procedures included transplants (except for patients with liver cancer), hip replacements and neonatal care. However, treatment for the common cold, viral hepatitis or a viral sore throat are not covered on the ground that these conditions improve on their own and do not require proactive medical treatment.

[9]   CHA, s. 2.

[10] *Ibid.,* s. 2.

3. Universality

The provincial health insurance plan must entitle all insured persons in the province to the insured health services provided under the plan on uniform terms and conditions.[11] In some instances, provinces have attempted to reduce the cost of health care by redefining the meaning of "insured persons" to exclude recent immigrants to Canada, Canadian "snowbirds" vacationing south of the border, and others who are perceived to have a more transient link to the province.

4. Portability

Provincial health insurance plans must be designed in such a way that residents who move from province to province, or who are absent temporarily from their province, remain eligible for insured health services.[12] Independent actions by some provinces have impaired the operation of the portability principle in Canada. For example, the fee schedule for physicians in Quebec is substantially lower than the fee schedule for physicians in Ontario. Although Quebec has signed an agreement guaranteeing the portability of insured services provided by doctors, it has refused to pay the higher rates of Ontario and other provinces, except in limited circumstances.[13]

5. Accessibility

The provincial plan must provide insured health services on a basis that "does not impede or preclude, either directly or indirectly whether by charges made to insured persons or otherwise, reasonable access to those services by insured persons".[14] The collection by some provinces of premiums or payroll taxes to fund the health insurance system has been criticized as being regressive in nature and for placing a heavy burden on large numbers of people with low or modest incomes.[15] Although premium assistance may be available for some individuals, this method of collection may offend the accessibility principle.

Each province has enacted legislation providing funding for medical and institutional health care services in conjunction with the federal government. The federal and provincial legislation constitutes a unique national medicare system that on the international scene is extremely progressive.

---

[11]   *Ibid.*, s. 10.
[12]   *Ibid.*, s. 11.
[13]   See *Health, Healthcare and Medicare*, a report by the National Council of Welfare (Ottawa: Ministry of Supply and Services Canada, 1990).
[14]   CHA, s. 12.
[15]   *Supra*, note 13, at 55-62.

ELIGIBILITY

Eligibility is based upon residency. Individuals who have been resident in a province for a certain duration are entitled to membership in the provincial plan. Tourists, transients, and students from outside the province, and individuals visiting residents of the province, who are not themselves resident in the province, do not qualify. Residents who go abroad, but who are only temporarily absent from their province, continue to be eligible for coverage in relation to health care treatment received abroad.

FEDERAL FUNDING

Government-sponsored health insurance plans in Canada are administered by the individual provinces. The federal government plays its most significant role in the plan through its financial contribution.

Generally speaking, the government of Canada contributes approximately 50 per cent of the net operating costs of the provincial plans both in respect of hospital and medical services. For the purpose of calculating the federal contribution, a formula is employed which favours poorer provinces. The effect of the formula is that less thrifty provinces receive a lower contribution from the federal government than the more efficient provinces. In recent years, the federal government's contribution has dropped.

In funding the cost of hospital and other designated health care facility services the federal contribution is restricted to operating costs. In calculating the contribution, any amounts spent on land or buildings or for the depreciation of land and buildings are excluded. As a result, health care facilities in the various provinces, and by extension, the provincial governments, have exclusive responsibility for the financing of construction and renovation of facilities. However, the federal contribution does take into account expenses incurred by health care facilities as a result of wear and tear on furniture and equipment.

The important responsibility of purchasing updated equipment and treatment facilities in hospitals rests exclusively with individual provinces. Not surprisingly, this is a weighty financial obligation that has the potential to leave already cash-strapped hospitals with insufficient resources for day-to-day operation. In some cases, hospitals will have insufficient resources to ensure that buildings, facilities and equipment remain up-to-date and available for the use of patients seeking treatment.[16]

---

[16]   See *Federal-Provincial Fiscal Arrangements Act*, R.S.C. 1985, c. F-8.

PROVINCIAL FUNDING

In some provinces, residents become members of the provincial health insurance plan by payment of a "premium" or a "tax" which in turn entitles the resident to the provision of insured health services. In other provinces, the province's share of the cost of the plan is funded exclusively from the general revenues of the province and there is no requirement that residents pay into the plan specific sums or "premiums" targeted to the funding of the plan itself.

In provinces where the plan is structured on the basis of "premiums", subsidies are available to individuals who can demonstrate a reduced income or financial difficulties. Generally, premium assistance is available to individuals who have been resident in the province for a certain length of time and who can show taxable income which does not exceed certain minimum limits. In some instances, residents such as senior citizens are eligible for complete premium exemption regardless of their level of income.

It should be noted that even in a province where residents are required to pay a premium for the entitlement of insured health services, premium assistance and premium exemption regulations, along with the sometimes extraordinary cost of modern health care, can result in a substantial payment by a provincial government out of its general revenues to subsidize the provision of insured health services not covered by the premiums received by the provincial authority. Although the federal legislation speaks of *insured* health services,[17] and although premiums form the conceptual base for the accumulation of funding in most provinces, in practice the Canadian medicare system more closely resembles a government-funded social program than it does an insurance scheme.[18]

INSURED SERVICES

The federal legislation requires each province to set out a tariff or system of authorized payments to individuals and institutions providing health care services. In order to qualify for payment under the provincial plan, a particular service is specifically included as an insured health service under the provincial legislation.

Schedules that identify insured health services are created by the province in consultation with such bodies as the Canadian Medical As-

---

[17]   CHA, s. 12(1)(b).

[18]   In 1989, the Ontario government modified its health insurance plan so that ordinary residents who apply are no longer required to pay premiums: Ontario *Health Insurance Act*, R.S.O. 1980, c. 197, s. 11 [am. 1989. c. 76, s. 41(2), now R.S.O. 1990, c. H.6, s. 11].

sociation, the Canadian Hospital Association, the Canadian Nurses' Association and other health care organizations. From time to time, schedules of insured health services are updated and revised.

In Ontario, for example, the provincial health insurance scheme provides coverage for services performed by duly licensed doctors in the province including:

- physician's services in the home, office, hospital or institution;
- services of specialists certified by the Royal College of Physicians and Surgeons of Canada;
- diagnosis and treatment of illness and injury;
- treatment of fractures and dislocations;
- surgery;
- administration of anaesthetic;
- x-rays for diagnostic and treatment purposes;
- obstetrical care, including prenatal and postnatal care;
- laboratory services and clinical pathology when ordered by and performed under the direction of a physician.[19]

In addition, the Ontario plan provides coverage for qualified patients who are treated at an approved health care facility by a licensed physician. The plan covers the cost of hospital services when medically necessary and the diagnosis and treatment of illness or injury, on an in-patient or out-patient basis, for such areas as:

- standard ward accommodation;
- necessary nursing services, when provided by the hospital;
- laboratory and x-ray diagnostic procedures;

---

[19] *Fifth Report on Accident and Sickness Insurance, 1981*, Government of Ontario, Select Committee on Company Law, p. 16. (Queen's Printer for Ontario, 1981). Reproduced with permission. Some physician's services are not insured, such as telephone advice at the patient's request, renewal of a prescription by telephone, completion of various forms, documentation and associated medical assessments, some patient-related interviews and discussions with other professionals at the patient's request. A physician may choose to offer patients a block payment plan whereby the patient is charged a flat yearly fee for all uninsured services. The payment is based on the average number of services used in the previous year. In s. 1(1) of O. Reg 857/93 under the *Medicine Act, 1991*, S.O. 1991, c. 30, the Ontario government changed the definition of professional misconduct to include the receipt of block payments. This regulation was challenged in *Szmuilowicz v. Ontario (Minister of Health)* (1995), 24 O.R. (3d) 204, 125 D.L.R. (4th) 688, 82 O.A.C. 183 (Div. Ct.), where it was ruled that block payments are permitted as long as physicians offer this payment option in accordance with the guidelines established by the College of Physicians and Surgeons. The Ontario government chose not to appeal this decision.

- use of operating and delivery rooms, anaesthetic and surgical supplies;
- use of radiotherapy facilities;
- services rendered by any person paid by the hospital.[20]

A similarly broad array of physician and health services are insured in other provinces. Specific reference should be made to the legislation of each province.

In addition to the cost of physician and health care services, provincial health insurance plans may provide limited coverage for such areas as:

- ambulance services;
- chiropractic and physiotherapy treatment;
- certain types of cosmetic surgery;
- certain types of dental and orthodontic treatment;
- certain types of optometric services.

As some services are not covered by the provincial plans, the patient is personally responsible for those costs. These services may include private or semi-private accommodation, charges for dental care not received in a hospital or other approved health care facility, private-duty nursing fees, cosmetic surgery and acupuncture.

INSURED NURSING SERVICES

In most provinces, direct billing of the health insurance scheme by a nurse is severely restricted. Most nursing services are insured on an ancillary basis in the course of medical services provided by physicians, health care facilities and community organizations.

In British Columbia, however, the *Medical Service Act Regulations* specifically extend coverage to certain nursing services. Insured services under the British Columbia plan include:

> the extended role services of a registered nurse where:
> (i) an arrangement for the rendering and for the payment of these services is approved by the Commission, and
> (ii) these services are rendered in an area of the Province where a medical practitioner is not normally available.[21]

---

[20] *Ibid.*, p. 17.
[21] B.C. Reg. 144/68, s. 4.09.

More recently, expanded roles for nurses in the health care system may have generated a potential need for the availability of direct access by nurses to health insurance schemes.

EXTRA-BILLING AND USER FEES

The contribution of the federal government to the provision of medical services has been somewhat complicated by the fact that for a lengthy period following the introduction of a programme of national health insurance, physicians and hospitals were permitted to "opt out" of the plan. Until fairly recently, in most jurisdictions there was no legal prohibition against physicians and hospitals charging patients a fee exceeding the fee schedules set by the individual provinces in conjunction with the federal government.

In recent years, controversy has arisen between the federal government and the various provinces over whether certain "extra-billing" practices engaged in by physicians have resulted in a breach of the "accessibility" requirement of the CHA.

Before the advent of government health insurance, physicians generally were paid on a fee-for-service basis. In other words, physicians were paid by their patients for their services on the basis of a fee set by the physician. There is no strong tradition in Canada of physicians being paid by salary or through some other mechanism that pools their services. Likewise, as private insurance schemes were introduced in the late 1940s and 1950s, private insurers continued to pay physicians a fee for specific services provided to insured patients. Although there may have been a limit on the amount of fee the health care market would bear in relation to a particular service, physicians continued to operate autonomously even though their fees were often paid through the intermediary of an insurer rather than by the patient. In constructing a national health insurance program, the fee-for-service method of payment was retained. It appears to have been regarded as a beneficial arrangement for patients, physicians and governments.[22]

---

[22] See Fain, *supra*, note 1, at 191-201. In an effort to cut budgets, government officials have questioned whether the fee for service is the most effective method of payment. Recently, a pilot project has been undertaken in Ontario whereby patients are asked to sign a contract with a group of physicians from whom they agree to receive all their non-emergency care. In return, that group of physicians must offer 24-hour care and telephone consultations. The group receives a budget in relation to the number of patients signed up in their roster, adjusted for sex and age. They physicians are still paid on a fee-for-service basis up to their maximum budget. The government reserves the right to charge patients who receive discretionary services from physicians other than

As noted, CHA requires individual provinces to establish a tariff or system of payment for health care services.[23] Aside from negotiations with professional bodies about the amounts that will form the tariff, the tariff undergoes constant revision to ensure that services that are medically necessary form part of the tariff and those that are not medically necessary do not. There is an incentive for individual provinces, beyond their own financial commitment, to ensure that the tariff is reasonable, as any federal contribution is reduced, by formula, to reflect the cost of insured services in a particular province in relation to all of the other provinces. As a result, provinces are penalized if the cost of insured services is more expensive on a per capita basis.

Under the originating federal legislation, it was possible for physicians and health care facilities to charge patients fees that exceeded the provincial tariff. There was some disincentive to physicians who might choose to do this as, in doing so, they would be required to "opt out" of the health insurance system. While "opted-out" physicians were not prevented from receiving payment indirectly under the provincial plan, physicians would be required to seek payment directly from the patient. The patient then could seek to recover from the provincial government an amount in respect of the physician's fee not exceeding the amount set out in the tariff. From an administrative point of view, this was a significant disincentive, and as of 1975, in provinces where "opting out" was permitted, physicians who had opted out comprised no more than nine per cent of the physician population with most of the provinces having an even lower percentage of opted-out physicians.[24]

In provinces where the practice of opting-out and extra-billing remained permissible under the provincial legislation, controversy arose between the federal government and the provinces. From the federal point of view, the practice of extra-billing offended the principles of universality and accessibility and contravened the federal requirement that the provincial plan not

[I]mpede or preclude, either directly or indirectly whether by charges made to insured persons or otherwise, reasonable access to [insured] services by insured persons.[25]

The introduction of revisions to the CHA, which were proclaimed April 17, 1984, meant that federal participation in any provincial health insurance plan would be reduced where it was permissible for physicians, or

those with whom they have signed a contract. This Primary Care Reform Initiative is currently in place in several designated Ontario centres.
[23] CHA, s. 12(1)(b).
[24] T.G. Fain (ed.), "National Health Insurance" in *Public Documents Series* New York: R.R. Bowker Co., 1977), at p. 205.
[25] CHA, s. 12(1)(a).

hospitals, to bill patients for fees or charges beyond the amounts authorized under the provincial health insurance plan. The CHA now stipulates that in order to "qualify" for a full cash contribution, no payments may be permitted by the province in respect of "extra-billing" by physicians or "user charges" by health care facilities. Extra-billing is defined as:

> [B]illing for an insured health service rendered to an insured person by a medical practitioner or a dentist in an amount in addition to any amount paid or to be paid for that service by the health care insurance plan of a province.[26]

User charges are defined as:

> [A]ny charge for an insured health service that is authorized or permitted by a provincial health care insurance plan that is not payable, directly or indirectly, by a provincial health care insurance plan, but does not include any charge imposed by extra-billing.[27]

In effect, in order for a province to qualify for the full federal contribution, physicians and health care facilities within that province cannot charge for insured services outside the government-sponsored health insurance scheme, except for certain limited exceptions contained in the legislation. Where extra-billing by doctors or user charges by hospitals continue to occur, the federal government may deduct from the federal contribution an amount equal to the total amount charged by physicians or hospitals outside of the provincial health insurance plan.

When the revisions to CHA were first introduced, only in British Columbia and Quebec were doctors barred from receiving any payment from the provincial health insurance plan, either directly or indirectly, if they chose to opt out. In Alberta, New Brunswick, Nova Scotia, Prince Edward Island and Saskatchewan, physicians were permitted to extra-bill without the necessity of opting out of the provincial plan. In Manitoba, Newfoundland and Ontario, the provincial legislation, with minor variations, permitted physicians to opt out and then recover a portion of their fee indirectly from the provincial plan. One of the provinces most significantly affected by the new federal position was the province of Ontario. By 1981, for example, approximately 62 per cent of its anaesthetists were opted out, or in other words, charging patients a fee that exceeded the provincial tariff.[28]

[26] *Ibid.*, s. 2.
[27] *Ibid.*, s. 2.
[28] Department of National Health and Welfare, *Preserving Universal Medicare* (Ottawa: Minister of Supply & Services Canada, 1983), p. 5. Excerpts reproduced with permission of the Minister of Supply and Services Canada, 1998.

In 1981 a Select Committee of the Ontario legislature rejected specifically the rationale of extra-billing because of its concern that fees charged
outside of the provincial system would "deny reasonable access to insured services by insured persons".[29] Furthermore, the Committee specifically rejected user fees as being a means to control the cost of health
care services and expressed agreement with a recommendation made by
an earlier committee which had been appointed to study health care financing.

> The Committee recommends that user fees not be introduced into the
> health-care system of the Province and that the arguments for the use of
> such fees as a means of controlling utilization of services, of cost contain-
> ment and of providing "*reasonable* compensation" to medical practitioners
> be rejected.[30]

In moving to reduce its contribution where the practice of extra-billing
continued in the various provinces, the federal government likewise rejected the position advanced by physicians' groups that a ban on extra-
billing would severely reduce the professional independence of physicians.

> Canada's system of Medicare has left physicians free to practise medicine
> on a fee for service basis unless they choose some form of salaried ar-
> rangement. They can practise anywhere they choose in any province in
> which they are licensed. At the same time, patients can choose any doctor
> they wish. Freedom of choice is a cornerstone of our Medicare system. The
> Government of Canada has no intention of changing any of this.
>   Doctors are not obliged to participate in Medicare if they want to oper-
> ate an entirely private practice. They can "opt out" and charge the patient
> directly, with or without extra-billing being involved. But the fact remains
> that the vast majority, nearly ninety per cent of Canada's more than 40,000
> doctors are part of Medicare and accept provincial plan payments as pay-
> ment in full.[31]

By 1985, the federal contribution to provinces had been reduced by mil-
lions of dollars to reflect extra-billing and user charges by physicians and
health care facilities in provinces where such practices continued to be
permitted.

In Ontario, in 1986, the provincial government enacted legislation to
ban extra-billing. The *Health Care Accessibility Act*[32] provides that physi-

---

[29]   *Fifth Report, supra,* note 19, p. 247.
[30]   *Ibid.,* p. 251.
[31]   *Preserving Universal Medicare, supra,* note 28, p. 12.
[32]   R.S.O. 1990, c. H.3.

cians, dentists and optometrists in Ontario who do not bill the provincial health insurance plan directly (*i.e.*, are "opted out") may not charge more than the amounts set out in the provincial health insurance tariff. A physician who does so may be charged with an offence under the Act, and if convicted, can be liable to a fine of $2,000 for the first offence and $2,000 for any subsequent offence.

ABUSE OF THE HEALTH INSURANCE SYSTEM

As government is the major, if not only, source for the payment of physicians' fees for medical services, governments are able to develop very comprehensive and detailed statistics on the distribution of payments, the number of claims being paid, the average cost per claim, the exact amount of the physician's income from the plan and a variety of other aspects of health care.[33] Consequently, provincial governments have at their disposal a very sophisticated basis upon which to assess the quantity and quality of medical services and are thereby able to detect abuses by both health practitioners and patients of the health insurance system. Abuses by the health practitioners may be the subject matter of an offence under the provincial health insurance legislation and will also be considered ethical contraventions by the practitioner's own self-regulating professional body. Such contraventions could lead to a suspension or complete abrogation of professional standing.

In *Re College of Physicians & Surgeons (B.C.) and Ahmad*[34] the British Columbia College of Physicians and Surgeons found a physician to have engaged in unprofessional conduct in over-servicing patients for his own financial benefit. Similarly, in *Re Casullo and College of Physicians & Surgeons (Ont.)*[35] proceedings were taken against a physician who had engaged in unprofessional conduct by ordering tests for patients in a laboratory in which he had a financial interest where the cost of such tests was unreasonable and excessive. In *Idicula et al. v. College of Physicians & Surgeons (Alta.)*,[36] several physicians were suspended and fined by the College for having overbilled the Alberta Health Care Insurance Plan for services for which there was no entitlement to compensation. On appeal, the Alberta Court of Appeal withdrew the suspension and reduced the fine as it was shown that the overbillings had resulted from a clerical error of an individual in the doctors' office. Although the physicians were

---

[33] See for example, Ministry of Health of Ontario, *OHIP Practitioner Care Statistics, 1984-1985 (Pre-Audit)*.

[34] [1973] 6 W.W.R. 412, 43 D.L.R. (3d) 381 (B.C.S.C.).

[35] (1973), 2 O.R. (2d) 261, 42 D.L.R. (3d) 43 (C.A.).

[36] (1987), 79 A.R. 181 (C.A.).

reprimanded for having given inadequate instruction and supervision to the billing clerk, it was recognized that the extra-billing did not result from an intentional act on the part of the physicians to deceive the provincial authorities.

There have been no reported cases in Canada to date which involve abuse of the health insurance system by nurses. However, to the restricted extent that nursing services qualify as insured services under provincial legislation, any abuse by nurses may lead to similar sanctions by government or self-regulating bodies. Likewise, as many nurses are directly involved in the billing process by physicians, and in some instances may be responsible for the preparation and submission of accounts to the provincial authorities, a legal onus lies on the nursing professional to protect the system by preventing and reporting abuse.

Similar to the problem of abuse of the health insurance system by health care professionals is the potential for abuse of the system by patients. The continuation of extra-billing or user charges within a government-sponsored health insurance scheme has been advanced on the basis that these charges can limit the overall cost of the scheme by shifting a portion of health costs from government to the individual recipients, discouraging "frivolous" or "unnecessary" use of health care services by patients, impressing in recipients of health care services a greater appreciation of the total costs involved, improving the quality of care provided to patients, and during difficult financial times, assisting in the remuneration of health professionals.[37]

It could be argued that the health care professional has a legal obligation to deter patients from overusing the health care system in circumstances where there is no valid medical reason for treatment. Likewise, where abuse of the system by a patient is obvious, there may be an obligation to register a report with the appropriate government authority.

THE FUTURE OF NATIONAL HEALTH INSURANCE

Since the introduction of a national health insurance scheme in Canada, the cost of health care services has increased dramatically. These rising costs have been employed as a further rationale for the retention of extra-billing and user charges.

> Some proponents of direct charges have claimed that [the] provinces can no longer afford to pay all of the costs of their current programs, and that user charges could be an added source of financing. We hear talk of

---

[37] R. F. Badgley, *User Charges for Health Services: A Report of the Ontario Council of Health* (Toronto: The Council, 1979), at 30.

"spiralling" health costs and the need to get government spending on health under control.[38]

In 1982, hospital expenditures in Canada increased by 17 per cent. From 1970 to 1981, there was an overall increase in expenditures of about 100 per cent, which was well in excess of the general inflation rate.[39] Nonetheless, in support of its opposition to extra-billing and user charges, the federal government asserted that while the cost of health care services had increased dramatically over the past decade, as a component of national expenditures, health care spending in Canada has been relatively constant. Moreover, in comparison with other countries in the western world, in particular the United States, the increase in the cost of health services has been modest.[40]

The financial ability of governments to meet the costs imposed by the health care insurance system has become an issue that threatens the viability of the system.

OTHER FORMS OF HEALTH CARE INSURANCE

The advent of government-sponsored health insurance in Canada has not removed the need for other insurance schemes, both private and government-run, to supplement national health insurance. It should be understood that while the Canadian health insurance system provides a comprehensive basis for the provision of basic health care services in the individual provinces, it does not finance all of the health care needs of residents within the provinces.

For example, if provinces continue to permit extra-billing and user charges, despite the reduced federal contribution, residents (unless otherwise insured for such costs) will be responsible for paying these direct charges. Individuals who do not qualify for membership in the provincial health care insurance plan, or for other reasons choose not to enroll, will be responsible for the full cost of their own health care services. Medications are not covered in most instances by the provincial plans and there are a number of other areas for which patients will bear the financial responsibility unless private insurance is obtained. Private insurance is available to meet the cost of semi-private and private accommodation in, for example, hospital, nursing-home care, prescription drugs, dental care, health care outside Canada, and special duty nursing.

---

[38]   *Ibid.*, p. 7.
[39]   *Preserving Universal Medicare, supra*, note 28, at 12.
[40]   *Ibid.*

There are a number of other areas for which patients will bear the financial responsibility unless private insurance is obtained. Private insurance is available to meet, for example, the cost of semi-private and private accommodation in hospital, nursing home care, prescription drugs, dental care, health care outside of Canada, and special duty nursing.

Other provincial statutes supplement health care expenses in certain situations. Workplace safety and insurance legislation, in addition to providing income benefits to injured workers, provides comprehensive medical rehabilitation benefits to workers who are injured while on the job. Such coverage may provide health care services, without charge, that are not covered under health insurance laws. In some provinces, medical and rehabilitation benefits are available to victims of motor vehicle accidents through mandatory insurance legislation. Under federal legislation, health care benefits, not otherwise available under provincial legislation, are made available to veterans who demonstrate a disability attributable to their military service.

There are also a great many health care benefits provided through clinics, assistance programs, hospitals for the chronically ill, senior citizens' homes, programs for the disabled, visiting nurses, public health nurses, and rehabilitation centres. For the most part, these are services funded through the general revenues of the provinces or municipalities that provide a variety of services, many relating to health care, and are available to qualified residents in the province.

Lastly, both federal and provincial governments allow taxpayers to deduct from taxable income certain medical expenses incurred in relation to themselves or disabled dependants. Also, provinces that have a provincial sales tax traditionally grant exemptions in respect of products that relate to health care needs.

CURRENT ISSUES: HEALTH INSURANCE

As a nurse in a general practitioner's office, your duties include remitting billings to the provincial health insurance plan. You notice that the billings you completed the previous week did not go out in the mail on schedule. To ensure that you've included the appropriate documentation, you decide to review it one last time before mailing it. To your surprise, you notice that your paperwork has been altered to include different fee codes.

You suspect that your employer is defrauding the health insurance system. What do you do?

A prudent first step is to double-check your own work, and not leap to any conclusions. If possible, verify whether there is an established pattern of fraudulent activity, or whether this is simply an oversight that can be explained.

If you still believe that an employer or colleague is engaged in fraudulent activity, you may have a legal, professional and ethical duty to take action. Although you may have concerns about how this will affect your relationship with your employer or colleague (including the possibility of losing your job), you do not want to risk becoming a party to fraud.

You should contact your provincial nurses' association for confidential advice. This will allow you to make an informed decision regarding the options available to you.

Relevant Legislation

CANADA

Canada Health Act, R.S.C. 1985, c. C-6

ALBERTA

Alberta Health Care Insurance Act, R.S.A. 1980, c. A-24

Alberta Health Care Insurance Amendment Act, 1998 [Royal Assent: December 9, 1998]
  Alberta Health Care Insurance Regulation, Alta. Reg. 216/81

BRITISH COLUMBIA

Hospital Insurance Act, R.S.B.C. 1996, c. 204
  Hospital Insurance Regulations, B.C. Reg. 16/58, 25/61

Medicare Protection Act, R.S.B.C. 1996, c. 286
  Medical and Health Care Services Regulation 281/92
  Medical Service Act Regulations, B.C. Reg. 144/68

MANITOBA

The Health Services Insurance Act, R.S.M. 1987, c. H35
  Diagnostic Laboratories Regulation, Man. Reg. 16/95
  Hospital Services Insurance and Administration Regulation, Man. Reg. 48/93
  Payments for Insured Medical Services Regulation, Man. Reg. 95/96

NEW BRUNSWICK

Health Services Act, R.S.N.B. 1973, c. H-3
  General Regulation, N.B. Reg. 84-115

Hospital Services Act, R.S.N.B. 1973, c. H-9
  Elimination of Authorized Charges Regulation, N.B. Reg. 86-74
  General Regulation, N.B. Reg. 84-167

NEWFOUNDLAND

Hospital Insurance (Agreement) Act, R.S.N. 1990, c. H-7
  Regulation 577

Medical Care Insurance Act, R.S.N. 1990, c. M-5
  Medical Care Insurance (Beneficiaries & Enquiries) Regulations, Cons. Nfld. Reg. 20/96
  Medical Care Insurance (Insured Services) Regulations, Cons. Nfld. Reg. 21/96
  Newfoundland Medical Care Insurance (Physicians and Fees) Regulations, Cons. Nfld. Reg. 576/78

NOVA SCOTIA

Health Services and Insurance Act, R.S.N.S. 1989, c. 197
  Hospital Insurance Regulations, N.S. Reg. 11/58

NORTHWEST TERRITORIES

Medical Care Act, R.S.N.W.T. 1988, c. M-8
  Medical Care Act Regulations, R.R.N.W.T. 1990, c. M-4

ONTARIO

Health Insurance Act, R.S.O. 1990, c. H-6
  General Regulation, R.R.O. 1990, Reg. 552

PRINCE EDWARD ISLAND

Health Services Payment Act, R.S.P.E.I. 1988, c. H-2
  General Regulations, R.R.P.E.I., EC 56/77
  Health Services Payment Regulations EC 453/96

Hospital and Diagnostic Services Insurance Act, R.S.P.E.I. 1988, c. H-8
  General Regulations, R.R.P.E.I., EC 539/63

QUEBEC

Health Insurance Act, R.S.Q. 1977, c. A-29
  Regulation respecting the application of the Health Insurance Act, R.R.Q.
  1981, c. A-29, r. 1

*Health Insurance Board of Quebec Act (An Act respecting the Régie de
l'assurance-maladie du Québec)*, R.S.Q. 1977, c. R-5
  Regulation respecting contributions to the Quebec Health Insurance Plan,
  R.R.Q. 1981, c. R-5, r. 1

Hospital Insurance Act, R.S.Q. 1977, c. A-28
  Regulations respecting the application of the Hospital Insurance Act, R.R.Q.
  1981, c. A-28, r. 1

SASKATCHEWAN

The Saskatchewan Hospitalization Act, R.S.S. 1978, c. S-23 (will be repealed
by the *Miscellaneous Statutes Repeal (Regulatory Reform) Act, 1997*, c. 12
when it comes into force)
  The Saskatchewan Hospitalization Regulations, 1978, Sask. Reg. 82/78

The Saskatchewan Medical Care Insurance Act, R.S.S. 1978, c. S-29
  The Medical Care Insurance Beneficiary and Administration Regulations,
  R.R.S., c. S-29, Reg. 13

YUKON

Health Care Insurance Plan Act, R.S.Y. 1986, c. 81
  Health Care Insurance Regulations, Yukon C.O. 1971/275, 1974/019,
  1977/256, 1984/236, 1984/333, 1984/061, 1988/145, 1994/063,
  1995/020

CHAPTER 3

Professional Status of Nurses

SYNOPSIS

This chapter highlights the role of nurses as professionals in the health care community. It sets out the nurse's entry into the profession, continuing education obligations and practice requirements, and the registration and licensing process.

INTRODUCTION

The law in Canada gives nurses a professional status similar to that enjoyed by other health care professionals like physicians and dentists. At one time, the role of the (usually female) nurse was considered secondary or subordinate to the trained (and usually male) physician. This notion is outdated in every respect. Nurses in Canada have won a place in the health care setting that increasingly recognizes the independent function of nursing and reflects its identity as a keystone of the health care system.

NURSES AS PROFESSIONALS

We have historically used the term "professional" to identify a distinct group possessing special skill or knowledge in an advanced area of learning. For example, law, medicine, dentistry, teaching and accounting are commonly referred to as professions. Nursing is now identified as a profession too. The term "professional" has come to designate an exclusive legal right to practise a particular profession. This, in theory, protects the public from those not qualified to practise. Those who claim to be qualified are regulated and monitored. In Canada, the law prevents unqualified individuals from claiming to be members of a professional body, or, in some cases, from practising the skills which are specifically identified with the particular professional body.

The laws that state that only qualified persons can practise a profession are of direct benefit to the members of the profession. They protect the reputation of the profession and limit the numbers of persons who can offer the professional service. The concept of "exclusivity" means there is a limited number of members. This will result in a form of monopoly. The fact that the members of a particular profession are limited in number can have a direct impact on the incomes of the professional members and the manner in which the members will practise. Some critics believe that the members of a profession enjoy a privileged position that outweighs the protection that the public actually receives.

PROVINCIAL REGULATION

In all provinces in Canada, nurses have professional status with all its responsibilities and privileges. The College of Nurses of Ontario stated in a submission to the Health Professions Legislation Review Committee:

> Nursing is a health discipline composed of practitioners prepared to accept the privileges and responsibilities of professional status. This position is supported by the people of Ontario who have granted the profession the privilege of self-regulation.[1]

Nurses have been granted an exclusivity of practise, a right of self-government and an obligation to monitor and discipline their own membership. Each province in Canada has legislation that provides for the registration of nurses by a governing body. The law in Canada prohibits individuals from holding themselves out as "nurses" or "registered nurses" unless they are listed as a duly qualified member in the provincial nursing register. In some provinces, the law prohibits individuals from practising any of the skills designated by the professional body to be those that require specialized nursing training.

Several provinces have umbrella legislation containing general provisions pertaining to all recognized health professionals within the province, as well as companion legislation relating to each profession. For example, in Ontario, the nursing profession is governed by the *Regulated Health Professions Act*,[2] and the *Nursing Act*.[3] This legislation establishes the College of Nurses of Ontario as the governing body responsible for the regulation of nursing in the province. Section 11 of the *Nursing Act* prohibits any person from holding himself or herself out as competent to practise as a registered nurse or as a registered nursing assistant unless that person has been issued a certificate by the College of Nurses. Also,

---

[1]   College of Nurses of Ontario, Submission to the Health Professions Legislation Review Committee, January 12th, 1984, p. 2.

[2]   S.O. 1991, c. 18.

[3]   S.O. 1991, c. 32.

no person may use the title "registered nurse" or adopt any of the designations commonly associated with registered nursing — Reg. N., R.N. or R.S.A. — unless the College of Nurses has issued a certificate to that person.

In other provinces, each individual health profession is regulated by an independent, self-contained statute that sets out the basis for self-regulation. For example, in Manitoba, *The Registered Nurses Act*[4] establishes the Manitoba Association of Registered Nurses to be the governing body for nurses in that province and provides that "no person shall practise as a registered nurse or hold herself [or himself] out for employment as a registered nurse unless her [or his] name is entered in the register" of the Association.[5]

In Nova Scotia, the *Registered Nurses' Association Act*[6] appoints the Registered Nurses' Association of Nova Scotia as the governing body responsible for regulating the nursing profession within the province. In Nova Scotia there is a broad prohibition that "no person shall engage in nursing practice in the Province" unless that person has been authorized to do so by the governing body.[7] In addition, no person is entitled to use the designation "registered nurse" or "R.N." either "alone or in combination with other words, letters or description to imply that person is entitled to practise as a registered nurse" without the authority of the provincial association.[8]

In Newfoundland, the governing legislation for the nursing profession is *The Newfoundland Registered Nurses Act*.[9] It appoints the Association of Registered Nurses of Newfoundland as the professional governing body, provides for the granting of a "licence to practise" to qualified nurses and prohibits any person from practising as a nurse or holding herself or himself out to be a registered nurse until "she [or he] has obtained a licence and has been registered as a member of the association."[10]

In Saskatchewan, *The Registered Nurses Act, 1988* enables the Saskatchewan Registered Nurses' Association to act as the governing body for the province's nurses.[11] It regulates education and continuing education for nurses in the province. The Act provides for the "certification" of nurses and the granting of licences and temporary licences. Under this legislation, any person other than a "nurse" (defined to be a "graduate nurse or a registered nurse") who practises as a registered nurse in the

---

[4]   R.S.M. 1987, c. R40.
[5]   *Ibid.*, s. 8(1).
[6]   S.N.S. 1996, c. 30.
[7]   *Ibid.*, s. 19.
[8]   *Ibid.*, s. 18.
[9]   R.S.N. 1990, c. R-9.
[10] *Ibid.*, ss. 8, 16.
[11] S.S. 1988-89, c. R-12.2.

province or uses the title "Registered Nurse", is guilty of an offence under the Act and is liable to a fine of not more than $1,000 for the first of-
fence.[12] The legislation of other provinces contains similar provisions for
prosecution and sentencing.

In British Columbia, the *Nurses (Registered) Act*[13] provides that the
Registered Nurses' Association of British Columbia is responsible for the
registration and regulation of nursing within the province. No person
who has not been registered by the Association is entitled to use the title
"Registered Nurse" or any abbreviation thereof.[14] Licensed practical
nurses (LPNs) are now regulated by the *Health Professions Act*.[15]

In Alberta, the governing legislation is the *Nursing Profession Act*.[16] The
Alberta Association of Registered Nurses is the governing body appointed under the legislation and is responsible for ensuring that no person, unless authorized by the Association, engages in "exclusive nursing
practice" within the province.[17] The Council may apply for an injunction
to prevent people using the name "Registered Nurse" or any other name
or abbreviation that represents that they are registered Nurses when they
are not.[18]

In New Brunswick, the *Nurses Act*[19] appoints the Nurses' Association
of New Brunswick to be responsible for the regulation of nursing within
the province. The legislation provides that no person other than a person
whose name is entered in the Association's registers shall "publicly or
privately — practise or offer to practise nursing".[20]

In Prince Edward Island, the *Nurses Act*[21] establishes the Association of
Nurses of Prince Edward Island to govern the affairs of professional
nurses in the province. It is responsible for issuing "licences". The legislation prohibits any person who is not a member of the Association from
using the titles "Nurse" or "Registered Nurse".[22] It also prohibits any
person from practising "as a nurse before first obtaining a licence and
being registered as a member in the register."[23]

In Quebec, the governing legislation is the *Nurses Act*.[24] It deems all
nurses "qualified to practise the profession of nursing in Quebec" to be

---

[12] *Ibid.*, s. 46.
[13] R.S.B.C. 1996, c. 335.
[14] *Ibid.*, s. 23.
[15] R.S.B.C. 1996, c. 183; see also *Licensed Practical Nurses Regulation*, B.C. Reg. 71/96.
[16] S.A. 1983, c. N-14.5.
[17] *Ibid.*, s. 3(1).
[18] *Ibid.*, s. 7.
[19] S.N.B. 1984, c. 71.
[20] *Ibid.*, s. 19.
[21] R.S.P.E.I. 1988, c. N-4.
[22] *Ibid.*, s. 17.
[23] *Ibid.*, s. 15.
[24] R.S.Q. 1977, c. I-8.

members of a corporation called the "Corporation professionnelle des infirmières et infirmiers du Québec" or alternatively, the "Ordre des infirmières et infirmiers du Québec".[25] No person may engage in nursing unless that person's name has been "entered on the roll" of the Corporation.

A common thread throughout the legislation in the various provinces is the designation of a statutory body or bodies, whose role is to register, monitor and discipline nurses within the province. In each case the chief responsibility of the statutory body is the regulation of nursing within the province for the benefit of the public. In some provinces there is a separate body, funded and operated by nurses within the province, whose role is to promote nursing interests in the province. These non-statutory bodies are active in the negotiation of wage rates and working conditions on behalf of the profession and engage in other activities that are designed to promote the interests of the profession.

In Ontario, the distinction between the legislative arm of the profession, the College of Nurses, and the non-statutory body, the Ontario Nurses' Association, is particularly apparent. The College itself emphasizes:

> The Ontario legislation separates regulatory functions from voluntary functions. The former is the responsibility of the regulating bodies; the latter, of the professional associations. This division of function has been generally accepted as appropriate and effective.[26]

In other provinces the separation between regulatory and voluntary functions is less stringent. For example, the Association of Nurses of Prince Edward Island is charged under that province's legislation with the objects of raising the standards of nursing service, and at the same time, the promotion of the professional, social and material welfare of nurses within the province. Arguably, these dual objects may conflict with one another in situations where, for instance, the maintenance or elevation of nursing standards impinges upon the promotion of nurses' economic interests.

In all provinces except Ontario the body established by the legislation to govern the nursing profession within the province is a provincial "Association". As mentioned above, the governing body in Ontario is entitled the College of Nurses. The legislation in the various provinces generally provides that the governing body shall have its affairs managed and conducted by a board of directors or a council elected by the members. The legislation may set out requirements for the election and appointment of officers, the composition of the board of directors or council, the requisite quorum, the term of office of a director or officer,

---

[25]　*Ibid.*, s. 2.
[26]　*Supra*, note 1, p. 4.

reporting requirements to the members and provisions to ensure that the governing body will be representative of the members and operate in a democratic manner consistent with the aims of the profession.

In some provinces, the legislation specifically provides for non-nursing participation in the governing body of the profession. For example, in Alberta the *Nursing Profession Act* provides that there must be one "member of the public" appointed to the Council for every 10 registered nurses.[27] The member of the public is to be appointed by the provincial government.

In Saskatchewan, *The Registered Nurses Act, 1988,* provides that a council "shall govern, manage and regulate the affairs and business" of the Association. The council is made up of not less than nine council members elected by the practising members of the Association and no more than two non-member residents of Saskatchewan appointed by the government.[28]

The board of directors or council of each governing body has the power to make by-laws or regulations that relate to its day-to-day operation and to the management and supervision of the members. Generally, the governing body of the profession in each province may enact regulations or by-laws to do the following:

- fix the number of appointees to the board of directors or council (subject to any legislated requirements);
- govern the election and appointment of members to the board or council;
- set guidelines for issuance, renewal, suspension and restoration of certificates to practise;
- establish, maintain and inspect provincial nursing registers;
- manage and provide continuing education to members;
- establish and collect annual fees from members;
- develop procedures for banking, finance, execution of documents, and ownership of property;
- develop procedures for the delegation of powers, the appointment of special committees, communication and association with other governing bodies;
- establish and regulate standards of nursing practice and, ethical guidelines; and,
- establish and enforce guidelines for determination of professional misconduct.

---

[27]   S.A. 1983, c. N-14.5, s. 10(1).
[28]   S.S. 1988-89, c. R-12.2, ss. 7 and 8.

ENTRY TO PRACTICE

Each of the provinces has legislation that establishes a basic threshold of competence that an applicant must meet in order to qualify for registration as a registered nurse, registered practical nurse, or nursing assistant.

Generally, an applicant is entitled to have his or her name entered upon the provincial nursing register once he or she has met the basic educational criteria set out in the governing legislation. You may refer to the provincial legislation for the criteria for entry to practice set by each province. In some provinces, the legislation states a requirement beyond the basic criteria of education and experience. In British Columbia, an applicant must satisfy the Registered Nurses' Association of British Columbia that he or she is "of good character,"[29] in addition to the other prerequisites of the Act. In Saskatchewan, an applicant is entitled to registration if he or she is "of good character".[30] There is no definition in either statute as to what is meant by "good character".

While all of the provinces implicitly want people bearing a professional designation to have good character, a ruling that bars an applicant who is considered to be of bad character leaves a broad scope for differing opinions. Most likely, this requirement would have to be interpreted rather restrictively so as not to offend human rights legislation either on the basis of discrimination or on the basis of simple fairness to the applicant. It is interesting to note that the Manitoba legislation provides:

> No person shall be denied membership in the association because of the race, nationality, religion, colour, sex, marital status, physical handicap, age, source of income, family status, political belief, ethnic or national origin of that person.[31]

This provision recognizes a principle which is inherent in the legislation of all of the provinces, even if not expressly stated: all applicants for membership in the nursing profession must be treated fairly and any refusal of entry into the profession must be based upon a legitimate concern about the applicant's ability to provide competent and reliable nursing services.

In most provinces, where an application for registration or renewal is refused, or about to be refused, by the governing body of the profession, the legislation provides for an appeal or review process designed to ensure that the applicant is treated fairly. For example, in Alberta, where an application is refused or deferred by the Registration Committee, the

---

[29] *Nurses (Registered) Act*, R.S.B.C. 1996, c. 335, ss. 14-17.
[30] *Registered Nurses Act*, 1988, S.S. 1988-89, c. R-12.2, s. 19(1)(b).
[31] *Registered Nurses Act*, R.S.M. 1987, c. R.40, s. 7(5).

Registration Committee must supply "written reasons for the decision".[32] The applicant is then entitled to either request the Registration Committee to reconsider its decision, or in the alternative, have a body called the Registration Review Committee do so. The applicant is entitled to appear before the Registration Review Committee with legal representation and to address the Registration Review Committee at the time that it reviews the application.

In most provinces, the legislation outlines a procedure similar to that contained in the Alberta legislation, in some instances, the legislation entitles the applicant to seek further relief from the courts. Although it is not explicit in the legislation of each province, there is an overriding legal obligation on the part of the decision-making body responsible for the consideration of applications for registration or renewal to treat the applicant fairly and impartially. The courts are likely to overturn a decision, review or hearing which does not provide the applicant with a basic level of justice or fairness, such as allowing the applicant to be heard, even where there has been no direct breach or omission regarding the governing legislation.

CONTINUING EDUCATION AND PRACTICE REQUIREMENTS

Once a member of the nursing profession is considered to be in good standing, the nurse is entitled to adopt the title "registered nurse" and thereby becomes eligible to be employed in those institutions which make registration a condition of employment. In some provinces, as noted, membership in the profession will mean an exclusive right to practise nursing with other nursing professionals. The nurse will be obliged to meet standards set by an employer — whether in a hospital, a clinic, a chronic care environment, a public health setting or with a private patient. Most provincial legislation gives the professional nursing authority the obligation to monitor the performance of nurses within the province on an on-going basis. It is not sufficient merely that a nurse be registered and have met the "entry to practice" criteria of registrations. There is a legal obligation upon the nurse to remain familiar with professional developments and to remain able to carry out tasks which the public would expect a competent nurse to be able to perform.

One way of ensuring that nurses meet, on an on-going basis, reasonable standards of performance is to require nurses to renew their certification or registration on an annual basis. There is no automatic right to renewal, and ordinarily, the applicant must meet certain criteria set out in

---

[32] *Nursing Profession Act*, S.A. 1983, c. N-14.5, s. 41.

the provincial legislation or in regulations or by-laws enacted by the professional body, in order to qualify for renewal.

For example, in New Brunswick, the Registrar of the Nurses' Association of New Brunswick is required, under the *Nurses Act*, to keep the following:

> (a) a register in which shall be entered the name and address of every person who has met the qualifications for registration as a nurse pursuant to this Act, the by-laws and the rules and is thereby entitled to engage in the practice of nursing in the Province;
>
> (b) a temporary register in which shall be entered for such period of time as the by-laws or rules prescribe the name and address of every person who has completed a nursing education program at an approved school of nursing and who is eligible for registration as a nurse upon the completion of the requirements for registration established by the by-laws and rules; and
>
> (c) rosters of members in which shall be entered the name and address of every person who is entitled to membership in any category of membership established by the by-laws, other than persons whose names are entered in the register or the temporary register.[33]

Those nurses whose names are entered in the register are entitled to engage actively in the practice of nursing within the province. Those nurses whose names are entered upon the temporary register have demonstrated to the Association that they have met the minimum criteria of education and experience required of nurses in the province and are entitled to engage in the practice of nursing, but this right may be subject to a limited period of time or other conditions, limitations and restrictions set out in the by-laws or rules of the profession.[34]

A member whose name is on a roster has demonstrated qualifications that entitle the member to membership, but not without some further qualification or approval by the Association, to engage actively in the practice of nursing.

Generally speaking, once an applicant has met the basic criteria for membership, and has become a member of the professional body of the province, the applicant is entitled to practise nursing and, apart from a material change in circumstances, is entitled to have his or her certificate of registration renewed on an annual basis. In most provinces there is an employment or practice requirement for eligibility to renew certificates or licences. These requirements may include a minimum number of hours, days or shifts within a stated period. If the applicant for renewal cannot meet the employment or practice requirements, he or she may be obliged

---

[33] S.N.B. 1984, c. 71, s. 11.
[34] *Ibid.*, s. 12(2).

to take a refresher course, or alternatively, may have certain restrictions applied to the type of practice in which the applicant may engage.

Aside from the renewal of certificates or licences, most provincial governing bodies of the nursing profession have a statutory obligation to furnish to members educational programs for nurses, who can attend on a voluntary basis. A number of states in the United States have mandatory continuing education requirements in their legislation which practising nurses must fulfill in order to qualify for renewal. In Canada, continuing education is a voluntary matter, although it is a nurse's legal and ethical obligation to remain current with standard nursing practices and new developments within the profession.[35]

REGISTRATION VS. LICENSURE

In all provinces where a nurse has had his or her name entered upon the provincial nursing register, that person is entitled, by law, to adopt the title, "registered nurse". In some provinces, persons who engage in nursing activities are not prohibited from engaging in those activities even though they are not registered nurses. They are prohibited only from adopting the title "registered nurse". The kind of protection afforded to the public and to the profession by this type of statutory mechanism is often referred to as "registration". It does not prevent individuals from engaging in nursing activities, but does provide a designation by which members of the public who wish to obtain nursing services can identify qualified personnel.

In a number of provinces, however, it is not only the title of "registered nurse" which is protected by statute, but the entitlement to engage in nursing practice. In those jurisdictions it is unlawful for an individual to perform nursing services or engage in nursing activities unless he or she is a registered member of the provincial nursing body. In other words, an individual must be licensed to engage in nursing practice. In those provinces, it is not just a matter of the title to be employed by the particular nursing practitioner.

Before organized professional bodies existed, and before their endorsement in legislation, any person who carried out nursing duties, either in the home or in the hospital, would have been referred to as a nurse. There was no regulatory body to ensure that a basic level of skill was met, and as a result, a practising nurse might possess only the most rudimentary of skills, or worse, might engage in practices which were more harmful than helpful to a patient.

---

[35] See, for example, College of Nurses of Ontario, *Guidelines for Ethical Behaviour in Nursing* (Toronto: The College, 1985), "Competence", p. 7.

From a practical point of view, most individuals who now carry on nursing in the various provinces are registered nurses. Most employers in the health care field stipulate that any nurse employed by the health care institution must be a member of the professional nursing body. While this guarantees, in most cases, that the patients will be treated by nurses who have met the basic criteria of registration, and who are monitored and regulated by the self-governing statutory body, it nevertheless leaves open the possibility that individuals who are unqualified and who have no regulatory authority to monitor and regulate their performance, will engage in nursing. This situation is to be contrasted with the situation of physicians in the various provinces. In Canada, no person may hold himself or herself out to be a doctor or a physician without being registered with the professional body, and the legislation of each province goes further by prohibiting any person from engaging in the practice of medicine without a licence from the provincial licensing body. In contrast, legislation in some provinces (*e.g.*, Manitoba) does not prohibit people from performing the duties of a nurse if they are not registered under the governing body for the province; instead, the legislation prevents the individual from representing herself or himself as being registered when that individual is not.

In Alberta, New Brunswick, Newfoundland, Nova Scotia, Prince Edward Island, Quebec and Saskatchewan, however, the legislation expands the regulation of nursing within the province to prohibit non-registered persons from engaging in the practice of nursing. In other words, the legislation grants to nurses in the province an exclusive licence to practise nursing in the province which is similar to that granted to physicians and dentists throughout Canada. For example, Nova Scotia's legislation provides that

19 (1) No person shall engage in the practice of nursing in the Province unless

(a) that person's name is entered in the Register and in the roster of active-practising members and that person is the holder of a current license;

(b) that person is the holder of a temporary permit;

(c) that person is a student nurse enrolled in a school of nursing that offers a nursing education program approved by the Board and is required to engage in the practice of nursing in a course of the nursing education program; or

(d) that person is permitted to engage in the practice of nursing as provided in this Act or the regulations, or as otherwise provided by law.[36]

---

[36] S.N.S. 1996, c. 30.

The section goes on the make an exception for nurses registered in other jurisdictions who temporarily accompany a client into the province as long as she or he does not claim to be registered in the province.

Ontario has enacted legislation that restricts the performance of certain procedures to qualified professionals. The *Regulated Health Professions Act*[37] sets out a detailed list of procedures[38] that are restricted to registered health professionals or their duly appointed delegates. The *Nursing Act*[39] further clarifies the restricted procedures that nurses are allowed to perform:

- performing a prescribed procedure below the dermis or a mucous membrane;
- administering a substance by injection or inhalation;
- putting an instrument, hand or finger beyond the external ear canal, beyond the point in the nasal passages where they usually narrow, beyond the larynx, beyond the opening of the urethra, beyond the labia majora, beyond the anal verge or into an artificial opening into the body.[40]

Some acknowledgment of advanced nursing practice is now present in the legislation: a registered nurse who holds an extended certificate of registration may be allowed to perform certain other functions, as long as there is no condition restricting that function placed on his or her certificate.[41] Such other functions include making certain kinds of diagnoses (in consultation with other health professionals as set out in the prescribed standards of practice), prescribing certain drugs, and ordering certain procedures, as set out in the regulations.

In British Columbia, the governing legislation achieves a blend of the registration and exclusive licensing systems. The *Nurses (Registered) Act* sets out a registration system that does not specifically exclude persons from engaging in "nursing practice". It only prohibits persons who are not registered with the provincial association from adopting the title of Registered Nurse or the abbreviation "R.N."[42]

However, the government of Brtish Columbia has enacted the *Health Professions Act*[43] and one of the regulations that has been enacted under the Act is the *Licensed Practical Nurses Regulation*.[44] In that regulation, the

37 S.O. 1991, c. 18.
38 *Ibid.*, s. 27(2).
39 S.O. 1991, c. 32.
40 *Ibid.*, s. 4.
41 *Ibid.*, s. 5.1 [added 1997, c. 9, s. 2].
42 R.S.B.C. 1996, c. 335.
43 R.S.B.C. 1996, c. 183.
44 B.C. Reg. 71/96.

title "licensed practical nurse" or "L.P.N." is reserved for people registered with the College of Licensed Practical Nurses of British Columbia.
The regulation limits the activity of a Licensed Practical Nurse to the
following nursing activities:

> A registrant may provide such nursing services related to the care of pa-
> tients as are consistent with his or her training and ability;[45] and except in
> an emergency, all nursing services provided by a registrant must be car-
> ried out under the direction of a medical practitioner who is attending the
> patient or under the supervision of a registered nurse who is providing
> services to the patient.[46]

In short, a licensed practical nurse in the province of British Columbia is
not permitted to engage in nursing practice unless supervised and directed by a qualified physician or registered nurse.

It has been suggested that in provinces where the legislation provides
only a registration mechanism, and not an exclusive right to practise
nursing, the public is not sufficiently protected:

> Registration (Certification) and licensure of the health professions exist be-
> cause the public has the right and the responsibility to protect itself from
> unsafe practitioners. As the health care system becomes more complex,
> more categories of health-care providers come into being. Consequently,
> the need increases to monitor and coordinate the emergence of these new
> categories and the expansion of the roles of existing categories ... nursing is
> the only profession now regulated through the *Health Disciplines Act* which
> does not have the authority to license its members. Under the present sys-
> tem (certification) it is possible that a member who has been disciplined for
> incompetence by the College and whose certificate has been revoked may
> be reinstated in the same employment position by a Labour Arbitration
> Board. Situations like those are not in the public interest, in order to fulfill
> its mandate to protect the public, it is essential that the Colleges of Nurses
> have the right to license those who practise nursing within the defined
> scope of practice and that these licensees have the exclusive right to prac-
> tise within that defined scope ... the present system of certification protects
> the titles "R.N." and "R.N.A." but does not provide nurses with the exclu-
> sive right to practise nursing, it therefore permits unqualified "nurses" to
> practise and is inadequate to protect the public from unsafe and unethical
> nursing care.[47]

The issue, however, is not only protection of the public from unqualified
or incompetent nursing practices. It is also the extent to which the public

---

[45] *Ibid.*, s. 4.
[46] *Ibid.*, s. 5(1).
[47] *Supra*, note 1, pp. 8-9.

ought to be entitled to obtain the services of individuals who can provide rudimentary and affordable health care services in a competent manner. Non-registered "nurses", as well as the public, might argue that the imposition of an exclusive licensing system impedes the provision of routine services, competently administered, where there are not sufficient registered nurses to meet the demand. Alternatively, the cost of providing some routine nursing services through registered nurses may be prohibitive.

NEW AREAS OF PRACTICE

We have briefly mentioned advanced nursing practice, which is a recent (and ongoing) development in Canadian health care. Advanced nursing practice goes beyond regular nursing duties into areas that were previously the domain of doctors. Nurses in advanced practice find employment in a range of settings, but perhaps their most usual role is in remote areas of the country where doctors are scarce. The Canadian Nurses Association identifies three general categories within advanced nursing practice: the clinical nurse specialist (CNS), the nurse practitioner (NP), and a variety of new roles that are often local solutions to specific needs in a facility or region.[48] A variety of titles is used in the provinces for nurses in advanced practice, without much consistency and often without any legislative definition of the titles. However, in all provinces there is an underlying acknowledgement of a higher level of expertise and responsibility for these nurses.

There are two main ways that advanced nursing practice have been addressed in the provinces of Canada: the enactment of separate legislation for nurses who provide extended health services, and the delegation of authority from doctors to nurses where it is not prohibited by some legislation.

Two provinces have enacted separate legislation which create a special class of nurse engaged in advanced practice. In Alberta and Ontario, nurses who meet extended professional qualifications are licensed to carry out a larger number of procedures in consultation with doctors, dentists, and other medical professionals.

Alberta's *Registered Nurse Providing Extended Health Services Regulation*[49] (enacted under the *Public Health Act*)[50] defines a "registered nurse providing extended health services" as:

---

[48] "Out In Front 'Advanced Nursing Practice'", *Nursing Now: Issues and Trends in Canadian Nursing,* Canadian Nurses Association, January 1977, No. 2, p. 1.
[49] Alta. Reg. 224/96.
[50] S.A. 1984, c. P-27.1 [am. S.A. 1996, c. 31, s. 2].

[A] registered nurse as defined in the *Nursing Profession Act* who is employed or engaged by a regional health authority or provincial health board established under the *Regional Health Authorities Act* or the Department of Health to provide extended health services under the regulation.[51]

The extended health services that these nurses may provide include diagnosis and treatment of common disorders affecting the health of adults and children, and referral and emergency services. A nurse's ability to provide these services, however, may be limited by the terms of an employment agreement, which is required under s. 4(1) of the regulation. The employer and the registered nurse providing the extended services must comply with the Guidelines for Registered Nurses in Advanced Nursing Practice Providing Health Care Services in Under-Serviced Communities in Alberta.

Ontario's *Regulated Health Professions Act,*[52] discussed in an earlier section, focuses on "controlled acts" that may be performed by regulated health professionals. The *Expanded Nursing Services for Patients Act*[53] proclaimed in February, 1998 authorized R.N.s who hold an extended certificate of registration to perform certain controlled acts like communicating a diagnosis, prescribing certain drugs and ordering the application of certain forms of energy to a patient. Although the term "nurse practitioner" is frequently used in Ontario, that title is not protected by the legislation. ("Registered Nurse in the Extended Class" is the term used by the College of Nurses of Ontario).

The other provinces provide for advanced nursing practice through the delegation of authority from doctors to nurses. This is done within the framework of existing legislation. It seems fair to state that in most provinces, delegation is likely an interim solution until legislative reform occurs which will both reflect or improve upon the current practice and clarify the responsibilities and rights of nurses in advanced practice.

Another development in recent years has been the regulation of midwives and their renewed acceptance as a part of the health care mosaic. Traditionally, midwives were women who assisted at childbirth and who may or may not have had formal training apart from their practical experience. Their role was overtaken by doctors in the early part of the 20th century as childbirth began to be viewed as a medical event. The reintroduction and redefinition of midwifery was, and perhaps still is, a hotly contested issue among diverse stakeholders like health professionals, women's rights organizations, and pregnant women. For years it existed in the grey area between legal and illegal (a situation which continues in

---

[51]   *Supra*, note 49, s. 1(v.2).
[52]   S.O. 1991, c. 18.
[53]   S.O. 1997, c. 9.

some provinces). Now, certain provinces have moved to regulate the provision of midwifery services. While in some provinces midwives are not required to be R.N.s, midwifery and the advanced practice of nursing have been linked in other jurisdictions.

In Alberta, there is a *Midwifery Regulation*[54] under the *Health Disciplines Act* which sets up a registration scheme for midwives who have satisfied the requirements of the Health Disciplines Board and the Midwifery Health Disciplines Committee, including an approved program of studies and an examination.[55] Midwives may:

(a) provide counselling and education related to childbearing;
(b) carry out assessments necessary to confirm and monitor pregnancies;
(c) advise on and secure the further assessments necessary for the earliest possible identification of pregnancies at risk;
(d) identify the conditions in the woman, fetus or newborn that necessitate consultation with or referral to a physician or other health professional;
(e) care for the woman and monitor the condition of the fetus during labour;
(f) conduct spontaneous vaginal births;
(g) examine and care for the newborn in the immediate postpartum period;
(h) care for the woman in the postpartum period and advise her and her family on newborn and infant care and family planning;
(i) take emergency measures when necessary;
(j) perform, order or interpret screening and diagnostic tests in accordance with Schedule 1;
(k) perform episiotomies and amniotomies and repair episiotomies and lacerations not involving the anus, anal sphincter, rectum and urethra;
(l) prescribe and administer drugs in accordance with Schedule 2; and,
(m) on the order of a physician relating to a particular client, administer any drugs by the route and in the dosage specified by the physician.[56]

The Health Disciplines Board is empowered to approve guidelines for midwifery practice, and midwives attending normal pregnancies are considered primary health care providers and are allowed to provide services in a variety of settings. If medical conditions arise that may require a physician's management, the midwife is required to consult with a physician. If the consultation determines that a physician is necessary for the management of a patient's care, the midwife must transfer primary responsibility for care to the physician (although the midwife re-

---

[54] Alta. Reg. 328/94.
[55] *Ibid.*, s. 2(1).
[56] *Ibid.*, s. 8.

tains the ability to engage in midwifery practice to the extent agreed to by the client, physician and midwife).[57]

Midwives are held to a high standard of practice governed by the best interests, welfare and informed consent of the client.[58] Investigations concerning the practice of Alberta midwives is initially handled by a Practice Review Committee consisting of three midwives, two consumer representatives and one member of the College of Physicians and Surgeons of Alberta, who have each been appointed by the Alberta Association of Midwives.[59] The Committee has the power to refer a matter to the Midwifery Health Discipline Committee of the Health Discipline Board if it discovers conduct or competence problems or if the midwife does not cooperate with the investigation.[60] Finally, a midwife is required to carry Board-approved professional liability insurance.[61]

British Columbia has also regulated midwifery under its *Health Professions Act*[62] in the *Midwifery Regulation*.[63] It provides for registration of qualified applicants with the College of Midwives of British Columbia, and only people registered with the College may use the title "midwife".[64] In addition to allowing registrants to perform the types of services already outlined in the Alberta legislation, aboriginal registrants are allowed to practice aboriginal midwifery, defined as:

(a) traditional aboriginal midwifery practices such as the use and administration of traditional herbs and medicines and other cultural and spiritual practices,

(b) contemporary aboriginal midwifery practices which are based on, or originate in, traditional aboriginal midwifery practices, or

(c) a combination of traditional and contemporary aboriginal midwifery practices.[65]

For the purposes of midwifery, only registrants or aboriginal people (on a reserve) who practised aboriginal midwifery prior to the regulation are allowed to conduct internal examinations, manage spontaneous normal vaginal deliveries and perform episiotomies and amniotomies and repair episiotomies or lacerations.[66] Under the legislation, midwives are required to advise their clients to consult a medical practitioner for a medical exam during the first trimester of pregnancy and to consult with a medical

---

57   *Ibid.*, s. 9.
58   *Ibid.*, s. 10.
59   *Ibid.*, s. 11(1).
60   *Ibid.*, s. 11(4).
61   *Ibid.*, s. 12.
62   R.S.B.C. 1996, c. 183.
63   B.C. Reg. 103/95.
64   *Ibid.*, s. 3.
65   *Ibid.*, s. 1.
66   *Ibid.*, s. 5(1).

practitioner about any deviations from the normal course of pregnancy, labour and delivery and to transfer responsibility where necessary.[67] Until December 31, 1998, midwives were allowed to take part in the "home birth demonstration project" administered by the Ministry of Health; it remains to be seen whether any new legislation will be proclaimed to allow midwives to participate in home births on a regular basis.

Some other provinces are in the process of considering separate legislation for midwives,[68] while in others, midwives appear to be considered part of the advanced practice of nursing.[69] This is another area where both new legislation and new practice guidelines may be anticipated.

CURRENT ISSUES: HISTORY OF NURSING REVISITED

The following joke was told by one nurse to another in 1922:

A public health nurse was asked by one of her patients "if she didn't think it was nice weather." The nurse replied, "I don't know, you had better ask your physician".[70]

While nursing has certainly come a long way from the days when holding an opinion was strictly a physician's prerogative, this period is perhaps not so far out of memory that it seems impossible to relate to current practices. Some historians of nursing have contended that in the late nineteenth century, "a certain class of men . . . took the more prestigious function of "curing" away from women, leaving them with "caring" (often undistinguishable from domestic work).[71] Others have contended that while there was tension between the perception of the role of nurses and doctors during

---

[67] *Ibid.*, s. 6.

[68] For example, Manitoba's *Midwifery and Consequential Amendments Act* L.M. 1997, c. 9.

[69] See, for example, "Plan of Action for the Utilization of Nurses in Advanced Practices Throughout Newfoundland and Labrador", Association of Registered Nurses of Newfoundland, May 1997.

[70] Letter of Edna Squires to Miss Knox, 7 April 1922, AO, RG 62, Flb. Box 475, cited in B. Boutilier, "Helpers or Heroines? The National Council of Women, Nursing and 'Woman's Work' in Late Victorian Canada", D. Dodd and D. Gorham, eds., *Caring and Curing: Historical Perpectives on Women and Healing in Canada* (Ottawa: University of Ottawa Press, 1994), pp. 17-47, at 26.

[71] J. Coburn, "'I See and Am Silent': A Short History of Nursing in Ontario", J. Acton et al., eds., *Women at Work, Ontario, 1850-1930* (Toronto: Canadian Women's Educational Press, 1974), 128, cited in K. McPherson, "Science and Technique: Nurses' Work in a Canadian Hospital, 1920-1939" D. Dodd and Gorham, eds., *Caring and Curing, ibid.*, pp. 71-101, at 72.

this period, it cannot be said that nurses' role was solely "unscientific",[72] and that the contribution of nurses cannot be summarized so tidily.

It is worth noting that the law has played a role both in responding to and in shaping the power balance between doctors and nurses. Early legislation reinforced the division of labour by profession (and, tacitly, by sex). It was also assumed that physicians could be all things to all patients. As professional and gender barriers have proceeded to erode in both professions, a new legal synthesis has emerged which reflects a far different understanding of the relationship between two professions that are, for better or worse, intricately linked. It is perhaps interesting to note that while a symbolic bridge has been built between the professions, there has still not been much recognition of a community of interest between female nurses and female physicians. Such a network might be able to focus on issues, like workplace abuse and harassment, which have not had much time in the limelight.

Relevant Legislation

ALBERTA

Health Disciplines Act, R.S.A. 1980, c. H-3.5
  Licensed Practical Nurses Regulation, Alta. Reg. 103/97
  Mental Deficiency Nurses Regulation, Alta. Reg. 194/89
  Midwifery Regulation, Alta. Reg. 328/94
  Psychiatric Nurses Regulation, Alta. Reg. 509/87

Nursing Profession Act, S.A. 1983, c. N-14.5
  Code of Ethics Regulation, Alta. Reg. 456/83
  General Regulation, Alta. Reg. 454/83
  Registration Regulation, Alta. Reg. 453/83

Public Health Act, S.A. 1984, c. P-27.1
  Registered Nurse Providing Extended Health Services Regulation, Alta. Reg. 224/96

BRITISH COLUMBIA

Health Professions Act, R.S.B.C. 1996, c. 183
  Licensed Practical Nurses Regulation, B.C. Reg. 71/96
  Midwives Regulation, B.C. Reg. 103/95

Nurses (Registered) Act, R.S.B.C. 1996, c. 335

---

[72] K. McPherson, *ibid.*, at 73.

MANITOBA

Licensed Practical Nurses Act, R.S.M. 1987, c. P100
  Licensed Practical Nurses Regulation, Man. Reg. 318/88

Practical Nurses Education Programs, Man. Reg. 65/86

Registered Nurses Act, R.S.M. 1987, c. R40
  Registered Nurses Regulation, Man. Reg. 459/88

The Registered Psychiatric Nurses Act, R.S.M. 1987, c. P170
  Registered Psychiatric Nurses Regulation, Man. Reg. 319/88

NEW BRUNSWICK

Health Professionals Act, S.N.B. 1996, c. 82

Nurses Act, S.N.B. 1984, c. 71

Registered Nursing Assistants Act, S.N.B. 1977, c. 60

NEWFOUNDLAND

Nursing Assistants Act, R.S.N. 1990, c. N-6
  Nursing Assistants Regulations, Nfld. Reg. 10/96

Registered Nurses Act, R.S.N. 1990, c. R-9 (as am. by S.N. 1996, c. 16)

NORTHWEST TERRITORIES

Certified Nursing Assistants Act, R.S.N.W.T. 1988, c. C-2
  Certified Nursing Assistants Investigation Regulations, R.R.N.W.T. 1990,
  c. C-1

Nursing Profession Act, R.S.N.W.T. 1988, c. N-4
  Nursing Profession Regulations, N.W.T. Reg. 004-96

NOVA SCOTIA

Licensed Practical Nurses Act, R.S.N.S. 1989, c. 319
  Licensed Practical Nurses Regulations, N.S. Reg. 177/96

Registered Nurses Act, S.N.S. 1996, c. 30
  Registered Nurses' Regulation, N.S. Reg. 72/97

Nursing Assistants Act, R.S.N.S. 1989, c. 319

ONTARIO

Expanded Nursing Services for Patients Act, S.O. 1997, c. 9.

Nursing Act, 1991, S.O. 1991, c. 32
  Committee Composition Regulations, O. Reg. 653/93
  General Regulations, O. Reg. 275/94

Professional Misconduct Regulations, O. Reg. 799/93

Regulated Health Professions Act, 1991, S.O. 1991, c. 18

PRINCE EDWARD ISLAND

Licensed Nursing Assistants Act, R.S.P.E.I. 1988, c. L-10
  Licensed Nursing Assistants Act Licensure Regulations, EC 778/89

Nurses Act, R.S.P.E.I. 1988, c. N-4
  Registration and Licensing of Nurses Regulations, R.R.P.E.I., EC 583/86
  Discipline Regulations, EC 504/89
  Schools of Nursing Regulations, EC 333/76

QUEBEC

Nurses Act, R.S.Q. 1977, c. I-8
  R.R.Q., c. I-8, rr. 1 to 15

Professional Code, R.S.Q. 1977, c. C-26

SASKATCHEWAN

Licensed Practical Nurses Act, S.S. 1988-89, c. L-14.1

The Registered Nurses Act, 1988, S.S. 1988-89, c. R-12.2
  Registered Nurses Act, 1988, Bylaws, 1995, SRNA

Registered Psychiatric Nurses Act, S.S. 1993, c. R-13.1

YUKON

Registered Nurses Profession Act, S.Y. 1992, c.11
  Registered Nurses Association Regulations, Yukon O.I.C. 1993/185

Nursing Assistants Registration Act, S.Y. 1987, c. 19
   Nursing Assistants Registration Regulations, Yukon O.I.C. 1987/168

CHAPTER 4

Professional Discipline and Nursing

SYNOPSIS

This chapter provides an introduction to nursing standards, the complaint process, the content of a discipline hearing, findings of incapacity, the penalties that may be assessed, the appeal process, and the steps to reinstatement.

INTRODUCTION

One of the most important features of professional self-regulation is the disciplinary process. The nursing profession in every province of Canada has a legal obligation to ensure that its members are performing nursing activities in a competent and appropriate manner. For example, Section 1 of Nova Scotia's *Registered Nurse Regulations*[1] offers the following summary of the mandate of the professional conduct process:

(1) The objects of the professional-conduct process are the protection and the preservation of the integrity of the nursing profession.
(2) The professional-conduct process shall seek to inhibit professional misconduct, conduct unbecoming a nurse, incompetence and incapacity by investigating, on its own initiative or on the complaints of others, alleged instances of such misconduct and, when appropriate, disposing of the matter or matters.
(3) Except when considered prejudicial to the attainment of the above objects, the professional-conduct process shall take into account the potential for the rehabilitation of the respondent [nurse].

This mandate arises out of the privilege afforded to nurses to be registered within some provinces, and in others, to have the exclusive right to engage in the practice of nursing. The public is entitled not only to expect that nurses admitted to the profession are competent and qualified, but

---
[1] N.S. Reg. 7.

in addition, that nurses will continue to be competent and qualified throughout their professional career. The fact that the nursing profession itself, and not some other body, is responsible for ensuring that the public is well-served and protected is a measure of the high degree of responsibility with which the profession is charged.

NURSING STANDARDS

The law insists upon an objective standard of nursing care which nurses must meet if we are to agree that they are treating patients in a competent manner. There are five main types of legal proceedings that may probe a nurse's professional abilities:

1. *Disciplinary proceedings* occur when a complaint is made to the College of Nurses about the competence or capacity of a nurse. If the College's investigators find reason to proceed, there will be a hearing. Disciplinary hearings are conducted by the College of Nurses in front of a disciplinary panel. If a nurse is found to be incompetent or to lack the capacity to perform nursing care to an acceptable standard, the nurse's registration may be suspended or revoked. This chapter will discuss disciplinary proceedings in further detail.
2. *Inquests* are proceedings, conducted by a coroner, that investigate suspicious deaths. While the purpose of an inquest is to find out what happened with a view to understanding how to prevent it from happening again, the purpose of an inquest is not to place blame on individuals who may have had something to do with the circumstances that caused the death. Chapter 10 will discuss inquests in more depth.
3. *Malpractice actions* occur where a patient or the family of a patient sue a nurse and allege that a nurse (and usually his or her employer and some of her co-workers) has not met an acceptable standard of nursing care and the patient has suffered harm as a result. Malpractice trials are conducted in a law court by a judge. The person who started the action is referred to as the plaintiff and the nurse (and anyone else who is named in the lawsuit and alleged to have done something wrong) is referred to as the defendant. If a defendant is found to have committed malpractice, the defendant (or its insurer) will be ordered to pay money (damages) to the plaintiff. Malpractice will be discussed at length in Chapter 9.
4. *Criminal charges* may be brought against a nurse (or anyone else) if there are grounds to believe that a criminal act has occurred. For example, if an investigation into suspicious deaths reveals evidence that suggests that a nurse has administered a lethal drug to patients

in excess of the prescribed dosage, the nurse may be charged with murder. Criminal charges against nurses are rare, and will not be covered in depth in this book.

5. *Grievance arbitrations* occur in settings where a nurse who belongs to a union in the workplace has been subject to discipline by an employer. He or she may choose to file a grievance and have the case heard by an arbitrator. Chapter 11, "Employment Law", discusses grievance arbitrations in greater detail.

Malpractice hearings and disciplinary hearings are forms of investigation in the list above that have the most in common, and the standard of care that they insist upon is similar. However, they are not the same. In a malpractice hearing, adequate or inadequate nursing will be demonstrated through the oral evidence of other nurses and health care practitioners who have expertise in the field and are able to provide a reliable opinion on what constitutes an accepted standard of nursing care in a given situation. It is essential to remember that a nurse will not be held responsible for malpractice simply on the basis that a patient has suffered harm during an unexpected medical event. Rather, malpractice occurs when the nurse fails to meet the acceptable standard of nursing care when faced with such an event. Where a nurse's conduct falls below that standard and causes grave risk to a patient, but no actual harm is incurred, court proceedings are unlikely, because there is no basis for making a damage award. These concepts will be discussed in greater detail in Chapter 9, "Nursing Malpractice".

A nurse may, however, become involved in disciplinary proceedings, even where no harm results to the patient. The purpose of the disciplinary provisions contained in provincial nursing statutes is not only to identify and sanction nurses whose conduct has resulted in harm to the patient, but more importantly, to identify and sanction nurses whose nursing practice has the potential to cause harm to the patient. The disciplinary proceeding is designed to determine whether professional misconduct occurred (a failure to maintain the standard expected of a nurse), even if it does not meet the test for malpractice (a failure to maintain a standard of care which has resulted in harm to a patient). Therefore, the standard in a disciplinary proceeding is higher than in a malpractice action.

Professional misconduct may arise from a single occurrence or event where a nurse fails to comply with appropriate nursing standards. Nurses may also be disciplined for a general failure or inability to carry out nursing duties. This condition is often referred to as "incompetence". The Ontario *Health Professions Procedural Code* (Schedule to the *Regulated Health Professions Act, 1991*) states:

[a] panel shall find a member to be incompetent if the member's professional care of a patient displayed a lack of knowledge, skill or judgment or disregard for the welfare of the patient of a nature or to an extent that demonstrates that the member is unfit to continue to practice or that the member's practice should be restricted.[2]

In Nova Scotia, incompetence means:

[T]he display of lack of knowledge, skill or judgment in the respondent [nurse's] care of a client or delivery of nursing services that, having regard to all the circumstances, renders the respondent [nurse] unsafe to practise nursing or unsafe to continue in the practice of nursing without remedial assistance.[3]

In some provinces, the professional governing body has the power to enact detailed regulations or by-laws governing the establishment of professional standards. For example, in Manitoba, the Manitoba Association of Registered Nurses has the power to enact by-laws to "develop, establish and maintain standards of professional ethics among its members".[4] In Nova Scotia, the Registered Nurses' Association is empowered to enact regulations to "develop, establish and maintain standards for the practice of nursing".[5] In Ontario, 37 acts that constitute professional misconduct are set out in the *Professional Misconduct Regulations*.[6] While not every province has this type of code that details each instance of misconduct, all provinces would agree in substance about the general standards such a code suggests.

The prohibition against "contravening a standard practice of the profession or failing to meet the standard of practice of the profession", as the Ontario code puts it, is a broad and all-inclusive assertion of nursing responsibility. The "standards of practice", in addition to being established by legislation, may also be based upon standards of performance of nursing duties established by nursing practice. A more comprehensive description of these standards may be delineated by the provincial governing body of the profession. The Saskatchewan Registered Nurses' Association has published a manual for nurses detailing 14 standards and examples of measurement criteria it will apply in order to determine whether the standard has been met. For example, the first standard and its measurement criteria are transcribed below:

---

[2] S.O. 1991, c. 18, s. 52(1).
[3] *Registered Nurses' Act*, S.N.S. 1996, c. 30, s. 26(c).
[4] *The Registered Nurses Act*, R.S.M. 1987, c. R40, s. 4(1)(j).
[5] *Registered Nurses' Act*, S.N.S. 1996, c. 30, s. 8(1)(e). See N.S. Reg. 72/97, s. 29, which sets standards for nursing education.
[6] O. Reg. 799/93.

Standard I – Assessment: The nurse collects client data

Examples of Measurement Criteria
  (a) Collects relevant data concerning the client's health status, environment, perception of health, and expectations.
  (b) Determines the priority of data collection by the client's immediate needs.
  (c) Involves the client, significant others, and health care providers in data collection.
  (d) Collects data in a systematic and ongoing method.
  (e) Validates the data with the client and appropriate others.
  (f) Documents relevant data in a retrievable form.[7]

This format communicates the expectations of the Association to nurses and tells nurses how those expectations can be met in actual situations.

An important area of a nurse's professional conduct is the responsibility to avoid conflicts of interest. For example, item 26 in the Ontario *Professional Conduct Regulations* defines "practising the profession while the member is in a conflict of interest" as an act of professional misconduct.[8] This particular standard is unlikely to affect those nurses practising in public hospitals, but for nurses practising at private hospitals, sanitoria, nursing homes, and senior citizen's residences, the prohibition against conflicts of interest may become quite relevant. This is especially true where the nurse's role goes beyond nursing and includes administrative and management duties.

One of the most important nursing standards, and one of the most difficult, is the obligation to report the suspected incompetence or misconduct of colleagues. Members of the nursing profession often come from similar backgrounds, have studied at the same institutions of learning and have a great deal of empathy towards one another in the practice. Nevertheless, professional status, as noted earlier, brings with it a statutory obligation on the part of the profession to self-govern in a manner that ensures that its members are performing nursing activities in a competent and appropriate manner. For a nurse to ignore or overlook incompetence or misconduct by colleagues, or even friends, is not only an act of professional misconduct, but may also lead to civil proceedings against both nurses if a colleague's incompetence or misconduct results in harm to a patient. In Manitoba, nurses are also required to disclose to the Association when they have reason to believe that a registered nurse is suffering from a physical or mental condition of such a nature that it is desirable in the interest of the public that the nurse no

---

[7] Saskatchewan Registered Nurses' Association, *Standards For Nursing Practice* (Regina: SRNA, 1994), p. 3.
[8] O. Reg. 799/93.

longer be permitted to practice.[9] Failure to do so is deemed professional misconduct.

Nurses should also know that the ethical obligation to report suspected incompetence or misconduct is not restricted to nursing colleagues. If you are a nurse, and you have a well-founded belief that the conduct of other health care practitioners may endanger the safety of a patient, you have an obligation to take steps to report that conduct as well. One situation where failure to warn about a colleague's misconduct may be mitigated is in a situation where a nurse is a victim of abuse by the colleague. In British Columbia, a nurse was sexually abused by a psychiatrist who worked at the same hospital. She obtained a settlement from him, but feared that disclosing this information would cause him to sue her. The Conduct Committee found that the nurse had a professional obligation to protect patients when she came to believe that patients were at risk of abuse by the physician. They held that in failing to warn others, she placed her own interests above her responsibility to her patients. The Committee imposed conditions on her membership, including a requirement to complete a biomedical ethics course. She appealed the decision to the Board, which reversed the decision. The Board found that the Committee was in error when it concluded that the member was obliged to report that patients might be at risk. The Association also published a letter of apology to the nurse for not protecting her identity as a victim of sexual abuse.[10]

It is also true that employers may have an obligation to report to the professional disciplinary body those nurses whose conduct falls below professional standards. Likewise, if a nurse or a nursing assistant is terminated from employment as a result of a failure to meet nursing standards, that termination may result in disciplinary proceedings. For example, in Ontario, an employer who terminates the employment of a member for reasons of professional misconduct, incompetence or incapacity is required to file with the registrar a written report setting out the reasons for termination. And, if a person intended to terminate the employment of a member, but did not do so because the member resigned, the person must a written report with the registrar setting out the reasons upon which the person had intended to act.[11]

Sexual abuse of patients is an area of misconduct that now receives specific mention in the legislation of several provinces. For example, the *Regulated Health Professions Amendment Act* in Ontario contains detailed

---

[9]   *Registered Nurses Act*, R.S.M. 1987, c. R40, s. 46(1).
[10] *Barr (Registration No. 569402)*, "Nursing BC" (Registered Nurses' Association of British Columbia, August/September 1995), p. 37 and November/December 1995, p. 31.
[11] *Regulated Health Professions Act,1991*, S.O. 1991, c. 18 [am. S.O. 1993, c. 37, s. 85.5].

provisions concerning sexual abuse, the purpose of which is articulated in s. 5:

> The purpose of the provisions of this Code with respect to sexual abuse of patients by members is to encourage the reporting of such abuse, to provide funding for therapy and counselling for patients who have been sexually abused by members and, ultimately, to eradicate the sexual abuse of patients by members.[12]

New Brunswick has similar legislation.[13] In addition, the *Nurses Act* requires the Association to report to the Minister of Health and Community Services regarding measures taken by the Association to prevent and deal with the sexual abuse of patients by its members. The Association must report annually to the Minister respecting complaints received respecting sexual abuse of patients.[14]

In British Columbia, if a member fails to authorize a criminal record check under the *Criminal Records Review Act* or an adjudicator under that Act has determined that a member presents a risk of physical or sexual abuse to children, the committee must take this into account, investigate the matter and decide whether to set limits or conditions on the practice of nursing by the member or whether to suspend or cancel the member's registration.[15]

THE COMPLAINT

Most discipline proceedings begin as complaints to the provincial governing body about an individual nurse. These complaints may come from patients, their families, other nurses, other health care practitioners or the administrators of health care facilities.

In some provinces, the investigation or review of a complaint by the governing body is mandatory, no matter how frivolous the complaint may appear. In Alberta, the chairperson of the Professional Conduct committee "shall, within 30 days after the date on which a complaint is received by [him or] her, commence a preliminary investigation of the complaint or appoint an investigator to conduct the investigation".[16]

---

[12] S.O. 1991, c. 18.
[13] For example, *Nurses Act*, S.N.B. 1984, c. 71 and *Registered Nursing Assistants Act*, S.N.B. 1977, c. 60.
[14] *Nurses' Act*, S.N.B. 1984, s. 45.5.
[15] *Nurses (Registered) Act*, R.S.B.C. 1996, c. 335 (Supp.), s. 39.1.
[16] *Nursing Profession Act*, S.A. 1983, c. N-14.5, s. 62(1).

Similarly, in Manitoba, the complaints committee "shall receive and review complaints brought against any member in writing".[17]

In a number of provinces, the complaint may be dealt with informally, often through the medium of a Complaints Committee. The Complaints Committee may meet with the complainant, the nurse who is the subject of the complaint and any other individuals who may have input. In some instances, the complaint may be resolved through informal means, for example, by apology by the nurse if that is appropriate. In other instances, the Complaints Committee may determine that the complaint is without merit and may recommend that no further proceedings be taken against the nurse.[18] In more serious cases where the complaint appears to have merit, the Complaints Committee may recommend that the complaint be dealt with by way of a discipline hearing. Nova Scotia's legislation gives the Complaints Committee the power to informally resolve the complaint, dismiss the complaint, provide the complainant an opportunity to appear before the Complaints Committee and to submit representations or explanations.[19] The Committee may also require the nurse to submit to physical or mental examinations, to a review of practice by qualified persons, or to such other examination as is required to determine whether the nurse is competent. If the nurse does not comply, his or her license may be suspended or restricted.[20]

In Ontario, an investigator has extensive powers to inquire into and examine the practice of the member to be investigated.[21] An investigator may apply to a Justice of the Peace for a search warrant and it will be granted if the Justice of the Peace has reasonable and probable grounds for believing that the member being investigated has committed an act of professional misconduct or is incompetent, and that there is something relevant to the investigation at the place.[22] British Columbia has an even broader provision in Section 36 (3) of the *Nurses (Registered) Act*:

On application under subsection (1), the Court may make an order under this section if satisfied on oath that there are reasonable grounds for believing that evidence may be found:

(a) that a person who is not a member has contravened this Act or the Rules, or
(b) that a person who is a member
   (i) has contravened this Act or the Rules,

---

17 *The Registered Nurses Act*, R.S.M. 1987, c. R40, s, 23(1).
18 In a number of provinces, a complainant has a right to appeal the decision of the Complaints Committee not to proceed further.
19 *Registered Nurses Regulations*, N.S. Reg. 72/97, s. 14.
20 *Ibid.*
21 *Health Professions Procedural Code*, S.O. 1991, c. 18, s. 76.
22 *Ibid.*, s. 77.

(ii) has failed to comply with a limit or condition imposed under this Act or the Rules,

(iii) has acted in a manner that constitutes professional misconduct,

(iv) is not competent to practice nursing, or

(v) is suffering from a physical or mental ailment, an emotional disturbance or an addiction to alcohol or drugs that impairs the person's ability to practice nursing.[23]

Some provinces have not followed this model and some critics argue that such wide powers are too coercive for a non-criminal investigation.

DISCIPLINE HEARINGS

In all provinces, legislation governing the nursing profession creates a Discipline Committee (which in some provinces may be called a "professional conduct committee", or by a similar title), which has the purpose of hearing and deciding discipline proceedings taken against members. The Discipline Committee is composed of nurses and is allowed to have non-nurse members as well. Proceedings before the Discipline Committee take the form of a hearing.

If discipline proceedings are taken against a nurse, the nurse's professional status is placed in jeopardy and the consequences can be serious. Accordingly, the nurse should be in a position to exercise full rights at a hearing. The nurse will likely wish to hire a lawyer to advise and represent before the Discipline Committee, to examine and cross-examine witnesses and to speak on the nurse's behalf to the committee.

In some provinces, the legislation contains a detailed description of the procedural protection to which a nurse is entitled in a hearing before the Discipline Committee. For example, the Nova Scotia legislation provides:

35 (2) In a proceeding before the professional conduct committee, the parties have the right to

a. be represented by legal counsel, a union representative or another representative;

b. the opportunity to present evidence and make submissions, including the right to cross-examine witnesses; and

c. receive written reasons for a decision within a reasonable time.

(3) Evidence is not admissible before a professional conduct committee unless the opposing party has been given, at least ten days before the hearing,

---

[23] R.S.B.C. 1996, c. 335.

a.   in the case of written or documentary evidence, an opportunity
     to examine the evidence;
b.   in the case of evidence of an expert, a copy of the expert's written
     report or if there is no written report, a written summary of the
     evidence; or
c.   in the case of evidence of a witness, the identity of the witness.[24]

The above components of the disciplinary process in Nova Scotia, even if
not set out in the governing legislation of a particular province, constitute
the components of a fair and impartial hearing. Nurses are entitled to
similar procedural protections at hearings before a Discipline Committee
of a particular province even if such procedural protections are not specifically elaborated in the legislation.[25] In Newfoundland, the lack of
statutory ability for the Discipline Committee to issue subpoenas (which
are used to force witnesses to appear in person in order to give testimony
at a hearing) has been held to be a breach of procedural fairness and a
nurses' suspension was overturned because he was unable to subpoena
the appropriate witnesses.[26]

Traditionally, hearings by the Discipline Committees of the various
provinces have been held in private. It has been suggested that the willingness of the public and of other nurses and health care practitioners to
report suspected incompetence or misconduct might be compromised by
holding such hearings in public.[27] Recent changes to legislation in some
provinces have distinguished between various types of hearings for the
purposes of determining whether a public or private hearing is necessary.
In Ontario, the legislation specifically provides that disciplinary hearings
shall be held in public unless the panel orders otherwise. However, incapacity hearings before the Fitness to Practice committee are to be closed
to the public unless the person who is alleged to be incapacitated requests the hearing to be held in public. The panel may refuse the request
if, for example, matters involving public security may be disclosed, a
person involved in a criminal proceeding may be prejudiced, or otherwise unfairly treated.[28] In Nova Scotia, the professional conduct committee is empowered to exclude any or all persons from the hearing or determine conditions for such persons remaining.[29] In Manitoba, all hearings of the Discipline Committee are held in private unless the person

---

[24] *Registered Nurses Act*, S.N.S. 1996, c. 30, s. 35.

[25] *Re Crandell and Registered Nurses' Assn. (Man.)*, [1977] 1 W.W.R. 468, 72 D.L.R. (3d) 602
     (Man. Q.B.).

[26] *Rubia v. Association of Registered Nurses of Newfoundland* (1996), 134 D.L.R. (4th) 741
     (Nfld. S.C.).

[27] See *Ontario Report of the Inquiry and the Civil Rights*, Vol. 3, p. 1198.

[28] *Health Professions Procedural Code*, S.O. 1991, c. 18.

[29] *Registered Nurses Regulation*, N.S. Reg. 72/97, s. 20(2).

whose conduct is the subject of the inquiry applies to the board for a public hearing and the board grants the application.[30]

Nonetheless, the exclusion of the public and the press from disciplinary proceedings may create the impression that the profession is willing to protect the reputations and careers of incompetent nurses at the expense of the public. Arguably, there is some legitimacy in suggesting that the public has a right of access to disciplinary proceedings, or at least, some portions of disciplinary proceedings.

A Discipline Committee is a specialized tribunal that is recognized by the courts to have "expertise" for judging competence. The Discipline Committee is entitled to make a finding of professional misconduct or incompetence based upon its own judgment that there is sufficient evidence to conclude that nursing errors have endangered the life of a patient.[31] An Ontario case also concluded that the committee has the discretion not to make a finding of professional misconduct despite its finding that the respondents failed to maintain the standards of the profession.[32]

However, a nurse's professional conduct and skill must be judged in relation to the "welfare of the patient". Courts have held that an allegation that there is a general lack of skill, knowledge or judgment is not sufficient for a finding of professional misconduct or incompetence.[33] Similarly, the British Columbia Court of Appeal has ruled that a nurses' apparent untrustworthiness and lack of remorse before an inquiry is neither the subject of the inquiry, nor sufficient grounds to establish that a nurse violated the ethical standards of the profession of nursing.[34]

A finding of incompetence on the part of a nurse must relate to what nurse's professional practice, in *Re Crandell and Registered Nurses' Association (Man.)*,[35] the Association suspended a nurse for incompetence where it was found that she had significant problems in getting along with other staff members. The court found that poor interpersonal skills on the part of a nurse ought not to deprive that nurse of registration unless those poor interpersonal skills resulted in risk of harm to patients. The suspension was quashed. The court suggested that the nurse's inability to get along with other staff members was an obstacle to her employment in the particular institution, but that nursing employment might be available elsewhere which would not involve a significant level of interpersonal skills.

---

[30] *Registered Nurses Act*, R.S.M. 1987, c. R40.
[31] *Re Reddall and College of Nurses (Ont.)* (1981), 33 O.R. (2d) 129, 123 D.L.R. (3d) 568 (Div. Ct.).
[32] *College of Nurses (Ont.) v. Eng* (1995), 84 O.A.C. 314 (Div. Ct.).
[33] *Re Singh and College of Nurses (Ont.)* (1981), 33 O.R. (2d) 92 (Div. Ct.).
[34] *Brock-Berry v. Registered Nurses' Assn. (British Columbia)* (1995), 127 D.L.R. (4th) 674, 12 B.C.L.R. (3d) 169 (B.C.C.A.).
[35] [1977] 1 W.W.R. 468, 72 D.L.R. (3d) 602 (Man. Q.B.).

In *Re Brown and College of Nurses (Ont.)*, an unreported decision referred to in *Re Matheson and College of Nurses (Ont.)*,[36] the court distinguished between a Discipline Committee's right to scrutinize professional incompetence as opposed to its inability to scrutinize "administrative duties or the other responsibilities which do not relate directly to the administration of health care to a patient for whom the nurse is responsible".[37] In other words, while the professional governing body is empowered to make findings and administer penalties for incompetent nursing activities, its jurisdiction does not allow it to discipline a professional nurse for conduct which occurs in the context of non-nursing activities.

In *Re West and College of Nurses (Ont.)*[38] a nurse had been found guilty by the College of professional misconduct. After working as a nurse for nearly five years, the nurse obtained employment as a private investigator. One method of investigation she employed was to pretend to be a staff member of a fictitious doctor's office in order to obtain access to confidential medical information. However, on appeal the Ontario Divisional Court overturned the decision of the College on the ground that the nurse was "not engaged in the performance of nursing services," and therefore, her conduct was outside the jurisdiction of the College.

INCAPACITATION

In addition to discipline proceedings which may arise against a nurse as a result of complaints made about specific acts of incompetence or professional misconduct, proceedings may also arise against a nurse who is considered to be incapacitated. Under the Ontario *Health Professions Procedural Code*, "incapacitated" means:

> [I]n relation to a member, that the member is suffering from a physical or mental condition that makes it desirable in the interest of the public that the member no longer be permitted to practise or that the member's practise be restricted.[39]

Findings of incapacity on the part of a nurse are often associated with such things as drug and alcohol addiction, physical or mental illness, or sometimes, a general determination by the disciplinary body that the

---

[36] (1979), 27 O.R. (2d) 632, 107 D.L.R. (3d) 430 (Div. Ct.). Appeal dismissed on consent (1980), 28 O.R. (2d) 611, 111 D.L.R. (3d) 179 (C.A.).

[37] *Ibid.*, at 635 O.R.

[38] (1981), 32 O.R. (2d) 85, 120 D.L.R. (3d) 566 (Div. Ct.).

[39] S.O. 1991, c. 18, s. 1(1).

nursing skills of the nurse in question have so deteriorated as to make continued practice dangerous to patients. Findings of professional misconduct or incompetence most often relate to a specific occurrence or series of occurrences in which a nurse has failed to meet appropriate nursing standards. Considerations of professional incapacity are often prospective in nature and the disciplinary body must determine whether it is likely, in the future, that a particular nurse is likely to engage in unacceptable nursing practice.

The notion of incapacitation is similar to that of incompetence except that it need not arise in the context of a specific complaint relating to patient care. In most provinces there is specific reference in the legislation which gives jurisdiction to the profession to restrict or suspend the nursing practice of members who are judged to be unable — for mental, physical or emotional reasons — to carry out their professional responsibilities.

PENALTIES

Where the provincial governing body, through its Discipline Committee, concludes that there has been professional incompetence or misconduct, the legislation of all provinces gives the profession jurisdiction to impose a penalty. The range of penalties available are the following:

(a) revocation of a nurse's membership in the professional body;
(b) suspension of a nurse's registration in the professional body for a specified period;
(c) imposition of limitations upon the areas of practice in which a nurse may engage;
(d) requirement that the nurse engage in remedial education or training;
(e) reprimand of the nurse and a record of the fact that such reprimand was made;
(f) imposition of a fine.

Reference should be made to the legislation of a particular province. The penalty imposed may involve a combination of penalties. For example, a nurse may be fined and at the same time receive a suspension, or may receive a suspension until such time as the nurse has completed a retraining program.

The penalty imposed must be fair and must conform to the statute.[40] In *Mason v. Registered Nurses' Association (B.C.)*,[41] a nurse was found to have

---

[40] In *Re Milstein and Ont. College of Pharmacy* (1978), 20 O.R. (2d) 283, 87 D.L.R. (3d) 392, 2 L. Med. Q. 297. The Ontario Court of Appeal commented that "The cancellation or

engaged in professional misconduct and the Discipline Committee decided that her nursing licence would be suspended indefinitely. On appeal to the British Columbia Supreme Court it was held that the penalty of "indefinite suspension" constituted a vague penalty which was not consistent with the provincial legislation. However, in *Hannos v. Registered Nurses Assn. (British Columbia)*,[42] interim suspension was held to be a legitimate order where the panel had identified a real and serious threat to patients' safety. For the purposes of an interim measure, it had sufficient material to conclude that suspension was a reasonable measure to take.

In *Re Singh and College of Nurses (Ont.)*,[43] the nurse was suspended by the Discipline Committee pending specified retraining. The nurse appealed the penalty imposed on the ground that it, as with the penalty in *Mason*, constituted an indefinite suspension. However, the court held that suspension pending retraining constituted a suspension for a "stated period" and denied the appeal.

Where a court, on appeal, concludes that the particular penalty imposed is inappropriate or unduly severe, it may intervene. In *Re Cunningham and College of Nurses (Ont.)*,[44] the Discipline Committee had cancelled the registration of a nurse upon a finding of professional incompetence. On appeal to the Ontario Court of Appeal it was held that although the "findings did merit some discipline," the particular penalty imposed was inappropriate and ordered the nurse to be reinstated.

APPEAL

In most provinces there is provision in the legislation for an appeal or review of the decision of the Discipline Committee by the profession's governing body itself or by an appeal committee authorized to hear appeals from the Discipline Committee. Such appeals do not constitute rehearings. In most cases, the appeal will be restricted to a review of transcripts of oral testimony and documents that constituted the evidence before the Discipline Committee in conjunction with the written reasons of the Discipline Committee. If the appeal tribunal finds that the decision reached by the Discipline Committee cannot be justified by the evidence, or is in some measure inappropriate, the decision of the Discipline Committee may be overturned or modified. While a nurse may be pres-

---

revocation of a professional licence to practise, is an extreme penalty and ought ... to be reserved for the most serious cases." (at 290 O.R.).

[41] [1979] 5 W.W.R. 509 (B.C.S.C.).

[42] Unreported, July 5, 1996, Doc. Vancouver A953585 (B.C.S.C.).

[43] (1981), 33 O.R. (2d) 92 (Div. Ct.).

[44] (1975), 8 O.R. (2d) 60, 56 D.L.R. (3d) 697 (Div. Ct.).

ent at the appeal, it is unlikely that the nurse would be given a further opportunity to testify or to call evidence and this fact highlights the importance of the original proceedings before the Discipline Committee.

In a number of provinces there is also a right of appeal to the courts. Appeal proceedings before the courts will be restricted to a review by the court of the decision of the Discipline Committee in conjunction with the evidence that was before it. A court will rarely hear evidence on appeal unless the evidence is new evidence that was unavailable at the time of the proceedings before the Discipline Committee. Moreover, it should be recognized that the courts, in dealing with an appeal from the decision of an administrative tribunal such as a professional Discipline Committee, are unlikely to second-guess that tribunal in areas where it considers the tribunal to have expertise, and will restrict its own review to legal issues as opposed to nursing issues.[45] In other words, unless there has been manifest legal error in the discipline process, a Court is unlikely to overturn or modify the Discipline Committee's decision. In *Bailey v. Saskatchewan Registered Nurses' Assn.*,[46] a nurse applied to have a penalty suspended until after her appeal. The Saskatchewan Court of Queen's Bench decided that while it might have been able to grant this request at the stage when the appeal was to the Court of Queen's Bench, it had no such power now that the appeal was to the (higher-ranking) Court of Appeal.

REINSTATEMENT

Most provincial statutes specifically provide for the restoration or reinstatement of a nurse to the provincial nursing register where a nurse's registration has been suspended or revoked. Ordinarily, the governing body will consider such an application, upon notice to other members of the profession, and order reinstatement where the nurse is able to demonstrate that those problems which lead to the suspension or revocation in the first place have been remedied and that the nurse is likely to engage in acceptable nursing practice in the future. For example, under section 20 of the *Nurses (Registered) Act*,[47] a former member is entitled to be reinstated as a member if the former member applies for reinstatement and meets the requirements for reinstatement. The applicant must provide evidence which is satisfactory to the Board of Directors, that the former member is of good character and is fit to engage in the practice of nursing.

---

[45] See *Reddall, supra,* note 31.
[46] (1996), 146 Sask. R. 6 (Sask. Q.B.).
[47] R.S.B.C. 1996, c. 335, s. 20.

In Ontario, an application for reinstatement cannot be made earlier than one year after the revocation or suspension of a certificate of registration. If the application fails, a new application can only be made after six months have passed.[48] In the Yukon, members whose registration and annual certificate have been revoked has no right to be reinstated; they may apply for reinstatement after two years have elapsed and must wait an additional two years after an unsuccessful application before applying again.[49] In Saskatchewan, if the Council refuses to reinstate the person as a nurse, the applicant may appeal the order to a judge of the court.[50]

CURRENT ISSUES – DISCIPLINE

You work at a private rehabilitation clinic. The staff physician has suggested that you receive training in alternative therapies, to better serve his clientele.

What are the implications of using therapeutic touch or other alternative therapies in a Canadian health care setting?

At present, many jurisdictions are examining the use of alternative (or "complementary") therapies in health care facilities. Two issues must be addressed:

- Is the therapy permitted? What if a patient claims to have suffered harm?
- If the therapy is not permitted, what if the patient claims to have suffered harm by not receiving it?

As a nurse, you may be asked to administer an alternative therapy, either at the request of the patient or your employer. The issue of informed consent cannot be ignored. However, before agreeing to participate in an alternative therapy, it would be wise to acquire further information about any responsibilities and liabilities you may incur.

Some professional colleges are already taking steps to examine alternative therapies. They may choose to develop standards of education, accreditation, and methods to evaluate health professionals. Related legislation is being considered by some jurisdictions.

---

[48] *Health Professions Procedural Code,* S.O. 1991, c. 18, s. 72.
[49] *Registered Nurses Profession Act,* S.Y. 1992, c. 11, s. 41(2).
[50] *Registered Nurses Act,* S.S. 1988-89, c. R-12.2, s. 38.

Relevant Legislation

See Chapter 3, "Professional Status of Nurses" for a list of relevant legislation.

CHAPTER 5

Health Records

SYNOPSIS

This chapter discusses the general common law obligation of health professionals (including nurses) to keep treatment records. Many of the statutes that regulate health professionals contain provisions that stipulate a minimum standard for record-keeping. Legislative initiatives are underway federally and in many provinces, which may lead to new rules surrounding the protection of personal health information and related duties of health professionals.

INTRODUCTION

Health records are prepared for the purpose of keeping a contemporaneous account of the care and treatment of patients. The broad range of health care services available in Canada results in the compilation and storage of records at a multitude of locations. A frequent source of health records is the hospital; records are compiled by physicians in their own offices and often contain a detailed history of their patients' health conditions. Public health nurses prepare records when seeing patients at homes, schools or clinics. Physicians may be asked to prepare medico-legal reports for the purpose of litigation. Health providers may be requested to prepare confidential reports for social workers. The Canadian health insurance system generates records which are used for monitoring cost, analyzing general health trends in the population, and tracking down abuses.

A patient's health record is an important vehicle of communication among health providers participating in the patient's treatment. It gives providers from various disciplines the precise medical status of a patient. It immediately familiarizes hospital staff with the past medical history of a patient. It informs physicians treating a patient about medications that have been prescribed and about the medications to which the patient may be allergic.

The health record will show whether there have been material changes in the patient's heart rate, blood pressure, temperature, urine content, fluid balance and other pertinent medical data. By writing an order a doctor can communicate to the nursing staff a particular form of treatment which is to be administered. This serves as notice that the particular order constitutes an aspect of the treatment plan. By signing off the order a nurse in turn communicates to other members of the health care team that the order has been carried out.

Health records may be used for other purposes. A patient (or a patient's lawyer) may require a copy of the record to establish the patient's condition while he or she was in the institution. A record may be subpoenaed to court to support or to contradict allegations of injuries sustained in an accident. Records may also be used to support or to contradict claims for workers' compensation, disability insurance, life insurance and similar claims. Patient records may be used for monitoring the cost of health care, analyzing health trends in the population, and tracking down abuses.

The health record provides a retrospective account, sometimes on a minute to minute basis, of the health care team's activities in treating a patient. Where the adequacy or propriety of treatment is under scrutiny — by a hospital committee, professional disciplinary body or a court — the contents of the health record may be the most detailed and reliable evidence available.

THE USE OF HEALTH RECORDS IN LEGAL PROCEEDINGS

Traditionally, courts have preferred the oral testimony of witnesses as the most reliable form of evidence. Witnesses are sworn to tell the truth. Their evidence can be tested by cross-examination and, where appropriate, rebutted by other oral evidence. Courts are reluctant to have evidence introduced into the proceedings that does not constitute sworn oral evidence, on the ground that such evidence may not constitute the "best evidence".

Written communications purporting to reflect the sworn evidence of a witness may be secondary to the sworn oral testimony of the actual witness. This is because the written communication may be self-serving; it has not been prepared under oath to tell the truth, nor is it susceptible to cross-examination.

Nonetheless, courts have recognized that in certain circumstances a written record may be more reliable than a witness's personal recollection, especially when the witness is attempting to recall events which took place months or years earlier, and detailed facts and information are involved that a witness ordinarily would not be able to recollect accurately. Accordingly, in court proceedings, as well as in proceedings before other tribunals, health records will be admitted into evidence where it can be established that the making of the record was contemporaneous with the occurrence of the events recorded, and that the record was made as a part of a general system for recording the care and treatment of a patient.[1]

In a malpractice proceeding, where a nurse's management of a patient may be under scrutiny, the availability of a comprehensive written record is crucial for two reasons:

1. It assists the nurse who was involved in the care of the patient to recall details of treatment, which might be difficult or impossible to recall after a period of months or years; and
2. It assists the nurse in persuading a court that the nurse's own testimony is accurate and can be believed when that testimony is consistent with contemporaneous notations shown on the record.

Where the particular health practitioner who created the notation on the records is available, that individual may be required to testify orally, although the health record may form the basis of that individual's testimony by refreshing his or her memory. It is not unusual in a medical malpractice case for a witness, who treated the patient some years before, not to have any recollection of the treatment. Such a witness must rely entirely upon the actual record in giving evidence. Where the individual who made the notation on the record is no longer available, the record itself may be evidence of the facts it contains.

GENERAL DUTY TO CREATE AND MAINTAIN RECORDS

Health professionals in all provinces and territories have professional obligations depending upon the nature of their profession and practice. In Ontario, "[f]ailing to keep records as required" is an act of professional misconduct.[2]

In addition, the College of Nurses of Ontario has established a minimum standard for record-keeping for its members. The requirements set out in this standard are probably applicable to nursing throughout Canada even where no formal standard has been established. In Ontario, registered nurses and registered practical nurses:

---

[1] *Ares v. Venner*, [1970] S.C.R. 608, 14 D.L.R. (3d) 4, 12 C.R.N.S. 349. Also, most if not all provinces have now passed legislation which permits the admission of health records into evidence.

[2] O. Reg. 799/93, ss. 1, 13, made under the *Nursing Act, 1991*, S.O. 1991, c. 32.

A. [keep] records in compliance with the policies of the employing agency.
B. where no forms are provided, [maintain] records for each period of duty which include at least:
    1. individual's name, address, age;
    2. person to be notified in case of emergency;
    3. physician's name, address, telephone number;
    4. physician's orders;
    5. date, time and relevant information about:
        a. assessment of emotional, social and physical status of individual;
        b. nursing actions, including administration of nursing medications and outcomes.[3]

Health professionals may, from time to time, delegate record-keeping to one another. A resident or intern may be directed by the staff physician to reduce an order to writing or to dictate an operative report. A nurse may write out a verbal order that is subsequently countersigned by the physician who made the order. Nurses may also be obliged, as part of their duties, to assist other health practitioners in the preparation and maintenance of the health care record. Physicians are obliged by law to maintain a medical record of patient treatment. In British Columbia, for example, rules made under the *Medical Practitioners Act*[4] set out minimum requirements for physician record-keeping. Health care providers must have the support of health administrators in recognizing the professional obligation, common law duty and in some jurisdictions, the legislative requirement, to create and maintain good-quality records.[5]

INSTITUTIONAL RECORDS

Many jurisdictions have enacted legislation setting out minimal requirements for record-keeping by health care institutions. Section 15 of the Regulation passed pursuant to the Nova Scotia *Hospitals Act*[6] provides that a "hospital shall maintain a record of the diagnostic and treatment services provided in respect of each in-patient and out-patient."[7] Section 16 of the Regulation sets out the minimum components of the hospital record, which must contain at least the following:

---

[3] *Professional Standards for Registered Nurses and Registered Practical Nurses in Ontario* (Toronto: College of Nurses of Ontario, June, 1996).
[4] R.S.B.C. 1996, c. 285.
[5] *McInerney v. MacDonald* (1990), 66 D.L.R. (4th) 736 (N.B.C.A.); affd. (1992), 93 D.L.R. (4th) 415, [1992] 2 S.C.R. 138.
[6] R.S.N.S. 1989, c. 208.
[7] N.S. Reg. 16/79.

(a) full name of the patient, including all previous surnames, where applicable;
(b) date of birth;
(c) history of present illness;
(d) history of previous illness;
(e) family history;
(f) physical examination;
(g) provisional diagnosis;
(h) orders for treatment;
(i) medical, nursing and other notes on the progress of the patient;
(j) condition on discharge;
(k) reports if any of
 (i) consultations;
 (ii) follow-up care;
 (iii) laboratory, radiological, and other diagnostic examinations;
 (iv) medical, surgical, obstetrical and other therapeutic treatment, including renal dialysis treatment;
 (v) operations and anaesthesia;
 (vi) the hospital autopsy report; and
(l) the final diagnosis;
(m) on decease of the patient in hospital, a copy of the death certificate under the *Vital Statistics Act*; and
(n) such other items as the board may prescribe.

The public hospitals legislation of Ontario provides that an admitting note clearly describing the reason for the admission of the patient and authenticated by a member of the medical or midwifery staff is to be entered in the medical record of the patient within 24 hours of admission.[8] The Ontario legislation also codifies a common practice, namely, that all orders for treatment must be in writing and signed by the "physician, dentist or midwife giving the order."[9] Alternatively, a physician, dentist or midwife may dictate an order by telephone to a "person designated by the administrator to take such orders"[10] but is obliged to "authenticate the order on the first visit to the hospital after dictating the order".[11]

In Alberta, the original or a copy of a record from another institution, which is "sufficiently recent to be relevant to the patient's current status", is to be included in the health record of the institution currently treating the patient.[12] The Alberta regulation even deals with a rule of record-keeping which may be more honoured in the breach: "[d]iagnostic and treatment service records shall be *legible*, accurate and complete." [Emphasis added].[13]

---

[8] *Hospital Management*, R.R.O. 1990, Reg. 965, s. 25 [am. O. Reg. 761/93, s. 12].
[9] *Ibid.*, s. 24(1) [rep. & sub. O. Reg. 761/93, s. 11].
[10] *Ibid.*, s. 24(2) [rep. & sub. O. Reg. 761/93, s. 11].
[11] *Ibid.*, s. 24(3)(b) [rep. & sub. O. Reg. 761/93, s. 11].
[12] Alta. Reg. 247/90, s. 13(3).
[13] *Ibid.*, s. 13(6).

Aside from hospitals, many other institutions are involved in the provision of health care, and thus, the generation of health records. For example, nursing homes, homes for the aged, chronic care facilities, psychiatric facilities, and even penal institutions are involved, to a greater or lesser extent, in health care. Many of these institutions are subject to provincial and federal legislation that may set out specific standards for record-keeping. Any review of such legislation is beyond the scope of this volume. However, those working in a particular type of institution ought to have regard for any legislation that governs health care and record-keeping in that institution.

"NON-STATUTORY" STANDARDS FOR RECORD-KEEPING

In addition to standards for record-keeping contained in legislation, institutions may develop their own internal policies regarding health records based upon the legislation itself, relevant professional standards and standards set by other health care agencies. The Canadian Council on Hospital Accreditation (hereinafter "CCHA") sets overall standards for hospital operations and provides a voluntary accreditation procedure. The CCHA sets basic requirements for the compilation of a hospital record, and those standards must be met by hospitals that seek to be approved by the Council. The standards set by the CCHA define what is meant by such terms as, for example, "admitting diagnoses", "progress notes", "discharge summary".[14]

Nursing departments within larger institutions may have established policies and guidelines for record-keeping by nurses based upon the legislative requirements and accepted professional standards. For example, in some provinces, professional nursing organizations have established standards of nursing practice which require nursing departments to develop guidelines for nursing documentation.

The standards for nursing practice developed by provincial nursing bodies require nurses to utilize the "nursing process" and a problem-oriented approach in giving patient care. This standard should be reflected in nursing documentation. The standard of care applied by a court of law will be derived from the professional standard. Consequently, nurses, to protect themselves from liability, should employ charting methods accepted and supported by the profession as well as by their employer.

---

[14] Canadian Council on Hospital Services Accreditation, *Standards for Acute Care Organization, 1995* (Toronto: The Council, 1995).

QUALITY OF RECORD-KEEPING

An inadequate or incomplete record may have an impact upon patient care. In legal proceedings where the standard of patient care is at issue, it is difficult to overstate the importance a good-quality record will have in demonstrating that the care provided was of a reasonable standard. In a malpractice proceeding, the record may carry more weight than any other evidence because the health professionals whose conduct is under scrutiny will typically place great reliance upon the record when giving oral evidence.

It is not unusual for a malpractice proceeding to reach trial five years or more after the events that gave rise to the action. In many instances, health care providers had no inkling at the time of treatment that their actions would give rise to a claim. A nurse may not discover that his or her conduct has become the subject matter of a complaint until months or years after the conduct of which the patient complains. It will be difficult to recall events precisely in the absence of accurate health records. The contemporaneous recording of information at the time that the events took place is likely to be received as more credible and objective evidence than the retrospective viewpoint of a witness or defendant whose recollections may be perceived as being influenced by the lawsuit.

Health records admitted as evidence in a court of law will be scrutinized closely. Discrepancies, inaccuracies or omissions will be used to discredit both the records and the witness who relies upon them. It is essential that nursing notes be prepared in an accurate, timely and professional manner. The following general guidelines may be useful to observe when documenting nursing actions.

1. Record at the Time of the Occurrence

Information obtained or actions taken should be recorded at the time of the occurrence or as shortly thereafter as possible. Failure to do so may lead to an inference that the record is inaccurate. Common sense dictates that the longer the period between the event and the recording of it, the more likely it is that the record will contain errors. Documentation created a considerable time after an occurrence may be influenced, inadvertently, by subsequent events. Information charted as soon after an event as possible will have the most persuasive value. The use of flow sheets placed at the bedside can make this an easier task.

2. Record Only What You Saw, Heard or Did

It is poor nursing practice to record as your own actions those carried out by another. Notations made in this manner risk a loss of credibility and may even suggest dishonesty. Nurses who record the actions or observations of someone else as their own will not be able to testify as to the truth of the event recorded as they have made no personal observations and carried out no personal treatment. Where policies of an institution require a nurse to document care given by others, the record should clearly identify both the caregiver and the individual who is documenting the information.

3. Record in Chronological Order

Entries should be made in chronological order. Failure to do so may place the accuracy of the record in doubt. An entry in the chart that is out of order may appear to have been placed there as an afterthought. It will not satisfy the criterion of contemporaneity. Where an entry has been forgotten or must be added out of order for some other reason, the entry should be dated and signed, indicating both the time of entry and the time the event occurred. This will avoid a suspicion of falsification. Spaces for later entry should never be left in the chart. Similarly, subsequent notations should never be added between the lines or in the margins. Late entries should be clearly marked as such.

4. Record in a Concise, Factual and Clear Manner

The record should show the pertinent facts clearly and objectively. Opinions or judgments should only appear when supported by sufficient documented information. For example, the notation "patient is depressed" by itself may be considered incomplete and possibly inaccurate. A court would wish to know what observations or information were relied upon to justify this conclusion. It is doubtful that any nurse could recall these details several years after the events in question unless they were recorded in the health record.

The terminology used should be as specific as possible. For example, in describing labour the phrase "progressing well" has little meaning and provides little indication that the patient was observed carefully and that the appropriate assessments were made. Nurses frequently must document under severe time constraints. However, abbreviations should be used sparingly and only where their meaning will be unmistakable. It is essential that notes be legible. Tragic errors may occur as a result of misunderstood abbreviations or illegible notes.

5. Record Frequently

The required frequency or extent of nursing documentation will be determined by the condition of the patient, generally accepted standards of care within the profession, applicable policies and procedures within the institution and any medical orders in the patient's chart. Care given or significant occurrences should be recorded. It may also be important to chart routine activities or events. In legal proceedings this charting will constitute evidence that the care and treatment of the patient was proceeding smoothly and without incident. Health practitioners often refer to the practice of "charting by exception". Such a practice should be employed cautiously, if at all. A patient's chart with routine observations and events recorded may be very valuable in demontrating that the preceding care was adequate and that a rapidly declining condition or sudden event could not have been anticipated or prevented.

The Ontario case of *Kolesar v. Jeffries*[15] concerned the death of a patient who was confined to a Stryker frame following back surgery. The hospital chart contained no record of nursing observations or activities during the eight hours preceding discovery that the patient had died. The trial judge stated:

On a ward with a great many patients the medical record becomes the common source of information and direction for patient care. If kept properly it indicates on a regular basis the changes in the patient's condition and alerts staff to developing dangers. And it is perhaps trite to say that if the hospital enforced regular entries during each nursing shift, a nurse could not make the entry until she had first performed the service required of her. In Kolesar's case the absence of entries permits of the inference that nothing was charted because nothing was done.[16]

The hospital was found liable in negligence for Mr. Kolesar's death. The court found that the ward was inadequately staffed and that the patient did not receive proper care. The trial judge made the following comments regarding the nursing records:

Finally there is the matter of nursing records. None worthy of the term were really kept. The nurses say it was their habit during the night shift to jot down on pieces of paper they were carrying, a note or two, and then at 5 or 6 a.m. they would get together, assisting each other to recall and record the events of the evening. An examination of all the records of the patients show little or nothing. I find it remarkable. Perhaps even more remarkable is what happened following Kolesar's death. On hearing of it, the Assistant Director of Nursing, Margaret Cameron, examined the medical record and noted the absence of any entry from 10 p.m. on December 30th, until 5 a.m. on the 31st. She asked Nurse Malette to write up a record which is ex. 29. One is always suspicious of records made after the event,

---

[15] (1976), 9 O.R. (2d) 41, 59 D.L.R. (3d) 367 (H.C.J.); vard. on other grounds, 12 O.R. (2d) 142, 68 D.L.R. (3d) 198; affd. on other grounds (*sub nom. Joseph Brant Memorial Hospital v. Koziol*), [1978] 1 S.C.R. 491, 2 C.C.L.T. 170, 15 N.R. 302 (*sub nom. Kolesar v. Joseph Brant Memorial Hospital*), 77 D.L.R. (3d) 161. This case is still followed on a regular basis.

[16] *Ibid.*, (1976) 9 O.R., at 47.

and if any credence is to be attached to ex. 29, it shows that at all times the patient was quite pale, very pale, and was allowed to sleep soundly to his death.[17]

In other circumstances the absence of nursing entries on the chart may lead to a different conclusion than the one reached in the *Kolesar* case. In *Ferguson v. Hamilton Civic Hospitals*[18] a patient became a quadriplegic following an angiogram. Justice Krever commented:

> While on the subject of nursing care, this is an appropriate place to say that, although invited so to find, I reject the submission that the absence of any nurse's entry in the nurses' record forming part of the hospital chart between 1:30 p.m. and 3:30 p.m. on June 27, 1973, is an indication of a failure in care on the part of the attending nurses. I infer that there was no observable change during that period that justified being recorded. With relation to nurses' notes this case is distinguishable from *Kolesar v. Jeffries* . . . in which [it was] held that where there is a positive duty on the part of a nurse to perform a physical act, the absence in the nurses' record of any reference to the performance of the act justifies the inference that the act was not performed. In the absence of any evidence that good nursing practice requires the making of a note every time a nurse attends to observe a patient, even when there is no observable change in the patient's condition, it would be extending that principle too far to apply it to routine inspections of the patient by the nurses.[19]

In effect, the frequency and extent of record-keeping by nurses requires balancing. Although it may be important to chart some routine, unexceptional events and treatment, this does not mean that every activity must be recorded.

6. Record Corrections Clearly

Corrections to the health record should be made in an honest and forthright manner. Notations that have been erased or obliterated may suggest that the record-keeper has something to hide. An error should be corrected by drawing a straight line through the mistake so that it remains legible. The error should be initialled, and the reader's attention should be directed to the corrected entry. The new entry should include the date, time and the writer's signature.

---

[17]   *Ibid.*, at 48 O.R.
[18]   (1983), 40 O.R. (2d) 577, 23 C.C.L.T. 254, 144 D.L.R. (3d) 214 (H.C.); affd. (1985), 50 O.R. (2d) 754, 33 C.C.L.T. 56, 18 D.L.R. (4th) 638 (C.A.).
[19]   *Ibid.*, at 602-603 O.R.

7. Record Accurately

Accuracy of the patient record is essential, for both medical and legal purposes. As professionals, nurses are required and expected to chart in an honest and truthful manner. In the British Columbia case of *Meyer v. Gordon*,[20] an action was brought on behalf of an infant plaintiff who had sustained permanent brain damage as a result of hypoxia at birth. In reviewing relevant nursing notes the trial judge found:

> [A]ccording to Nurse Webb's note in the hospital record, the fetal heart rate was monitored and found to be normal. She noted that Mrs. Meyer's labour was "good labour" and that she was experiencing a dilation of the cervix of 3 cm. with contractions every two minutes which were strong. Nurse Webb did not note or record the duration of each contraction. She noted that the fetus was at "mid" station.

> When Nurse Webb conducted her examination of Mrs. Meyer shortly after 11:30 she omitted to ascertain Mrs. Meyer's obstetrical history and that her first labour and delivery had been a rapid one. Nurse Webb agreed on cross-examination that if she had taken the history of the rapid first labour she would have realized that she must watch Mrs. Meyer more closely than she did.

> Nurse Webb's evidence of her understanding of the significance of her measurements of 3 cm. dilatation at 11:30 was imprecise. I found her appreciation of the progress of Mrs. Meyer's labour to be inaccurate. She testified that when she conducted the first vaginal examination, she thought Mrs. Meyer was in "early" labour. But that description was not used on the chart. She described the labour as "good" labour. In her incident report (Ex. 31) she described the labour as "hard". On cross-examination she described the stage of labour as "active labour" requiring a fetal heart rate check every 15 minutes . . .

> A further indication of her inexact approach was the use of the *expression* "mid" to describe the station or position of the fetus.[21]

Expert nursing witnesses in the case testified that the term "mid" was not specific enough in terms of evaluating the progress of labour.

In addition to finding the record-keeping inadequate, alterations and additions to the record caused the trial judge to suspect that someone had tampered with the record. The trial judge found that there was an entry on the record, a crucial entry for the purposes of this lawsuit, which

---

[20]   (1981), 17 C.C.L.T. 1 (B.C.S.C.).
[21]   *Ibid.*, at 7 and 11-12.

had been inserted by the nurse on the chart *after* the infant plaintiff had been sent to another hospital.

> I have concluded that after Nurse Webb subsequently became aware that the child was in trouble and after the child had been taken to Vancouver General Hospital, Nurse McAuley noted the inadequacy of Nurse Webb's charting. She communicated her concern of this inadequacy to Nurse Webb and Nurse Webb then made the interlineated entry. It was not until she was faced with proof at the trial that the interlineated entry was made after the copy of the chart had gone to Vancouver General Hospital that she changed her evidence.[22]

The record-keeping of the nurse was found to have contributed to serious injuries sustained by the infant plaintiff at birth. Both the nurse and the hospital were found liable.

INCIDENT REPORTS

When unusual incidents within the hospital place patients or staff at risk, an incident report must be completed. Generally, the report describes the incident, the surrounding events, any resulting injuries and the corrective action taken. The incident report does not ordinarily become part of the patient record. It is an internal document, the primary purpose of which is to provide data to the health care institution so that it may monitor, from a risk management and quality assurance perspective, actual or potential sources of harm to individuals.

Incident reports often involve patients and the incidents described may result in litigation. Where an incident report contains opinions or accusations it can be damaging to the health care institution. It is sometimes arguable that an incident report is not admissible in court on the grounds that it is privileged or confidential information. For example, if a court concludes that the incident report was made for the purpose of advising counsel about impending litigation, it may be considered privileged, and therefore, not admissible in court. In many cases, however, the incident report will be admitted into court as evidence. In *Levinson v. Royal Victoria Hospital*,[23] the Quebec Court of Appeal ruled that a patient who was injured while being treated in hospital was entitled to receive a copy of the incident report that had been prepared.

Consequently, incident reports, as well as the forms that are the basis for report, should always be prepared with the possibility of litigation in

---

22   *Ibid.*, at 18.
23   Unreported, November 18, 1982 (Que. C.A.).

mind. The report should contain accurate, concise, factual information and should be prepared by the person who actually witnessed the events. Information obtained from the patient or other individuals should be clearly identified as such. Opinions and judgments should be avoided when preparing these reports.

COMPUTERIZED RECORD-KEEPING

Legal obligations for record-keeping now include computerized records. Some jurisdictions have specifically amended their health legislation to cover situations in which the record is created, maintained or stored by computer. In Ontario hospitals, "every order for treatment" must be in "writing and shall be dated and authenticated by the physician, dentist or midwife giving the order".[24] Section 1 of O. Reg. 965 defines "writing" as including "an entry in a computer" and "authenticate" as identifying "oneself as the author of a document or a record by personal signature or by any other means authorized by the board" of the hospital. The regulation further provides:

> 34.(1) Where in this Regulation or under by-laws of a hospital, a notation, report, record, order, entry, signature or transcription is required to be entered, prepared, made, written, kept or copied, the entering, preparing, making, writing, keeping or copying may be done by such electronic or optical means or combination thereof as may be authorized by the board.
> (2) The board shall ensure that the electronic or optical means referred to in subsection (1) is so designed and operated that the notation, report, record, order, entry, signature or transcription is secure from loss, tampering, interference or unauthorized use or access.

The advent of computerized records and their use in health care raises legal issues in relation to confidentiality of patient records. Information systems that allow on-line access to health records may compromise a patient's right to privacy. The benefit of a computerized information system is the quick and easy access to patient records; however, if access is gained by third parties, even treatment providers, without the patient's consent and against the patient's wishes, a breach of patient privacy rights may result in legal liability. Several Canadian jurisdictions are contemplating broad legislation that would serve as a regulatory guide-

---

[24] R.R.O. 1990, Reg. 965, s. 24(1) [rep. & sub. O. Reg. 761/93, s. 11].

line for the creation of, and access to, electronic information systems containing patient records.[25]

RETENTION OF RECORDS

Once a health care record has been created it will be retained for a period of time. The retained record may be a reference source for future treatment of the patient, may be used as a source of data for teaching or research, may form the basis of an overall program for quality control within the institution, may be a source of measuring the standard of treatment and care afforded by the hospital or its staff, and may be a source of evidence in respect of disciplinary or legal proceedings that arise out of the care and treatment of the patient.[26]

Although legislation may suggest that certain parts of the patient's record can be disposed of once the patient has been discharged from hospital, this may not be prudent. In some cases, checklists or graphic charts may be an important part of the record should the care and treatment of the patient subsequently be called into question.

There is little consistency among the provincial statutes regarding retention of records. For example, Newfoundland[27] and Nova Scotia[28] provide for the maintenance of hospital records, but do not provide any specific guidelines in respect of the period for which they ought to be retained. In addition to the written documentation contained in the hospital chart, such things as x-ray films, microscopic slides, foetal monitoring tapes and other records created during the course of a patient's treatment may be considered part of the health care record and may be subject to the retention requirements of the governing legislation.

The importance of nurses' notes cannot be overemphasized. For the same reason that nurses' notes showing temperature, blood pressure, respiration, vital signs or fluid balance pose problems for retention and storage (they are bulky and can comprise hundreds of pages in relation to a single patient), they are also capable of providing a complete day-to-day, and even minute-to-minute account of the patient's treatment. In the context of malpractice actions, nurses' notes may become the focus of attention, as it is often the nurses who have the most frequent contact

---

[25] At the time of writing, Ontario's draft *Personal Health Information Protection Act, 1998*, had yet to receive First Reading.

[26] See L.E. Rozovsky and F.A. Rozovsky, *The Canadian Law of Patient Records* (Toronto: Butterworths, 1984), pp. 34-44 for a comprehensive summary of the purposes for which retained records may be employed.

[27] *The Hospitals Act, 1971*, R.S.N. 1990, c. H-9, s. 35.

[28] N.S. Reg. 16/79, ss. 15-16.

with the patient and who are responsible for noting the patient's progress on a continuous basis. Given that it is likely to be months or years following treatment before a patient may decide to start a malpractice action,[29] it may not be safe to assume that shorter retention periods can be safely applicable to nursing records.

CONFIDENTIALITY OF RECORDS

The Supreme Court of Canada has held that it is a patient's right to have records or information in regard to his or her treatment and health condition kept confidential.[30] Although the decision in *Halls v. Mitchell* concerned disclosure of confidential health information by a physician, the legal principle enunciated by the court is equally appropriate to the nursing profession:

> It is, perhaps, not easy to exaggerate the value attached by the community as a whole to the existence of a competently trained and honourable medical profession; and it is just as important that patients, in consulting a physician, shall feel that they may impart the facts touching their bodily health, without fear that their confidence may be abused to their disadvantage.[31]

In its *Guidelines for Professional Behaviour*, the Ontario College of Nurses recommends the following standard:[32]

Behavioural Directives
Nurses demonstrate regard for privacy and confidentiality by:

1. Keeping all personal and health information confidential within the obligations of the law and standards of practice.
2. Informing clients or substitute decision-makers that other health care team members will have access to any information obtained while caring for clients.
3. Refraining from collecting information which is unnecessary to provide health care.
4. Protecting clients' physical and emotional privacy.[33]

Because of the nature of modern medical treatment, health professionals, out of necessity, will have to communicate confidential information about

---

[29] See Chapter 9, "Nursing Malpractice".
[30] *Halls v. Mitchell*, [1928] S.C.R. 125, [1928] 2 D.L.R. 97.
[31] *Ibid.*, at 138 S.C.R.
[32] College of Nurses of Ontario, *Guidelines for Professional Behaviour* (February, 1995).
[33] *Ibid.*, at p. 9.

a patient's condition and background to other personnel who are responsible for the care of the patient. In some instances, the information communicated will not be noteworthy. The revelation by a health professional to a third party that a patient has a gall bladder disorder, has undergone routine minor surgery or is being treated for high blood pressure is unlikely to raise any complaint by the patient. On the other hand, there may be situations where the patient's condition is of a much more sensitive nature and a patient would be very disturbed at having it divulged unless it was necessary for the purpose of his or her treatment.[34] A current example would be that of a patient who is being treated for HIV/AIDS. If this condition were communicated without the permission of the patient it could result in severe harm to the patient, and consequently, in legal proceedings.

A breach of confidentiality may constitute an invasion of privacy, which is actionable at law.[35] A right to privacy includes not only a right to territorial or spatial privacy, but also a right to privacy of information. The Supreme Court of Canada has commented:

[S]ituations abound where the reasonable expectations of the individual that the information shall remain confidential to the persons to whom, and restricted to the purposes for which it is divulged, must be protected.[36]

Privacy has been defined as "the right of the individual to determine for himself [or herself] when, how, and to what extent he [or she] will release personal information about himself [or herself]".[37]

In some instances, an obligation may arise for health care professionals to divulge particulars of a patient's condition even though this may be contrary to the patient's wishes. For example, in the case of *Tarasoff v. The Regents of the University of California*,[38] a student informed his psychologist that he was going to kill another student. The psychologist did not report

---

[34] In *Peters-Brown v. Regina District Health Board* (1995), 26 C.C.L.T. (2d) 316, 136 Sask. R. 126 (Q.B.); affd. (1996), 31 C.C.L.T. (2d) 302, 48 Sask. R. 248 (C.A.), a hospital was found liable for breach of contract and negligence. A confidential list of patients requiring bodily fluid precautions was posted in an inner room in the Emergency Department in full view of police officers, ambulance workers and correctional officers who had access to the room. The plaintiff, a correctional officer who had been a patient at the hospital approximately eight years before, overheard her co-workers discussing her name in connection with the list. The court concluded that the hospital should have employed a more secure method for recording such information, and further, that the list should have been kept up-to-date. The judge held that it was foreseeable that the release of confidential information would cause harm to the plaintiff. Damages were awarded.

[35] *Roth v. Roth* (1991), 9 C.C.L.T. (2d) 141, 4 O.R. (3d) 740 (Ont. Gen. Div.).

[36] *R. v. Dyment* (1988), 55 D.L.R. (4th) 503, at 515 (S.C.C.).

[37] *R. v. Duarte* (1990), 53 C.C.C. (3d) 1 (S.C.C.).

[38] 551 P. 2d. 334 (Cal. 1976).

this to anyone. After the student carried out his threat, the family of the deceased student brought an action against the psychologist and alleged that he should have taken steps to warn their son or the proper authorities. The psychologist argued that to do so would have breached the confidential relationship he had established with his patient. Nonetheless, the Supreme Court of California held that despite the confidential nature of his relationship with his patient, the psychologist was under an obligation to inform the police of the danger so that appropriate steps could be taken. In circumstances where patients may harm themselves or others, a nurse may be compelled to breach the more general obligation of confidentiality.[39]

Specific legislation in most provinces obliges health professionals to disclose certain health information. For example, provincial highway traffic legislation may require physicians to notify government licensing authorities of any patient who may be suffering from a condition which makes it dangerous for that patient to drive. Likewise, legislation requires the mandatory reporting of births, deaths, stillbirths and suspected child abuse. Public health legislation may require health care practitioners to report such conditions as venereal disease, tuberculosis, polio, and more recently, HIV/AIDS, to public health authorities. In some instances, failure to comply with the legislation can result in prosecution.

The legislation of some provinces specifically states that health records are to remain confidential except in certain specified instances. For example, the Nova Scotia *Hospitals Act* provides:

> The records and particulars of a hospital concerning a person or patient in the hospital or a person or patient formerly in the hospital shall be confidential and shall not be made available to any person or agency except with the consent or authorization of the person or patient concerned.[40]

In Newfoundland, a person who publishes or discloses information obtained from hospital records may be subject to a summary conviction and a fine not exceeding $500 or in default of payment, 30 days' imprisonment.[41]

---

[39] L.E. Ferris, H. Barkun, J. Carlisle, B. Hoffman, C. Katzman and M. Silverman, "Defining the Physician's Duty to Warn: Consensus Statement of Ontario's Medical Expert Panel on the Duty to Inform" (1998), 158 C.M.A.J. 1473. See also *Final Recommendations of Ontario's Medical Expert Panel on Duty to Inform* (Toronto: Institute for Clinical Evaluative Sciences, Technical Report No. 97-04-TR, October 1997). Although the report examines the obligations of physicians and not nurses, many of its recommendations merit the attention of all health professionals.

[40] R.S.N.S. 1989, c. 208, s. 71(1).

[41] *The Hospitals Act*, R.S.N. 1990, c. H-9, s. 35(6).

Generally speaking, health professionals are well-advised not to discuss or disclose health care information about a patient unless the communication is made for the express purpose of treating the patient. Although it is difficult to put into practice, avoidance of discussions or "gossip" among health personnel about patients and their respective conditions should be avoided. If the need arises to disclose health care information about a particular patient outside the clinical context, consideration should be given to consulting legal counsel.

A patient who commences a legal proceeding relating to the provision of health care may be considered to have waived the right to confidentiality. In *General Accident Assurance Co. of Canada v. Sunnybrook Hospital*,[42] an issue arose as to whether legal counsel for a hospital's insurer was entitled to production of the health records of a patient without consent. The court held that the hospital was entitled to permit its insurers or their solicitors to inspect and to make copies of the health records in question for the purpose of dealing with, or defending, a civil action.

ACCESS TO HEALTH RECORDS

Most health care institutions are prepared to provide copies of the patient's health care record to the patient, at the patient's expense, upon presentation of a written authorization signed by the patient. In fact, contrary to the belief of some patients, the record belongs not to the patient, but to the hospital. Traditionally, hospital records have been considered as "property of the hospital and shall be kept in the custody of the administrator".[43] More recently, the Supreme Court of Canada has determined that health records are held in fiduciary trust by the administrator, for the patient.[44]

In Ontario, the practice of providing the patient with a copy of his or her record upon presentation of a signed authorization is prescribed by statute. The governing legislation specifically prohibits the hospital from permitting "any person to remove, inspect or receive information from medical records" except in limited circumstances.[45] The Regulation does provide that a hospital "may permit . . . a person who presents a written request signed by . . . the patient"[46] to obtain a copy of the record. It should be noted that in requesting the release of psychiatric records, a

---

[42] (1979), 23 O.R. (2d) 513 (H.C.J.).
[43] *Re Mitchell and St. Michael's Hospital* (1980), 29 O.R. (2d) 185, 112 D.L.R. (3d) 360, 19 C.P.C. 113 (H.C.).
[44] See *McInerney v. MacDonald* (1992), 93 D.L.R. (4th) 415, [1992] 2 S.C.R. 138.
[45] R.R.O. 1990, Reg. 965, s. 22(1).
[46] *Ibid.*, s. 22(6)(c).

clear authorization by the patient will not lead necessarily to release of the record.[47]

Most public hospitals legislation contains provisions governing access to patient records. The general rule is that patients are entitled to have access if they supply a written consent or authorization to the institution. In some instances, however, the right to access is restricted. For example, the Alberta *Hospitals Act* provides that a hospital board, the Minister of Health or a physician may:

> (a.1) with the written consent of a patient or his/her guardian or without that consent if the patient is not mentally competent and does not have a guardian, divulge any diagnosis, record or information relating to the patient to any person, if in the opinion of the person making the disclosure it is in the best interests of the patient to disclose the information.[48]

The Alberta statute does not define what is meant by "in the best interests of the patient". In fact, such a qualification conflicts with the developing common law and with statutes in other jurisdictions in which "competent" patients are given unlimited access to their health records. Although some mental health legislation restricts access to psychiatric records in situations where disclosure is likely to result in harm to the patient or others, in a time when access to records is routine and consistent with the principle of openness and reduced paternalism in health care, a provision that can deny access on a basis as broad and imprecise as the "best interests of the patient" is difficult to justify.

In many instances, despite the general rule of confidentiality, health records or information contained in those records will be released to third parties. Circumstances in which access to health records may be authorized without the consent of the patient include the following:

1. Where a court or other tribunal orders health care records to be produced;[49]
2. Where information from the record and particulars of a patient are furnished to a municipal official for the purpose of establishing a patient's entitlement to insured medical services;[50]
3. Where a professional governing body requires access to the health care records for the purpose of investigating a complaint.[51]

---

[47] See Chapter 6, "Mental Health Law".
[48] R.S.A. 1980, c. H-11, s. 40(5) [am. S.A. 1988, c. M-13.1, s. 55].
[49] Sask. Reg. 331/79, s. 16.
[50] *Hospitals Act*, R.S.N.S. 1989, c. 208, s. 71(6)(c).
[51] R.R.O. 1990, O. Reg. 965, s. 22(3).

4.   A person engaged in health or medical research may obtain access to the record for teaching purposes or for scientific research where such access is in the public interest.[52]

Generally, the cost of providing a copy of the record should be borne by the patient or the person authorized to receive a copy of the record. Any charge must be reasonable. A charge that is punitive or that exceeds the actual cost to the institution may be viewed as an unreasonable obstacle to access. In some jurisdictions, the issue of cost may be dealt with directly in the governing statute.

In *McInerney v. MacDonald*,[53] a physician was ordered to provide a patient with a copy of all medical documentation in his possession, including documentation he had received from other physicians who were acting as consultants. The physician had resisted releasing the consultants' reports in the belief that it would be unethical to provide documents that were the property of other physicians. This position was rejected. Rather, it was held that the patient had a right to access all medical documents involving her care and treatment which her physician relied upon in providing such care and treatment. This was subject to a physician's conclusion that release of some or all of the record would be harmful to the patient or to others. Furthermore, the physician's discretion in this regard was subject to the supervising jurisdiction of the courts. The patient, however, was required to pay a legitimate fee for the preparation and reproduction of the information by the physician. The access did not extend to information in the physician's file that was outside the doctor-patient relationship. *McInerney* supports the practice of most hospitals and other health facilities – the payment by the patient or other party who wishes to obtain access to the patient record.

In *Re Meyers and Wellesley Hospital*,[54] a patient had lapsed into a coma as a result of complications arising from childbirth. The patient's husband wished to obtain a copy of her hospital record for the purpose of evaluating the care received by his wife. The hospital took the position that the statutory regulation governing the disclosure of patient records permitted access only to a patient and disclosure of the record was subsequently ordered by the court. In *Halliday v. McCulloch*,[55] the court set out a procedure for the production of hospital records where a patient claimed privilege for some of the records. It is not within the exclusive purview of a health facility to decide what records are privileged. There is a distinction between patient records and other types of records.

---

[52]   *Hospitals Act*, R.S.N. 1990, c. H-9, s. 35(4).
[53]   *Supra*, note 44.
[54]   (1986), 57 O.R. (2d) 54 (H.C.J.).
[55]   (1986), 1 B.C.L.R. (2d) 194 (C.A.).

Nonetheless, in *Duras v. Welland General Hospital*,[56] a hospital was ordered to produce the personnel files of physicians who had been sued where such records were considered relevant to the issues in the action.

PEER REVIEW AND QUALITY ASSURANCE PRIVILEGE

In some Canadian jurisdictions, there may be a privilege preventing the disclosure of documents or reports prepared for the purpose of quality assurance or the ongoing assessments and review of health professionals (including nurses), and their peers. In *Smith v. Royal Columbian Hospital*,[57] the plaintiff in a malpractice action sought production of all documents relating to an investigation conducted by the Credentials Committee of the hospital. The hospital took the position that the documents were privileged and that their release would compromise the hospital's ability to obtain frank and honest opinions about the physician's competence from the physician's colleagues. It was argued that the hospital's inability to conduct such an investigation on a confidential basis would compromise patient care. In that case, the court accepted the hospital's claim for privilege on the ground that the interest in protecting the confidentiality of the inquiry process outweighed the public interest in having the particular documents disclosed.

CURRENT ISSUES – HEALTH RECORDS / CONFIDENTIALITY

You work in a public health clinic, and know most of the patients who come in by name. In the waiting room one morning, you recognize a man whose wife regularly brings in their three children. A while later, one of the clinic's physicians makes an off-handed comment to the effect that she would hate to be the last to know what was going on in her own marriage. When you ask what she means, she changes the subject.

At the end of the day, you look at the patient's chart. You see that the husband has been given an HIV test, but there is no indication of what prompted his decision to be tested.

When the wife comes in the following week suffering from what appears to be the flu, you worry that she should be tested for HIV as well. Should you raise it with her, or pretend you know nothing about her husband's test?

---

[56] (1985), 51 O.R. (2d) 284 (H.C.).
[57] (1981), 123 D.L.R. (3d) 723 (B.C.S.C.).

What *do* you know about her husband's HIV test? You know nothing about his reasons for being tested, nor what the test results will be. You are not part of the therapeutic relationship between him and his physician. Stop speculating immediately. Every patient has a right to confidentiality, and that right is only superseded in limited circumstances. There are reporting requirements in the public health legislation of every jurisdiction for communicable diseases, including HIV, which will be triggered only if the test results come back positive.

All health professionals have a duty to keep information about their patients confidential. Idle gossip undermines the trust patients place in their health care providers, and the husband's physician would be wise to keep her comments to herself.

It is never wise to take action where you do not have all the facts. If you have doubts about whether you have a positive obligation to involve yourself in this type of situation, call your provincial professional association for their advice. Their ethics guidelines and practice resources are available to assist you.

Relevant Legislation

There is no particular federal or provincial statute that deals in a general manner with health records. Usually, guidelines relating to the creation, maintenance, and retention of access to health care records are found in the legislation that regulates the management of the particular type of health care institution; *i.e.,* public and private hospitals and nursing homes. Legislation relating to health care records may be found in statutes that regulate public health and the various health care professions. Currently, the federal government and several provincial jurisdictions are drafting privacy legislation that would create guidelines for the collection, use and disclosure of personal health information. At the time of writing, only Manitoba had passed its health privacy statute, the *Personal Health Information Act.*[58]

---

[58]   S.M. 1997, c. 51.

CHAPTER 6

Mental Health Law

SYNOPSIS

This chapter provides an overview of the rules governing mental health, including involuntary and voluntary status, consent to health care treatment, review procedures, patients' rights, and mental health records.

INTRODUCTION

Special legal considerations apply to the treatment of patients suffering from conditions that affect their mental health. These considerations apply even when the patient is not being treated in a facility designated for the treatment of psychiatric patients. All provinces have passed legislation that sets out a statutory scheme for the treatment of the mentally ill. This legislation relates to the management of health facilities in which psychiatric patients are being treated, the voluntary or involuntary admission of psychiatric patients, the competence of psychiatric patients to consent to treatment, the retention and disclosure of psychiatric records, and the availability of legal remedies or review procedures for psychiatric patients who may wish to question the nature or propriety of their psychiatric care and treatment. This legislation applies to hospitals and to other health facilities that treat patients suffering from mental illness and is not exclusive to treatment of patients in institutions dedicated to psychiatric care.

The treatment of psychiatric patients raises legal issues that ordinarily do not arise in the treatment of other illnesses. The fact that patients are often detained against their will places a high priority on the protection of individual rights within the treatment facility.[1] Consequently, nurses who work in the mental health field may be required to be as sensitive to legal issues as they are to medical issues. Decisions about treatment for psychiatric patients often receive a high degree of scrutiny from tribunals or boards charged with the review of such decisions under the provincial

---

[1]   See Chapter 12, under "Charter of Rights and Freedoms".

legislation. The question of whether treatment is authorized by law may eclipse any question of the quality of the treatment administered, and whether or not it was effective.

INVOLUNTARY DETENTION AND CONFINEMENT

It is a well-accepted common law principle that a patient who is sufficiently competent to understand the nature and appreciate the consequences of his or her health condition can decide either to accept or reject treatment.[2] Even a patient who is suffering from a condition which is likely to be fatal, if untreated, is permitted to exercise his or her own free will about whether treatment will be administered.[3] A nurse who disregards the patient's wish and proceeds to administer treatment commits a battery and may be the subject of civil and criminal proceedings.[4] Likewise, if a patient wishes to discharge himself or herself from hospital, even against medical advice, the patient's decision must be respected. Preventing a patient from leaving a health care facility voluntarily may constitute the intentional tort of false imprisonment.[5]

However, in the mental health setting, a patient's right to accept or refuse treatment sometimes may be subordinated to other concerns. Provincial mental health legislation, in restricted situations, allows health care providers to detain patients for the purpose of examination and diagnosis, to admit and confine patients against their will to psychiatric facilities, and, in some provinces, to forcibly administer treatment to patients who are determined to be in need of it.

The underlying rationale of these legislative measures is based upon a societal desire to protect individuals whose decision-making ability regarding care and treatment has been undermined by the disease itself. The legislation assumes that in certain situations a patient or would-be patient is affected by illness in such a way that the patient is incapable of making rational or concrete choices about treatment. That determination may result not only in confinement of patients for the purpose of protecting them from themselves, but because of a risk of harm to others.[6] In

---

[2]   *Marshall v. Curry*, [1933] 3 D.L.R. 260, at 266, 60 C.C.C. 136 (N.S.) 136 (N.S.S.C.).

[3]   *Malette v. Shulman* (1990), 72 O.R. (2d) 417, 67 D.L.R. (4th) 321 (C.A.); *Nancy B. v. Hôtel-Dieu de Québec*, [1992] R.J.Q. 361 (C.S.).

[4]   *Mulloy v. Sang*, [1935] 1 W.W.R. 714 (Alta. C.A.).

[5]   *Burke v. Efstathianos* (1961), 34 W.W.R. 337, 27 D.L.R. (2d) 518 (Man. C.A.); *Ketchum v. Hislop* (1984), 54 B.C.L.R. 327 (S.C.).

[6]   In *Starnaman v. Penetanguishene Mental Health Centre* (1995), 24 O.R. (3d) 701, 100 C.C.C. (3d) 190, 83 O.A.C. 95, a pedophile with a long criminal record and a lengthy history of aggressive sexual misconduct directed primarily at young females was serving a prison sentence for uttering a death threat. A few days prior to his release the names and ad-

Canada, when individuals demonstrate that they could be a danger to themselves or to others, involuntary detention and treatment is considered.

In most jurisdictions, the test for involuntary detention and confinement is two-fold; it requires both that patients suffer from mental illness and that patients are a danger to themselves or others. The language varies from jurisdiction to jurisdiction. In Alberta, for example, a physician must certify that the patient is "suffering from a mental disorder" and is "in a condition presenting or likely to present a danger to himself [or herself] or others" before involuntary admission to a psychiatric facility is authorized.[7] In British Columbia a physician is required to certify that the patient requires "medical treatment" and requires "care, supervision and control" in a mental health facility "for his [or her] own protection or for the protection of others".[8]

In some jurisdictions, involuntary detention and confinement criteria may go beyond the two-fold requirement of a mental disorder and risk of harm to the patient or others. In Manitoba, a physician may make an application for the involuntary psychiatric assessment of a person suffering from a mental disorder where that disorder is likely to result in "substantial mental or physical deterioration of the person,"[9] even though the physician cannot certify that the patient presents a likelihood of "serious harm" to the patient or others. In Ontario, there is a similar criterion that may result in involuntary confinement, even in the absence of risk of "danger" or serious "harm" to the patient or to others, but the criterion is restricted to situations where the patient may sustain "imminent and serious physical impairment". It would seem that the likelihood of serious or substantial *mental* impairment, when coupled with the other criteria set out in the legislation, is insufficient to authorize involuntary detention in Ontario.[10]

---

dresses of children and single mothers in Kingston and Toronto areas were discovered in his cell. One of the doctors at the Mental Health Centre requested an assessment. The assessment was conducted by a staff psychiatrist and a certificate of involuntary admission was signed. The certificate was renewed on several occasions. The patient appealed the involuntary admission, but the Ontario Court of Appeal held that at the date of the review hearing the doctor had clearly established the criteria for involuntary admission. The patient also argued that his involuntary admission was a violation of ss. 7 and 12 of the *Canadian Charter of Rights and Freedoms*. These arguments were dismissed by the court.

[7] *Mental Health Act*, R.S.A. 1988, c. M-13.1, s. 2. In addition to this medical diagnosis, the two physicians must also certify that the patient is unsuitable for admission to a psychiatric facility other than as a formal (*i.e.*, involuntary) patient (s. 8).

[8] *Mental Health Act*, R.S.B.C. 1996, c. 288, s. 22(2).

[9] *The Mental Health Act*, R.S.M. 1987, c. M110, s. 8(1) [re-en. R.S.M. 1987 Supp., c. 23, s. 7].

[10] Ontario's *Mental Health Act*, R.S.O. 1990, c. M.7, s. 15(1), contains one of the most detailed set of criteria for involuntary commitment:

In addition to a medical determination that an individual should be the subject of involuntary detention and confinement, most provincial statutes permit police officers or courts to apprehend and convey individuals to psychiatric facilities for examination by a physician. In British Columbia, for example, where a person is acting in a manner likely to endanger his or her own safety or that of others, and is apparently suffering from a mental disorder, a police officer or constable is empowered to take that person into custody and to immediately convey that person to a physician who will assess him or her.[11] Likewise, in British Columbia, an application can be made to a provincial court judge to issue a warrant for the apprehension of a person and the subsequent "conveyance" and "admission" of that person to a psychiatric facility upon evidence that there is "good reason to believe that a person is a mentally disordered person and dangerous to be at large".[12]

Involuntary commitment has been attacked in the courts as contrary to the *Canadian Charter of Rights and Freedoms*.[13] In the case of *Thwaites v. Health Sciences Centre Psychiatric Facility*,[14] the Manitoba Court of Appeal struck down provisions in that province's *Mental Health Act* which permitted the detention of individuals for examination when a single medical practitioner believed that a person should be confined. The court determined that compulsory committal in these circumstances violated the *Charter's* guarantee of freedom from arbitrary detention or imprisonment. A revision of the offending section in the *Mental Health Act* was upheld by the court in a subsequent court challenge.[15] The court stated that compulsory detention, even authorized by statute, will be considered arbitrary under the *Charter* if the statute does not narrowly define the persons with respect to whom it may be properly invoked and does

---

Where a physician examines a person and has reasonable cause to believe that the person,
  (a) has threatened or attempted or is threatening or attempting to cause bodily harm to himself or herself;
  (b) has behaved or is behaving violently towards another person or has caused or is causing another person to fear bodily harm from him or her; or
  (c) has shown or is showing a lack of competence to care for himself or herself,
and if in addition the physician is of the opinion that the person is apparently suffering from mental disorder of a nature or quality that likely will result in,
  (d) serious bodily harm to the person;
  (e) serious bodily harm to another person; or
  (f) imminent and serious physical impairment of the person,
the physician may make application in the prescribed form for a psychiatric assessment of the person.

[11] R.S.B.C. 1996, c. 288, ss. 28(1) and (2).
[12] *Ibid.*, ss. 28(3), (4) and (5).
[13] *Constitution Act, 1982, enacted as Schedule B to the Canada Act 1982*, (U.K.) 1982 c. 11 [hereinafter the "*Charter*"].
[14] [1988] 3 W.W.R. 217 (Man. C.A.).
[15] *Bobbie v. Health Sciences Centre* (1988), 14 C.R.D. 125.40-03.

not prescribe the conditions under which the person may be detained. However, the court concluded that the more precise definition of "mental disorder" contained in the revised legislation, combined with the introduction of objective criteria which had to be met before an involuntary admission certificate was completed, satisfied the requirements of the *Charter*. Although the applicant in *Bobbie* was deprived of his liberty under the *Charter*, it was in accordance with the principles of fundamental justice. In effect, although the rights of an individual can be abrogated in limited circumstances, the abrogation is unlawful where the abrogating process is unlawful.

The Manitoba Court of Appeal held that the *Mental Diseases Act*[16] was breached when a woman was taken mistakenly to a psychiatric hospital, admitted without authority and held for 15 days.[17] In a more recent British Columbia case, the plaintiff successfully sued for false imprisonment when she was incarcerated unlawfully in a psychiatric facility and forcibly injected with prescribed drugs.[18]

CONTINUATION OF INVOLUNTARY STATUS

Because of the infringement of individual rights which is, by necessity, associated with involuntary status, the legislation of all provinces contains provisions which require the further verification of a patient's condition before involuntary status can be continued. In a number of provinces, the initial determination of involuntary status is only for observation and assessment; some further determination must be made before the individual is formally admitted.

For example, in Ontario, an initial determination of involuntary status is made during a "psychiatric assessment", at which time the patient is detained. A person cannot be held under an application for assessment in a psychiatric facility for longer than 72 hours.[19] Upon the conclusion of the initial examination and assessment, the physician must release the person or obtain consent from the person for admission on a voluntary basis. In circumstances where the physician concludes that the patient should be admitted against his or her will, and that the necessary criteria for involuntary admission have been fulfilled, the physician must complete a "certificate of involuntary admission".[20] The physician completing the certificate of involuntary admission must be different from the one

---

[16] R.S.M. 1954, c. 161.
[17] *Burke v. Efstathianos, supra*, note 5.
[18] *Ketchum v. Hislop, supra*, note 5.
[19] Ontario *Mental Health Act, supra*, note 10, s. 15(5)(b).
[20] *Ibid.*, s. 20(1)(c).

who completed the original application for psychiatric assessment.[21] An involuntary patient cannot be detained in a psychiatric facility in Ontario for more than 14 days under a certificate of involuntary admission, but must be made the subject of a series of renewal certificates which require a further examination and assessment of the patient's condition at stipulated intervals.[22]

The mental health legislation of each province contains legislative safeguards which require that patients be assessed at regular intervals to determine whether the patient's condition continues to meet the criteria set out in the legislation for involuntary status. If the criteria are not met, or, in the alternative, if further examination and assessment are not undertaken, the patient's involuntary status is terminated.

Generally, the authority to detain and to admit a patient involuntarily is reserved for a physician. Nurses are not permitted to involuntarily detain or admit a patient. The decision must be based on the physician's own observations and knowledge of the patient's condition, although it is not necessary for the patient to be in the physical presence of the physician for the certificate of involuntary admission to be issued.[23] It has been suggested that the issuing of a certificate of involuntary admission by a physician, based on information received over the telephone and without a face-to-face examination of the patient, is insufficient. However, the court has not been required to rule on that point.[24] It is likely that any determination would depend upon the particular facts of the case, and whether the physician had good reason to believe the patient was suffering from a mental illness that gave rise to a risk of harm to the patient or to others.

INVOLUNTARY DETENTION UNDER THE CRIMINAL CODE

In addition to involuntary detention and confinement under provincial mental health law legislation, there is also legislation under the federal *Criminal Code*[25] that can result in the involuntary detention and confinement in psychiatric facilities of persons who have been charged with a criminal offence. A person charged with a criminal offence can be admitted to a provincial psychiatric facility in two situations. First, a determination may be made in the course of criminal proceedings that the ac-

---

[21]   *Ibid.*, s. 20(2).
[22]   *Ibid.*, s. 20(4).
[23]   *Grieger v. Dua*, unreported, December 29, 1994 (Ont. Gen. Div.).
[24]   See *Cascone v. Rodney* (1981), 131 D.L.R. (3d) 593 (Ont. H.C.J.).
[25]   *Criminal Code*, R.S.C. 1985, C-46.

cused is "unfit to stand trial".[26] The presumption is that the accused is fit to stand trial, unless the court is satisfied otherwise, on a balance of probabilities.[27] A court may order, usually based upon medical and psychiatric evidence, that the accused be detained until he or she either is acquitted or becomes fit to stand trial. The *Criminal Code* sets out a complex procedural code to protect the rights of accused persons in this situation. The accused is likely to be detained in a psychiatric facility in the province where the criminal proceedings take place. In theory, the accused can be detained indefinitely until he or she has recovered sufficiently to be considered fit to stand trial. However, the *Code* mandates a continuing series of reviews to establish whether the accused's condition has changed.

Second, a person may also be detained at a provincial psychiatric facility because of a finding following a criminal trial, that the accused is "not criminally responsible on account of mental disorder".[28] Similarly, the accused will be held at an approved psychiatric facility for an indefinite period, subject to a continuing process of reviews in which the provincial review board determines whether continued custody is required by law.

An inmate in a federal correctional facility who requires care and/or treatment in a psychiatric facility may be transferred involuntarily. This has been supported by case law, in spite of the fact that it is no longer authorized by the *Criminal Code*. In *Khan v. St. Thomas Psychiatric Hospital*,[29] an inmate opposed her transfer to a provincial psychiatric hospital on the basis that she was already detained, in segregation for the most part, in a maximum security penitentiary. She argued that it could not be said that enforced custody in a psychiatric facility would prevent harm to others. It was suggested that the involuntary admission, in that case, was for the underlying purpose of involuntary treatment. The Court of Appeal disagreed, concluding that "[s]ince it is caused by mental illness, her dangerousness may be more easily anticipated, gauged and assessed in a psychiatric facility than in a prison setting".[30]

Generally, once an individual has been ordered into custody at a provincial psychiatric facility pursuant to the *Criminal Code*, the individual is considered, for practical purposes, to be an "involuntary patient" within the facility. Unlike patients who have been detained and confined under provincial mental health legislation, and who can be released by medical personnel, an accused who has been detained and confined under the

26 *Ibid.*, s. 672.11 [added 1991, c. 43, s. 4; am. 1995, c. 22, s. 10].
27 *Ibid.*, s. 672.22 [added 1991, c. 43, s. 4].
28 *Ibid.*, s. 672.54 [added 1991, c. 43, s. 4].
29 (1992), 7 O.R. (3d) 303 (C.A.).
30 *Ibid.*, at 310.

Criminal Code cannot be discharged from the facility without the authority of a court or a provincial review board.

VOLUNTARY STATUS

Individuals suffering from mental illness may be admitted voluntarily to a health care facility for the purpose of treatment just as individuals may be admitted for treatment of any other type of illness. They have an absolute right to refuse treatment and have an absolute right to discharge themselves, even against medical advice. Individuals must be provided with sufficient information about any proposed treatment to enable them to give an informed consent.

In most jurisdictions, there are provisions for voluntary patients to be considered for involuntary status. If a situation arises where a voluntary patient's conduct raises concern as to whether or not the patient's condition meets the criteria for involuntary status, steps must be taken to have the patient examined in accordance with the procedures stipulated by the legislation before the patient can be treated as other than a voluntary patient.

In some jurisdictions, special provisions in the governing legislation highlight the general obligation of health care providers (including nurses) and administrators to safeguard the distinction between voluntary and involuntary patients. In British Columbia, a nurse in charge of a ward in a mental health facility must ensure that a voluntary patient can "communicate without delay to the director ... any desire to leave".[31] The Manitoba legislation stipulates that a voluntary patient may leave the psychiatric facility at any time or refuse any treatment.[32] In the Yukon, the legislation states that a voluntary patient must be discharged "forthwith" if the patient so requests.[33] An involuntary patient, whose status has been changed from involuntary to voluntary, must be "promptly informed" of his or her right to leave the facility.[34]

TREATMENT OF INVOLUNTARY PATIENTS

In some jurisdictions, little or no distinction is made between involuntary admission and involuntary treatment. Authority and responsibility for the treatment of psychiatric patients may be delegated by statute to the

---

[31]   *Mental Health Act*, R.S.B.C. 1996, c. 288, s. 8(1)(a).
[32]   *Mental Health Act*, R.S.M. 1987, c. M1110, s. 7(4).
[33]   *Mental Health Act*, S.Y. 1989-90, c. 28, s. 4(2).
[34]   *Ibid.*, s. 17(3).

administrator of the psychiatric facility. For example, in British Columbia, the involuntary admission of a patient by the completion of two admission certificates, gives the director of the provincial mental health facility the authority to sign consent to treatment forms for a patient in order to ensure that:

> each patient in a provincial mental health facility is provided with professional service, care and treatment appropriate to his condition and appropriate to the function of the Provincial mental health facility . . .[35]

The British Columbia legislation further provides that a patient held in a provincial mental health facility under the *Criminal Code* provisions relating to accused persons who are unfit to stand trial or who are not guilty by reason of mental disorder "must receive care and psychiatric treatment appropriate to his or her condition as authorized by the director.[36] In effect, the British Columbia legislation suggests that the determination of involuntary status gives the facility and its health care providers a right to administer treatment to the patient without that patient's consent.

In Ontario, an involuntary patient retains the right to refuse treatment unless a finding is made that the patient is incapable of doing so. Where an involuntary patient is not mentally competent, consent may be given or refused by an authorized substitute decision maker.[37] Alternatively, a psychiatric review board may authorize specified psychiatric and other related medical treatment of a mentally incompetent patient if it is satisfied that:

> (a)(i)the treatment will or is likely to improve substantially the condition of the person to whom it is to be administered, and the person's condition will not or is not likely to improve without the treatment, or
> (ii) the person's condition will or is likely to deteriorate substantially or to deteriorate rapidly, without the treatment, and the treatment will or is likely to prevent the deterioration or to reduce substantially its extent or rate;
> (b) that the benefit the person is expected to obtain from the treatment outweighs the risk of harm to him or her;
> (c) that the treatment is the least restrictive and least intrusive treatment that meets the requirements of clauses (a), and (b); and
> (d) that the person's condition makes it necessary to administer the treatment before the final disposition of the appeal.[38]

---

[35] *Mental Health Act*, R.S.B.C. 1996, c. 288, s. 8(1)(a).
[36] *Ibid.*, s. 30.
[37] *Health Care Consent Act*, S.O. 1996, c. 2, s. 10(1).
[38] *Ibid.*, s. 19(2).

In Nova Scotia, as in Ontario, the legislation stipulates that an involuntary patient cannot be treated, if competent, without that patient's consent. Where the patient is incompetent, there is provision for a relative or the public trustee to exercise a substitute consent.[39]

In Manitoba, every patient of a psychiatric facility has the right to refuse consent to psychiatric or other medical treatment except in urgent situations where immediate treatment is necessary, or where a review board has authorized treatment against the expressed desire of the patient. That province's legislation requires that a physician, as soon as is reasonably possible after admission, determine whether the patient is mentally competent to consent to psychiatric or medical treatment by considering:

(a) whether the patient understands:
(i) the condition for which the treatment or course of treatment is proposed;
(ii) the nature and purpose of the treatment or course of treatment;
(iii) the risks and benefits involved in undergoing the treatment or course of treatment; and
(iv) the risks and benefits involved in not undergoing the treatment or course of treatment; and
(b) whether the patient's ability to consent is affected by his or her condition.[40]

If a determination is made by the health care provider that the patient is competent to consent to or refuse treatment, no treatment can be authorized without that patient's consent even though the refusal to accept treatment may be physically or mentally harmful to the patient.

It is interesting to note that in Alberta[41] there is a specific provision in the legislation to overturn the decision of the competent psychiatric patient. The attending physician may apply to a review board to authorize the giving of specified psychiatric treatment and other related medical treatment to an involuntary, but competent, patient where consent has been refused. The legislation empowers the review panel to "make an order that ... treatment may be administered"if the proposed treatment would be in the "best interest" of the patient having regard to certain criteria set out in the legislation. The criteria relate to the likelihood of the patient improving with treatment, the weighing of risks involved in treatment and whether the treatment being proposed is the least intrusive treatment available in the circumstances.[42] One mention of the com-

---

[39] *Hospitals Act*, R.S.N.S. 1989, c. 208, s. 54(2).
[40] *Mental Health Act*, R.S.M. 1987, c. M110, s. 24(3).
[41] *Mental Health Act*, R.S.A. 1988, c. M-13.1, s. 29.
[42] *Ibid.*

petent patient's rights is a provision that authorizes a competent patient to refuse psychosurgery.[43] A number of mental health statutes appear to treat psychiatric patients differently from other patients in that they purport to override the decision of a competent patient. In doing so, they may offend the equality rights set out in the *Charter*.

In contrast, the Ontario legislation, which also requires a determination of competency to be made in relation to consent to treatment, restricts the role of the Consent and Capacity Board to the determination of capacity or incapacity, but does not give the board the authority to make decisions on behalf of incapable persons. That decision must be made by a guardian of the person or an attorney for personal care who is authorized under the *Substitute Decisions Act, 1992* and who must act in a manner consistent with prior capable wishes of the patient, or if the patient's wishes are unknown, in the best interest of the patient."[44] In other words, a competent psychiatric patient, like any other patient, can refuse treatment, even if the refusal will have, from the health care providers' point of view, harmful consequences. The court has held that *parens patriae* jurisdiction cannot be invoked to abrogate the *Charter* rights of competent mentally ill patients, nor can it be invoked to authorize the medical treatment of an incapable person who has expressed prior capable wishes relating to the proposed treatment.[45] In *Re Howlett and Karunaratne*,[46] the court held that the provisions of the Ontario *Mental Health Act*, which permitted the involuntary treatment of a mentally *incompetent* patient did not infringe the patient's rights under the *Charter*.

COMPETENCY

The question of competency can arise in a variety of other settings. All provinces have passed legislation[47] providing for the appointment by the

---

[43] *Ibid.*, s. 29(5).

[44] *Substitute Decisions Act, 1992,* S.O. c. 30, s. 66 [am. S.O. 1996, c. 2, s. 43].

[45] *Fleming v. Reid* (1991), 4 O.R. (3d) 74 (C.A.).

[46] (1988), 64 O.R. (2d) 418 (Dist. Ct.).

[47] Alberta: *Dependent Adults Act,* R.S.A. 1980, c. D-32; British Columbia: *Patients Property Act,* R.S.B.C. 1996, c. 349; Manitoba: *The Mental Health Act,* R.S.M. 1987, c. M110, ss. 56-79; New Brunswick: *Infirm Persons Act,* R.S.N.B. 1973, c. I-8; Newfoundland: *The Mentally Disabled Persons' Estates Act,* R.S.N. 1990, c. M-9; Northwest Territories: *Guardianship and Trusteeship Act,* S.N.W.T. 1994, c. 34 [not yet in force]; Nova Scotia: *Incompetent Persons Act,* R.S.N.S. 1989, c. 218; Ontario: *Substitute Decisions Act, 1992,* S.O. 1992, c. 30, Prince Edward Island: *Mental Health Act,* S.P.E.I. 1994, c. 39, R.S.P.E.I 1988, c. M-6.1, s. 40; Saskatchewan: *The Mentally Disordered Persons Act,* R.S.S. 1978, c. M-14; *The Dependent Adults Act,* S.S. 1989-90, c. D-25.1. See also Gerald B. Robertson, *Mental Disability and the Law in Canada,* 2nd ed. (Toronto: Carswell, 1994), Part I: Property and Personal Guardianship.

court of a committee charged with managing the affairs of someone found to be mentally incompetent.[48] Generally, these statutes give the committee control over the individual's estate. Historically, this type of legislation was intended to deal with financial aspects of the individual's estate, but its use has been broadened to include other areas. In the treatment of the mentally ill there is sometimes a presumption that mental illness can be equated with incompetence. This is not the case. A patient cannot be considered incompetent to make decisions about treatment, finances, personal hygiene or anything else simply because that patient suffers from a mental illness.

In Prince Edward Island, competency legislation was used to allow a substitute consent to be given by the committee for treatment of a patient. In the 1983 case of *Re Casford*,[49] the Supreme Court of Prince Edward Island granted a provisional guardianship order to move a woman into an institutional setting where care and treatment could be administered. Her illness rendered her not only physically incapable of taking care of herself, but also so "unreasonable and uncooperative" that it was extremely difficult for anyone to provide the care she required. The *Mental Health Act*[50] defined "a person in need of protection" as a person "who is suffering from such a disorder of the mind" that he or she requires supervision and control. Without explicitly declaring Mrs. Casford to be incompetent, the court used the provisions of the Act to appoint a guardian and provide her with personal care.

In Alberta, Ontario and Saskatchewan, legislation has been passed specifically for the purpose of authorizing substitute decisions for treatment. Section 6 of the Alberta *Dependent Adults Act* notes that:

> When the Court is satisfied that a person named in an application for an order appointing a guardian is:
> (a) an adult, and
> (b) repeatedly or continuously unable
> (i) to care for himself [or herself], and
> (ii) to make reasonable judgments in respect of matters relating to his [or her] person the Court may make an order appointing a guardian.[51]

---

[48] This concept is best known as guardianship of the person, but some provinces use the term committee (pronounced committée) of the person. Originally created in English law to deal with the management of the mentally incompetent individual's property, guardianship of the person has been criticized for its lack of clarity in respect of basic issues such as authority of the guardian.

[49] (1983), 43 Nfld. & P.E.I.R. 240, 127 A.P.R. 240 (P.E.I.S.C.).

[50] R.S.P.E.I. 1974, c. M19 s. 2(o) [am. 1974, c. 65, s. 5(a)]; now S.P.E.I. 1994, c. 39; R.S.P.E.I. 1988, c. M-6, s. 1(m) "person in need of guardianship".

[51] Alberta: *Dependent Adults Act*, R.S.A. 1980, c. D-32; Saskatchewan, *The Dependent Adults Act*, S.S. 1989-90, c. D-25.1.

The Alberta and Ontario legislation is a departure from traditional mental incompetency statutes that authorize substitute decision making. It is justifiably discriminating in its ability to grant limited guardianship permitting dependent adults to exercise independent judgment, to the extent that they are capable of managing their own affairs. Compared to traditional incompetency legislation, this would appear to be an improved model for substitute decision making.

A question of competency may arise in circumstances where there is concern about a person's capacity to handle his or her financial affairs, to enter into contracts, to make a will, to testify in court, to vote, to marry, to be a witness in a court proceeding or to instruct counsel. In those instances, courts may be compelled to make determinations about competency, often with the assistance of health care personnel.

In *Clark v. Clark*,[52] Justin Clark, a resident at a government facility for the handicapped, expressed a desire to participate in a residential placement program, despite severe personal limitations from cerebral palsy. His father, who opposed this desire, applied to the court to have him declared mentally incompetent. However, the judge determined that Justin was mentally competent to make decisions about his own lifestyle and issued a declaratory order to that effect.

The subject of competency has become one of renewed interest in recent years. The fact that some provinces have passed legislation which specifically distinguishes involuntary patients from competent patients demonstrates a recognition that the two conditions cannot be equated. In many jurisdictions, there is a growing recognition that a determination of competency must be related to the particular transaction under scrutiny. Hence, a patient who is incompetent to make decisions about his or her psychiatric treatment may be quite competent to make a decision as to whether or not an appendix should be removed or about the financial management. A global determination that an individual is mentally incompetent without relating that incompetence to a particular subject matter or area of decision making may constitute an overly broad determination of incompetency, and hence, a denial of individual rights.

REVIEW PROCEDURES

In all Canadian jurisdictions, decisions about admission and treatment are subject to review by a board or tribunal appointed for that purpose. In some provinces, a patient who wishes to contest an involuntary admission may apply to the court. The Nova Scotia *Hospitals Act* provides:

---

[52]   (1982), 40 O.R. (2d) 383, 3 C.R.R. 342, 4 C.H.R.R. D/1187 (Co. Ct.).

[A] person in a facility of the guardian of that person or his spouse or next of kin or the Public Trustee may, on five clear days notice in writing to the administrator of the facility, apply to the judge of the county court for the district in which the facility is situate for the discharge of the person on the ground that he [or she] is not suffering from a psychiatric disorder or is not a danger to his [or her] own safety or the safety of others.[53]

Upon such an application, the judge is required to review the evidence and records. The judge may require the patient to be examined by one or more medical practitioners. If the judge, upon considering the evidence, determines that the person should not be detained in the facility, the judge may grant a discharge.[54] Similarly, in British Columbia, involuntary patients may apply to the court for discharge.[55] In the remaining provinces, a review board is appointed to consider such an application.

The nature of the review will depend upon the particular jurisdiction. In New Brunswick and Prince Edward Island, review boards are required only to "conduct an investigation", but are not required to hold a hearing.[56] In Ontario, an application to the review board in respect of an involuntary admission or a determination of incompetency requires a hearing at which the patient is entitled to be represented by counsel, examine and cross-examine witnesses, have full access to the health care record and exercise other procedural rights.[57] Furthermore, in some provinces where review boards are appointed, a party to proceedings before the review board is entitled to appeal the review board's decision to the courts. The legislation in both New Brunswick and Prince Edward Island is silent on this point, but further redress by judicial review would be possible in either jurisdiction.

PATIENTS' RIGHTS

The field of mental health law is subject to a constant tension between the concepts of individual rights and involuntary care and treatment. Personal freedom favours autonomy of the person and the right of individuals to make choices about treatment that are respected by others. Conversely, the intrusion of the state through legislation mandating care and treatment which contravenes the expressed desire of the patient may be justified on the ground that the state has an interest in preventing in-

---

[53]   R.S.N.S. 1989, c. 208, s. 47(1).
[54]   *Ibid.*, s. 47(2).
[55]   R.S.B.C. 1996, c. 288, s. 27.
[56]   R.S.N.B. 1973, c. M-10, s. 32(1); R.S.P.E.I. 1988, c. M-6, s. 26(1).
[57]   *Statutory Powers Procedures Act*, R.S.O. 1990, c. s. 22.

dividuals from harming themselves and others. This is particularly relevant in situations where the individual's expressed desires may be a function of illness and not the result of rational processes.

This state intrusion has been based historically on two seemingly contradictory principles: the *parens patriae* power and the police power. The term *parens patriae* refers to society's interest in protecting the vulnerable. Government has used this concept to support legislation mandating involuntary detention and admission. The police power has been used to uphold the traditional state interest in public order and welfare. Its primary goals have been to protect property and the physical safety of citizens, and not the individual interests of the mentally disordered.

Treatment of psychiatric patients in the context of these two concepts can lead to difficult decisions for health care providers. Statutory authority, which allows, in specific situations, compulsory detention, restraint and treatment, does not permit the unrestricted infringement of personal freedom. Several provincial statutes contain specific provisions that highlight the contradiction between personal freedom and compulsory treatment. In practice, however, the distinction will be one of judgment on the part of the individual caregiver, and no exhaustive list of possible situations can be prepared.

Caregivers have an obligation to ensure that patients who are being detained involuntarily are not released or permitted to escape without legal authority. Failure to fulfil that obligation may result in legal sanction. In British Columbia, a person commits an offence who:

(a) assists a patient to leave or to attempt to leave a Provincial mental health facility without proper authority;
(b) does or omits to do an act to assist a patient in leaving or attempting to leave a Provincial mental health facility without proper authority; or
(c) incites or counsels a patient to leave a Provincial mental health facility without proper authority.[58]

The fact that a patient is involuntarily detained, however, does not authorize care or treatment that is discriminatory or unfair. Involuntary patients must be treated like any other patient to the extent that their conditions and the security of the institution allow. In British Columbia, a person employed in a provincial mental health facility or private mental hospital (including a nurse) who "ill treats, assaults or wilfully neglects a patient" is guilty of an offence punishable by fine or incarceration.[59] In Newfoundland, the *Mental Health Act* provides:

---

[58] *Supra*, note 55, s. 17(1).
[59] *Supra*, note 55, s. 17(2).

[I]f the administrator, medical director or an officer, or other person employed in a treatment facility maltreats, abuses or neglects any patient, or obstructs patients from communication with the review board, such administrator, medical director, officer, or other person shall be guilty of an offence and shall be liable on summary conviction to a penalty not exceeding $500, or in default, to imprisonment for a period not exceeding 6 months.[60]

The mere fact that a patient is a psychiatric patient does not allow the obstruction, censoring or interception of the patient's mail or other forms of communication. In Alberta, communication written by or to a patient in a facility shall not be "opened, examined or withheld" and "its delivery shall not be obstructed or delayed in any way by the board or a member of the staff of a facility".[61] It has been held, however, that a policy at a psychiatric facility requiring that mail be opened under the observation of staff does not violate a psychiatric patient's rights under the *Charter*.[62] The Alberta legislation also provides that a patient may receive visitors during hours fixed by the board unless a physician considers that a visitor would be "detrimental to the patient's health".[63] This provision is very broad, and of doubtful legal validity, if one accepts that a competent psychiatric patient should be able to refuse or accept treatment (and by extension, choose to refuse or accept visitors) even though it may be harmful to the patient's health. A lawyer acting for a patient "may visit the patient at any time".[64]

In Nova Scotia, there are specific provisions relating to incoming and outgoing mail and telephone calls. No outgoing mail can be opened, examined or withheld or its delivery obstructed or delayed.[65] However, the administrator of a facility may insist on being present at the opening of the mail and may remove "contents detrimental to the addressee or others, but not the correspondence itself." Such withholding can only occur where it is the opinion of a psychiatrist that failure to withhold the contents would be "detrimental" to the patient. Similarly, patients are permitted to make and receive unmonitored telephone calls at reasonable times unless it is the opinion of the psychiatrist that the calls would be "detrimental" to the patient.[66] The legislation stipulates that patients shall be permitted to receive visitors at reasonable times and circumstances.[67]

---

[60] *Mental Health Act*, R.S.N. 1990, c. M-9, s. 20.
[61] R.S.A. 1988, c. M-13.1, s. 15.
[62] *Everingham v. Ontario* (1993), 100 D.L.R. (4th) 109 (Ont. Gen. Div.).
[63] *Supra*, note 61, s. 16(1).
[64] *Ibid.*, s. 16(2).
[65] *Hospitals Act*, R.S.N.S. 1989, c. 208. ss. 70(1), (2).
[66] *Ibid.*, s. 70(5).
[67] *Ibid.*, s. 70(6).

Psychiatric facilities in Nova Scotia are required to post copies of the legislation relating to patient rights "in a place within the hospital where they can be seen".[68] That province's facilities are required to provide advice in written form regarding patients' rights in respect of correspondence, telephone calls, visiting rights, "the right to counsel" and the right to have a "file reviewed by a review board or a court".[69]

In Quebec, the *Mental Patients Protection Act*[70] requires that each involuntary patient must be handed a form entitled "Rights and Recourses of Persons Admitted for Close Treatment" which sets out in detail the legal rights and remedies available to a patient who wishes to contest involuntary detention. In Saskatchewan, the *Mental Health Services Act* provides that an involuntary patient:

(a) shall be informed promptly of the reasons for his [or her] apprehension or detention, as the case may be; and
(b) is entitled on his own request to receive a copy of the certificate, warrant or order pursuant to which he [or she] has been apprehended or is detained, as the case may be, as soon as is reasonably practicable.[71]

The Saskatchewan legislation does not require, however, that the patient be provided with a written explanation of the rights and remedies to contest involuntary status.

In the Yukon, the mental health legislation stipulates that no person shall be deprived of any right or privilege by reason of having received mental health services or by reason of being named in any form or certificate under the statute.[72] The Act lists a number of rights of mental health patients, including the right to receive communications in the language with which the patient is most familiar, unrestricted access to visitors, legal representation, telephone and mail access, the right to wear clothing or apparel of the patient's choice unless doing so would constitute a danger or offend others, and the right to be informed about the legal process that has led to the patient's involuntary detention and the patient's right to challenge the involuntary status.[73]

The legislation of a particular province may not address the subject of patient rights in the detail that one finds in other provincial statutes. However, in any province a denial or restriction of basic rights simply because a patient suffers from a psychiatric illness, and not because of a clinical or therapeutic reason authorized by law, may amount to a

---

[68] *Ibid.*, s. 70(7).
[69] *Ibid.*, s. 70(8).
[70] R.S.Q. 1977, c. P-41, s. 27.
[71] S.S. 1984-85-86, c. M-13.1, s. 16(1).
[72] *Mental Health Act*, S.Y. 1989-90, c. 28, s. 40(1).
[73] *Ibid.*, ss. 40(1.2)-41.

denial of the patient's common law rights or the patient's rights under the *Charter*.

PSYCHIATRIC PATIENT ADVOCATES

In Ontario, health care providers must consider the impact of the Psychiatric Patient Advocate Office (hereinafter "PPAO") on mental health care. Established by the Ministry of Health in 1982, the PPAO appoints individuals to act as advocates on behalf of patients in each of the provincial psychiatric facilities. Although advocacy services are not mandated by legislation, the Minister has given the PPAO the authority under s. 9(1) of the *Mental Health Act*, to carry out its advocacy functions.

The advocates report to the Director of the P.P.A.O., who is accountable to the Minister and Deputy Minister on policy matters, and to the Assistant Deputy Minister for Institutional Health and Community Services on administrative matters. Rights advisors have also been assigned to each provincial psychiatric facility, and provide legal information to involuntary patients.

The PPAO is a quasi-independent agency of the Ministry of Health. It does not speak for the Ministry. Its mandate is as follows:

* to advance the legal and civil rights of psychiatric patients in all provincial psychiatric hospitals;
* to inform the patient, family, hospital staff and the community about patients' legal and civil rights;
* to assist, facilitate and help resolve the complaints made by psychiatric patients by providing an avenue for resolution for negotiation according to the patient's instructions;
* to investigate alleged incidents and assess institutional and systemic responses to them; and
* to refer patients, when necessary, to outside community advocacy resources such as community organizations, lawyers, or physicians who may offer a second psychiatric opinion.[74]

In Alberta, the patient advocate is appointed by the provincial cabinet and is charged with investigating complaints from, or relating to, formal patients.[75] The patient advocate is authorized to engage the services of lawyers, psychiatrists or other persons having special knowledge,[76] and is

[74] As discussed with Mr. Vahe Kehyayan, PPAO Director; January, 1999.
[75] *Mental Health Act*, S.A. 1988, c. M-13.1, s. 45.
[76] *Ibid.*, s. 46(2).

required to prepare an annual report summarizing his or her activities in the year. When investigating a complaint, a patient advocate is required to:

- notify the board of the facility in which the formal patient is detained of the nature of the complaint;
- notify the formal patient in writing that the complaint has been received and is under investigation;
- notify the other person named in the complaint of the investigation; and
- contact the formal patient and conduct any necessary investigation.[77]

The patient advocate may request, in writing, a copy of a policy or directive of the facility, and medical records or documents relating to the patient who is the subject of the complaint. The board of the facility must "within a reasonable time after [receiving] the request, provide access to the materials requested."[78]

In New Brunswick, the government "may designate persons, services or organizations as patient advocate services".[79] It is the duty of patient advocate services to offer advice and assistance to persons who are detained in a psychiatric facility or who have been certified as involuntary patients.[80] A patient advocate has the right at all reasonable times to meet with the patient, to attend hearings and to have access to books, records and other documents relating to the patient who is the subject of advocacy.

PSYCHIATRIC RECORDS

Access to psychiatric health care records in Canada may differ from access to non-psychiatric records. Generally, it is the practice in Canada for health care facilities to release records to patients upon receiving an authorization signed by the patient. In the case of psychiatric records, however, the psychiatric facility may have some concern that release of records to the patient may be harmful to the patient or others. In some instances, there may be justification for concluding that a psychiatric patient will misinterpret or distort the contents of the psychiatric record in a way that may be harmful to the patient's own health. Release

---

[77] *Patient Advocate Regulation* Alta. Reg. 310/89, s. 3.
[78] *Ibid.*, s. 5(5).
[79] *Mental Health Act*, R.S.N.B. 1973, c. M-10, s. 7.6(1) [added S.N.B. 1989, c. 23, s. 5].
[80] *Ibid.*, s. 7.6(2) [added S.N.B. 1989, c. 23, s. 5].

of the record may divulge to the patient the names of individuals (*i.e.*, family or friends) who have been in communication with caregivers and who may have been responsible for the patient's initial admission to the psychiatric facility. There may be a legitimate fear that divulging the names and participation of those individuals will put them at risk. In those circumstances, psychiatric facilities must consider carefully the advisability of releasing records to the patient simply on the basis of a signed authorization.

At the same time, there must be a legitimate concern that release of the record may lead to harm to the patient or others before a psychiatric patient's access is restricted. If access is refused simply because the request has been made by a psychiatric patient, a court will likely interpret the refusal as discriminatory and unacceptable. In addition, the facility will have to consider carefully whether part of the record should be released, rather than releasing the record in its entirety.

Several jurisdictions have provisions in their mental health legislation that restrict access to psychiatric records. In Ontario, the *Mental Health Act* contains a statutory mechanism for the review of requests for the release of psychiatric records. The legislation provides that no person shall "disclose, transmit or examine a clinical record" unless prescribed conditions are met. Generally speaking, a record cannot be disclosed until it has been examined by the "officer in charge" of the psychiatric facility and the "attending physician" who are then authorized to disclose, transmit or permit the examination of it to certain persons.[81] However, the psychiatric facility may choose not to release the record in circumstances where the attending physician states in writing that he or she is of the opinion that release of the record:

(a) is likely to result in harm to the treatment or recovery of the patient; or
(b) is likely to result in,
(i) injury to the mental condition of a third person, or
(ii) bodily harm to a third person.[82]

Where there is a refusal to release the record in the context of a court proceeding, the court is required to hold a hearing to determine if the concerns expressed by the attending physician can be supported. If the court concludes that the result expressed is "likely", the court "shall not order the disclosure, transmittal or examination unless satisfied that to do so is essential in the interests of justice".[83]

---

[81] *Mental Health Act*, R.S.O. 1990, c. M.7, ss. 35(2) [am. 1992, c. 32, s. 20] and (3) [am. 1992, c. 32, s. 20, 1996, c. 2, s. 72].
[82] *Ibid.*, s. 35(6) [am. 1992, c. 32, s. 20].
[83] *Ibid.*, s. 35(7).

The *Mental Health Act* provides for a review mechanism in circumstances where the psychiatric facility refuses to release a record to a patient outside a court proceeding. In those circumstances, the psychiatric facility may apply to the Review Board "for authority to withhold all or part of the clinical record".[84] When such an application is made, the legislation mandates the Board to:

> review the clinical record in the absence of the patient and by order in writing shall direct the officer in charge to allow the patient to examine or copy the clinical record or a copy of it unless the board is of the opinion that disclosure of the clinical record is likely to result in,
> (a) serious harm to the patient or recovery of the patient while in treatment at the psychiatric facility; or
> (b) serious physical harm or serious emotional harm to another person.[85]

In Manitoba, the *Mental Health Act* contains a statutory mechanism for the review of requests for release of psychiatric records. The legislation provides that no person shall "disclose, transmit or examine a clinical record" unless certain conditions set out in the legislation are met. A review board may choose not to release the clinical record to a psychiatric patient in circumstances where disclosure of the record is likely to result in harm to the treatment or recovery of the patient, or is likely to result in serious physical or serious emotional harm to another person.[86]

In Quebec, the restricted access provisions in the *Health Services and Social Services Act*[87] refer generally to the "user's record" and do not appear to be exclusive to the patient's psychiatric record. In that province, the access to some or all of the record may be denied if it is likely to be "seriously prejudicial to the user's health".[88] In the absence of an agreement in writing from a third person who is mentioned in the user's chart, a "user" is not entitled to information that would identify that third person or to any information that the third person may have communicated.[89] Ontario[90] and Manitoba[91] legislation also provides a right of correction to patients who have examined their psychiatric records and found the contents to be erroneous.

---

[84]   *Ibid.*, s. 36(4) [am. 1992, c. 32, s. 20].
[85]   *Ibid*, s. 36(6) [am. 1992, c. 32, s. 20].
[86]   *Mental Health Act*, R.S.M. 1987, c. M110, s. 26.9(2) [added S.M. 1987-88, c. 56].
[87]   R.S.Q. 1977, c. S-4.2.
[88]   *Ibid.*, s. 17.
[89]   *Ibid.*, s. 18.
[90]   *Mental Health Act*, R.S.O. 1990, c. M.7, s. 36(13).
[91]   *Mental Health Act*, R.S.M. 1987, c. M110, s. 26.9(9) [added S.M. 1987-88, c. 56].

Currently, health privacy legislation is being developed in several jurisdictions. To date, only Manitoba's *Personal Health Information Act*[92] is in force. Ultimately, proposed legislation in Ontario, Alberta and Saskatchewan may address mental health records, however, existing legislation must be relied on until these statutes become law.

CURRENT ISSUES – SECLUSION / RESTRAINTS

As a nurse at a provincial psychiatric facility, you are occasionally put in dangerous situations with forensic patients. In the past two years, you have suffered a broken wrist, a sprained knee, and several episodes resulting in scratches and bruises.

You have had training in the use of seclusion and restraints, and know that they should be used in situations where a patient poses a risk of harm to him or herself, or to others. However, you also suspect that some staff members use seclusion/restraints whenever a patient gets into an argument, even when it is not clear that the patient is a risk to anyone.

You ignore this practice but are uncomfortable with it. You believe that you do a very difficult job and deserve to work in a safe environment, but the use of seclusion and restraints is causing you stress.

The use of seclusion and restraints in psychiatric facilities are controversial issues, with no easy answers. From an occupational health and safety point of view, health professionals are entitled to a safe working environment. Mental health legislation in various jurisdictions across the country aims to create a proper balance between the rights of patients and those of health care providers and the public. In most cases, the use of physical and chemical restraints is permitted only in the most serious situations, in a manner that is as minimally intrusive as possible in the circumstances.

Psychiatric facilities would be wise to put in place appropriate policies and procedures to handle crisis situations that merit the use of seclusion and/or restraints. They should never be used routinely to silence or control patients. Documentation of the use of seclusion, restraints and authority for their use is critical.

A first step may be to find out whether the facility where you work has a policy on seclusion/restraints. The facility owes a duty to ensure that the policy is known both to employees and patients, and to see that it is followed. A second step is to inquire about any available training in their use. Lastly, your professional nursing association may have a position statement on the use of seclusion/restraints.

---

[92]   S.M. 1997, c. P33.5.

Relevant Legislation

CANADA

Criminal Code, R.S.C. 1985, C-46, Part XX.I, s. 672.1-672.2 (mental disorder provisions)

ALBERTA

Dependent Adults Act, R.S.A. 1980, c. D-32

Mental Health Act, S.A. 1988, c. M-13.1

BRITISH COLUMBIA

Health Care (Consent) and Care Facility (Admission) Act, R.S.B.C. 1996 c. 181 [not yet in force]

Mental Health Act, R.S.B.C. 1996, c. 288

Patients Property Act, R.S.B.C. 1996, c. 349

MANITOBA

The Mental Health Act, R.S.M. 1987, c. M110

The Mental Health Consequential Amendments Act, Bill 35, Fourth Session, 36th Legislature; Second Reading: June 17, 1998. Third Reading: June 29, 1998 [In effect on proclamation.]

NEW BRUNSWICK

Infirm Persons Act, R.S.N.B. 1973, c. I-8

Mental Health Act, R.S.N.B. 1973, c. M-10

NEWFOUNDLAND

The Mental Health Act, R.S.N. 1990, c. M-9

The Mentally Disabled Persons' Estates Act, R.S.N. 1990, M-10

NORTHWEST TERRITORIES

Guardianship and Trusteeship Act, S.N.W.T. 1994, c. 24 [not in force]

Mental Health Act, R.S.N.W.T. 1988, c. M-10

NOVA SCOTIA

Hospitals Act, R.S.N.S. 1989, c. 208 (note: Nova Scotia does not have a separate statute dealing with mental health)

Incompetent Persons Act, R.S.N.S. 1989, c. 218

ONTARIO

Health Care Consent Act, 1992, S.O. 1996, c. 2, Sch. A

Mental Health Act, R.S.O. 1990, c. M.7

Mental Hospitals Act, R.S.O. 1990, c. M.8

Statutory Powers Procedure Act, R.S.O. 1990, c. S.22

Substitute Decisions Act, 1992, S.O. 1992, c. 30

PRINCE EDWARD ISLAND

Mental Health Act, S.P.E.I. 1994, c. 39 [not yet proclaimed]; R.S.P.E.I. 1988, c. M-6

QUEBEC

Mental Patients Protection Act, R.S.Q. 1977, c. P-41

An Act respecting the protection of persons whose mental state presents a danger to themselves or others. Second session, 35th National Assembly, Bill 39. Royal Assent December 18, 1997, c. 35. In force on proclamation.

SASKATCHEWAN

The Dependent Adults Act, S.S. 1989-90, c. D-25.1

The Mental Health Services Act, S.S. 1984-1985-86, c. M-13.1

The Mentally Disordered Persons Act, R.S.S. 1978, c. M-14

YUKON

Mental Health Act, S.Y.T. 1989-90, c. 28

CHAPTER 7

Drugs

SYNOPSIS

This chapter examines the federal and provincial legislation governing drugs and controlled substances, the role of nurses in drug administration, and the problems associated with ease of access to powerful drugs.

INTRODUCTION

For many nurses, the administration of drugs is an integral component of daily practice and routines. When used as a tool to remedy illness, control disease or alleviate suffering, drug therapy has enormous benefits. Scientific advances have made drug administration and therapy one of the most important tools available to nurses and other health care professionals.

However, drug administration and ease of access occasionally lead to problems for health professionals. Many cases of professional negligence arise out of the improper or careless administration of drug therapies. The abuse of drugs by health care professionals is a common subject matter for disciplinary proceedings. Health care providers, because of their access to drugs, may become involved, willingly or unwillingly, in criminal activities. In Canada, drug administration is closely regulated by law and there are many restrictions on the conduct of professionals who administer drug therapy. Contravention of the law can result in severe professional and criminal penalties.

FEDERAL LEGISLATION

Federal and provincial legislation control the use and handling of drugs. Two federal acts control the manufacture, distribution and sale of drugs: the *Food and Drugs Act* (hereinafter "FDA")[1] and the *Controlled Drugs and*

---

[1] *Food and Drugs Act*, R.S.C., 1985, c. F-27. [hereinafter *"FDA"*]

Substances Act (hereinafter "CDSA").[2] The CDSA replaces the *Narcotic Control Act*[3] and Part III [Controlled Drugs] and Part IV [Restricted Drugs] of the FDA.

The FDA controls the manufacture, distribution, advertising and sale of food, drugs, cosmetics and certain medical devices. Under this Act, the definition of a drug is very broad and includes:

[A]ny substance or mixture of substances manufactured, sold or represented for use in:
(a) the diagnosis, treatment, mitigation or prevention of a disease, disorder or abnormal physical state, or its symptoms, in human beings or animals;
(b) restoring, correcting or modifying organic functions in human beings or animals, or;
(c) disinfection in premises in which food is manufactured, prepared or kept;[4]

The FDA and its regulations contain lengthy and detailed directives regarding the composition, labelling, advertising, manufacturing and sale of various drugs and groups of drugs. Many regulations refer to specific drug types, however, the Act and its regulations create a number of broader classifications, both directly and indirectly.

The CDSA merits particular attention, since it creates a new scheme for regulating certain dangerous drugs and narcotics (which are now referred to as "controlled substances"). The schedules to the CDSA set out the controlled substances which are significant:

- **Schedule I**: includes very dangerous drugs such as opium, heroin, morphine, cocaine
- **Schedule II**: includes cannabis (e.g. its preparations, derivatives and similar synthetic preparations, including marijuana)
- **Schedule III**: includes amphetamines and lysergic acid diethylamide (LSD)
- **Schedule IV**: includes drugs with therapeutic uses, such as barbiturates

"Traffic" means, in respect of a substance included in any of Schedules I to IV,

(a) to sell, administer, give, transfer, transport, send or deliver the substance,
(b) to sell an authorization to obtain the substance, or

[2]   1996, c. 19 in force May 14, 1997. [hereinafter "*CDSA*"]
[3]   R.S.C. 1985, c. N-1.
[4]   FDA, s. 2.

(c) to offer to do anything mentioned in paragraph (a) or (b),
otherwise than under the authority of the regulations.

A case argued before the Saskatchewan Court of Appeal outlined the range of medical procedures necessary to establish a physician-patient relationship.[5] The physician charged in the case was found to have pre-scribed demerol to an undercover police officer who was not his patient. The court observed:

> [He] failed to take her history; he made no inquiry as to her ailments; asked her no questions regarding the pain that demerol was to neutralize; nor sought to determine what drug, if any, she was then using. He con-ducted no physical examination to determine whether or not she was in need of the narcotic [under the then *Narcotic Control Act*]. There was none of that. Under the circumstances, she was not his patient . . .[6]

Nurses may be required by their employers to keep special records per-taining to the administration of controlled substances. Nurses involved in drug administration may have unparallelled access to certain drugs. By a rare few, this could be seen as an opportunity. However, unauthorized use or possession of a controlled substance is a criminal offence under the CDSA. Several specific offences are contained in the Act, including:

(a) possession (s. 4(1));
(b) trafficking (s. 5(1)); and
(c) possession for the purpose of trafficking (s. 5(2)).

Trafficking may not necessarily involve the wide distribution of large quantities of drugs. In a British Columbia case,[7] the accused was charged under the predecessor legislation with unlawful possession of narcotics and drugs for the purpose of trafficking contrary to both the *Narcotic Control Act* and the *Food and Drugs Act*. He was found in possession of L.S.D. tablets and cannabis resin which he was taking home for the use of only his wife and himself. The accused argued that this was merely pos-session and not trafficking. The court, however, found that transporting the drug to any other person, even a family member, rendered the ac-cused guilty of trafficking. In fact, it has been held that to make drugs

[5] *R. v. Tan*, [1985] 1 W.W.R. 377, 35 Sask. R. 74, 42 C.R. (3d) 252, 15 C.C.C. (3d) 303 (C.A.).

[6] *Ibid.*, at 380 W.W.R.

[7] *R. v. O'Connor*, [1975] 3 W.W.R. 603, 29 C.R.N.S. 100, 23 C.C.C. (2d) 110 (B.C.C.A.). Application for leave to appeal to S.C.C. dismissed 23 C.C.C. (2d) 110*n*.

available by giving a prescription falls within the definition of trafficking.[8]

PROVINCIAL LEGISLATION

Each province has legislation pertaining to pharmacists and the practice of pharmacy. This legislation provides for the establishment of a professional association that regulates the practice of pharmacy and has the power to make regulations regarding licensing, standards of practice, record-keeping, discipline of members, advertising and other matters of a similar nature. The statutes also set out guidelines for the packaging and sale of various groups of drugs. Each province has slightly different rules in this regard. Most of the statutes contain schedules listing those drugs which must be sold by prescription; those which must be labelled as "poisons" and their purchase recorded in a special register; those which may be sold without a prescription but must be stored in an area controlled by a licensed pharmacist, and those which, provided they are properly packaged, may be sold by anyone to anyone. The legislation should be consulted for a more detailed review of the requirements in each province.

The legislation in each province limits the practice of pharmacy, and the operation of a pharmacy, to a licensed pharmacist. The compounding, dispensing and sale of drugs are also functions specifically limited to pharmacists in all jurisdictions. For example, section 30(1) of the *Pharmaceutical Act* of Manitoba states:

> Save as in this Act otherwise provided, no person except a licensed pharmacist shall,
> (a) keep open a shop for retailing, dispensing, or compounding drugs, poisons or medicines including the articles from time to time named in any regulation made hereunder;
> (b) dispense or compound poisons, drugs, or medicines;
> (c) sell or attempt to sell or keep or expose for sale, poisons, drugs or medicines;[9]

A physician who attempted to refute a charge of trafficking by claiming that he was authorized to dispense drugs under the combined provisions of the Prince Edward Island *Pharmacy Act*[10] and the *Narcotic Control Act* was nonetheless found guilty. The Prince Edward Island

---

[8]   *R. v. Tan, supra*, note 5, at 381 W.W.R.
[9]   S.M. 1991-92, c. 28.
[10] R.S.P.E.I. 1974, c. P-5, s. 15(3) [now R.S.P.E.I. 1988, c. P-6, s. 14].

Court of Appeal approved the trial judgment which stated that "a doctor is not a full-fledged pharmacist or pharmaceutical chemist within the meaning of the *Pharmacy Act*."[11] Even read together, the provisions of the two Acts could not support a defence of authority to sell the narcotic in question.

Dispensing is an activity that can be somewhat difficult to define. Most of the provincial statutes pertaining to the practice of pharmacy provide no definition of the term. However, in the Nova Scotia *Pharmacy Act*, the definition states:

> [D]ispensing ... includes the responsibility for taking all reasonable steps to ensure pharmaceutical and therapeutic appropriateness as well as the preparing and releasing of the prescribed medication.[12]

The College of Nurses of Ontario has developed a guideline for dispensing which relates directly to nursing activities:

> Dispensing is the process of removing a medication from a labelled container, placing it in another container, and insuring that the container is properly labelled for distribution to a client.[13]

Although the College of Nurses' guideline does not have the force of law, it may be useful in assisting nurses to define the limits of their practice.

In some remote areas and in smaller health care facilities, pharmacists are not always available to dispense medications, which may be required at all hours of the day. Many of the professional nursing bodies have developed standards and guidelines for nurses practising under these circumstances. For example, Manitoba nursing guidelines suggest various methods of providing pharmacy services in the absence of a pharmacist, such as the use of a "Service Cabinet" containing a selected stock of prepackaged drugs prepared by a pharmacist in a limited number of doses.[14] This system avoids requiring the nurse to dispense drugs at any time.

---

[11] *R. v. Burke* (1978), 16 Nfld. & P.E.I.R. 132, 44 A.P.R. 132, 44 C.C.C. (2d) 33 (P.E.I.C.A.), at 146 Nfld. & P.E.I.R.

[12] R.S.N.S. 1989, c. 343, s. 2(f).

[13] College of Nurses of Ontario, *Medication Administration Standards* (Toronto: The College, 1996).

[14] Manitoba Association of Registered Nurses, *Guidelines for Extended Pharmacy Services* (Winnipeg: The Association, October 1985). (At the time of publication, Manitoba's present standards were being updated.)

ADMINISTRATION OF MEDICATIONS BY NURSES

The administration of medications pursuant to a physician's order is a basic nursing responsibility. Until recently, the *Nursing Profession Act* of Alberta made this particularly clear in that it defined "exclusive nursing practice" to include:

> [T]he administration of any drug or medicine, as defined in the *Pharmaceutical Act*, that is permitted by law to be prescribed and administered to a person;[15]

The narrow legal definition of "administer" applies most closely to the nurse's role. At least one court has determined that:

> [T]he meaning to be given to the word "administer" is the more limited meaning of "to apply, as a medicine" or "to give remedially", rather than "to make drugs available by giving a prescription"[16]

Under this analysis, the court concluded that a drug or narcotic [today, "controlled substance"] is not administered until it has entered an intended recipient's system parenterally or otherwise.

In administering medication, nurses will be held to the standard set by the profession. A competent nurse is expected to know the purpose and effect of any drug he or she is administering as well as the possible side effects and contraindications. It is also standard practice to administer medications while observing what some nurses refer to as the "five rights". Ask yourself:

- Is this the right patient?
- right drug?
- right dose?
- right route?
- right time?

Many of the professional nursing bodies have developed guidelines outlining nursing responsibilities in medication administration. Nurses administering medications will be expected to meet these standards. Failure to do so may result in the initiation of a lawsuit against the hospital and its nurses or in discipline proceedings against the nurse.

In a 1947 Nova Scotia case, a hospital was found liable for the negligence of two nurses who assisted in the administration by a doctor of a

---

[15] S.A. 1983, c. N-14.5, s. 1(f). It is interesting to note that this provision was removed by the *Professional Statutes Amendment Act*, S.A. 1990, c. 33, s. 1.

[16] *R. v. Tan, supra*, note 5.

local anaesthetic.[17] The doctor had requested a vial of novocaine. The nurses brought a vial from which the doctor drew a quantity into a syringe and injected it into the patient. The vial contained adrenalin, however, and as a result, the patient died within a short time. Neither of the nurses had followed the proper procedure in checking the vial label. The judge stated, at pp. 342-43:

> In the case of drugs where the consequences of a mistake may be so grave, I think that anyone who is procuring a drug should use whatever means are within his [or her] power to prevent a mistake. It is true that as these matters become routine, there must be a tendency to expect that everything will be right but the nurse whose duty it was to provide the material for the work which the doctor was about to do, must, I think, have a duty to use the reasonable means at her disposal to make sure that she had the right drug. It was only a matter of looking at the label in this case and I must hold that she was negligent in not doing so.

Nurses also have the responsibility, based upon professional knowledge and judgment, to clarify unclear orders and to question orders that appear incorrect or unsafe. A nurse who follows unclear orders may be found negligent for failure to contact the prescribing physician for clarification of the order.

In a 1962 American case, an infant died after receiving an overdose of digoxin by injection.[18] The physician had prescribed three cubic centimetres of Lanoxin Elixir, without indicating the intended route of administration. The nurse who administered the drug believed that the drug was only supplied in injectable form and thus assumed that the doctor intended the medication to be injected intramuscularly. She did suspect that the dose might be high and checked with two physicians, but she was not entirely clear in her communication with these doctors. She proceeded with the injection without checking with the prescribing physician. This method of administration was incorrect and resulted in the death of the child. The judge found the actions of both the nurse and the prescribing physician to be negligent and made the following comments regarding the standard of care expected of a nurse in this situation:

> [W]e are of the opinion that she was negligent in attempting to administer a drug with which she was not familiar. While we concede that a nurse does not have the same degree of knowledge regarding drugs as is possessed by members of the medical profession, nevertheless, common sense dictates that no nurse should attempt to administer a drug under the cir-

---

[17] *Bugden v. Harbour View Hospital et al.*, [1947] 2 D.L.R. 338 (N.S.S.C.).
[18] *Glynace N. Norton et al. v. Argonaut Insurance Co. et al.*, 144 So. 2d 249 (La. Ct. App. 1962).

cumstances shown in the case at bar. Not only was Mrs. Evans unfamiliar with the medicine in question but she also violated what has been shown to be the rule generally practiced by the members of the nursing profession in the community and which rule, we might add, strikes us as being most reasonable and prudent, namely, the practice of calling the prescribing physician when in doubt about an order for medication. True, Mrs. Evans attempted to verify the order by inquiring of Doctors Beskin and Ruiz but evidently there was a complete lack of communication with these individuals. ... For obvious reasons, we believe it the duty of a nurse when in doubt about an order for medication to make absolutely certain what the doctor intended both as to dosage and route. In the case at bar the evidence leaves not the slightest doubt that whereas nurses in the locality do at times consult any available physician, it appears equally certain that all of the nurses who testified herein agree that the better practice (and the one which they follow) is to consult the prescribing physician when in doubt about an order for medication.[19]

These principles are applicable to nursing practice in Canada.

Situations may also arise in which the physician's order is clear, but the nurse questions or ought to question the propriety or accuracy of the order. In such a case, nurses are under a duty to inform the responsible physician of any concerns. If the dosage is administered in spite of those concerns, a finding of negligence may be made. Similarly, if a physician's order is clearly improper, failure to recognize the error or impropriety may be grounds for civil or disciplinary proceedings.

Some of the provincial professional bodies have developed guidelines to assist nurses encountering this situation. The Ontario College of Nurses has created Medication Administration Standards that address this issue:

Behavioural Directives
The nurse will:

1. Avoid accepting verbal orders when the physician is present and can write her or his own orders.
2. Repeat verbal or telephone orders in their entirety to ensure their accuracy.
3. Assess whether the medication is appropriate for the client in the particular situation.
4. Document verbal or telephone orders in the client's record.
5. Take all necessary actions or follow-up required when a medication is ordered.[20]

---

[19]   *Ibid.*, at 260-261.
[20]   *Medical Administration Standards* (Toronto: Ontario College of Nurses, 1996), at 9.

Nurses should also be aware that the legislation pertaining to the particular health care setting in which they work may contain specific directives regarding administration of medication, checking of doctors' orders, record-keeping and other matters. Furthermore, most health care employers have developed policies and guidelines regarding the handling of medication in their own institutions. In particular, most institutions will have strict policies in place regarding the documentation required when prescribing, dispensing or administering drugs and the procedures for proper control of controlled substances. Nurses should be aware of the guidelines existing in their particular employment setting.

Nurses (particularly those working in public health) frequently administer immunizing agents to children and adults. In recent years, there has been considerable concern expressed regarding the rare but extremely serious adverse reactions experienced by certain individuals. This concern has led to amendments in Ontario to the *Health Protection and Promotion Act.*[21] Section 38(2) requires the following:

> If consent to the administration of an immunizing agent has been given in accordance with the *Health Care Consent Act, 1996,* the physician or other person authorized to administer the immunizing agent shall cause the person who has given consent to be informed of the importance of reporting to a physician forthwith any reaction that might be a reportable event.

Although the Act does not require that a signed consent be obtained, it would be advisable to obtain some evidence that the information was given and understood. The College of Nurses of Ontario recommends that each health care agency establish clear guidelines about the information to be given and provide a system for documenting that this information was given and that consent was received from the client to proceed. Where there is doubt as to the client's comprehension of the information and competence to give consent, a physician should be requested to make the necessary assessment.

---

[21] *Health Protection and Promotion Act,* R.S.O. 1990, c. H.7: ss. 38(2) [am. 1996, c. 2, s. 67(4)] duty to inform of importance of reporting to a physician forthwith any reaction that might be a reportable event; s. 38(3) duty to report reactions.

CURRENT ISSUES – EASE OF ACCESS TO DRUGS

Nancy has been a registered nurse for almost 10 years, working at a major teaching hospital. In that time, she has been recognized for her dedicated and tireless care of patients, contribution to continuing education, and mentoring of new nursing graduates. Lately, however, she does not have much energy to devote to anything but her work and home life.

Nancy's husband no longer works, due to an accident on the job. This has limited his ability to care for their three young children. With the cutbacks at her hospital and her increased professional and personal responsibilities, Nancy cannot shake her constant fatigue.

Although she's not sure when she started it, for a number of weeks Nancy has been halving the dosage of a controlled substance destined for one of her patients. She has new energy, and people are starting to remark on her change in spirit. In the back of her mind, she knows what she's doing is wrong, but doesn't everyone benefit when she is on top of the world?

In most health care settings, the dispensing of narcotics and other controlled substances is monitored very closely. The *Criminal Code* legislates the control of these substances to protect the general public. What happens when health professionals with access take their authority too far?

Nancy is in trouble, and needs to seeks help immediately. She could face the loss of her livelihood, professional sanction and criminal charges because of her behaviour. She is compromising her patients' care by altering their prescribed medication. To compound this, she may be facing an addiction problem.

If she has the inner resolve to put an end to this situation, she should contact her provincial nursing association immediately. This can be done anonymously, to seek assistance in dealing with this situation. Professional advice is recommended, and depending on the outcome, Nancy should also consider seeking legal advice.

Relevant Legislation

CANADA

Controlled Drugs and Substances Act, 1996, c. 19 (and its regulations)

Food and Drugs Act, R.S.C. 1985, c. F-27 (and its regulations)

ALBERTA

Pharmaceutical Association Act, S.A. 1988, c. P-7.1

Pharmaceutical Profession Act, S.A. 1988, c. P-7.1

Pharmaceutical Profession Regulations 322/94
Prescription of Drugs by Authorized Practioners Regulation, Reg. 83/98

BRITISH COLUMBIA

Pharmacists, Pharmacy Operations and Drug Scheduling Act, R.S.B.C. 1996, c. 363

Pharmacists, Pharmacy Operations and Drug Scheduling Act, 1997, S.B.C. 1997, c. 36
  B.C. Reg. 461/87
  Prescribed Health Care Profession Regulation, Reg. 277/97
  Access PharmaNet Patient Record Information Regulation, Reg. 401/97
  Drug Schedules Regulation, Reg. 9/98

MANITOBA

Manitoba Drug Interchangeability Formulary Regulation 66/98

The Pharmaceutical Act, S.M. 1991-92, c. 28
  Manitoba Drug Standards and Therapeutics Formulary Regulation, Man. Reg. 248/91
  Manitoba Prescription Drugs Regulation, Man. Reg. 317/88

Pharmaceutical Regulation, 56/92

NEW BRUNSWICK

Pharmacy Act, S.N.B. 1983, c. 100

NEWFOUNDLAND

Pharmaceutical Association Act, 1994, S.N. 1994, c.P-12.1
  Dispensing of Substitute Brand-Name Drug Regulations, Reg. 2/98
  Hospital Pharmacy Registration Regulations, Regs. 73/96, 74/96, 108/96.
  Interchangeable Drug Products Formulary (Volume 30) Regulations 1995, Reg. 89/95

NORTHWEST TERRITORIES

Pharmacy Act, R.S.N.W.T. 1988, c. P-6

NOVA SCOTIA

Pharmacy Act, R.S.N.S. 1989, c. 343
   N.S. Reg. 148/81
   N.S. Reg. 172/83
   N.S. Reg. 38/84
   N.S. Reg. 76/87
   Nova Scotia Pharmaceutical Society Regulations, N.S. Reg. 141/89
   Pharmacy Regulations, N.S. Regs. 50/89, 136/91, 133/92, 128/97

ONTARIO

Drug and Pharmacies Regulation Act, R.S.O. 1990, c. H.4

Drug Interchangeability and Dispensing Fee Act, R.S.O. 1990, c. P.23

Ontario Drug Benefit Act, R.S.O. 1990, c. O.10

Regulated Health Professions Act, 1991, S.O. 1991, c. 18

PRINCE EDWARD ISLAND

Pharmacy Act, R.S.P.E.I. 1988, c. P-6
   Authorization Regulations, EC 575/92
   Physician Dispensary Regulations, EC 617/87
   Standards Regulations, EC 618/87

QUEBEC

Pharmacy Act, R.S.Q. 1977, c. P-10

SASKATCHEWAN

Pharmacy Act, S.S. 1996, c. P-91
   Drug Schedules Regulations, 1997, R.R.S. c. P-9.1, Reg. 2

YUKON

Pharmacists Act, R.S.Y. 1986, c. 131

CHAPTER 8

Consent to Treatment

SYNOPSIS

This chapter analyzes consent to health care treatment, informed consent, emergency care, treatment of minors and the role of nurses in documenting consent.

INTRODUCTION

The notion that a patient must give consent to medical treatment has its roots in the common law. Recently, many provinces in Canada have moved to codify the common law to require that an informed consent be obtained before health care is provided. Nurses must understand and adhere to the new rules of consent in order to meet their professional, statutory and ethical obligations.

CONSENT TO PHYSICAL CONTACT

Health care requires frequent physical interaction. Physical examinations, diagnostic testing, administration of medication, surgery and physio-therapy all require physical contact between the health care provider and the patient. In some instances, for example, when a nurse checks a patient's blood pressure or pulse, the physical contact will be minimal and is unlikely to have any adverse consequences. In other circumstances, such as when surgery is performed, the physical contact will be invasive and can pose serious risks to the patient.

As a general principle, no person may touch another person without the consent of the person being touched.[1] This is true at common law, and has been codified in a number of provincial statutes. In Ontario's *Health Care Consent Act, 1996*,[2] consent to treatment is valid when:

---

[1]   *Reibl v. Hughes*, [1980] 2 S.C.R. 880, 14 C.C.L.T. 1, 33 N.R. 361, 114 D.L.R. (3d) 1.
[2]   *Health Care Consent Act, 1996*, S.O. 1996, c. 2, Sch. A (hereinafter "HCCA").

1.   it relates to the treatment;
2.   it is informed;
3.   it is given voluntarily; and,
4.   it is not obtained through misrepresentation or fraud.[3]

In some instances, consent can be inferred. When a nurse assists a patient in moving from a wheelchair to a bed, the conduct of the patient in reaching out to the nurse for assistance is clear evidence that the patient consents to being touched by the nurse for the purpose of that assistance. Similarly, when a patient holds out an arm for the purpose of receiving an injection or disrobes for a physical examination, the patient implies consent, making it reasonable for the health professional to conclude that consent has been given, even in the absence of communication.

There are, however, exceptions to the general principle. A police officer engaged in an arrest may be permitted to apprehend a suspect by physical coercion. Reasonable steps taken by health care providers to restrain patients who are an imminent danger to themselves or others would not result in legal liability. Nurses who use reasonable force to protect themselves from a patient who is attempting to harm them constitutes self-defence and is not actionable. A nurse who engages in cardiopulmonary resuscitation of an unconscious patient (who is unable to provide any consent, oral or implied) does so in the context of an emergency and does not require the express consent of the patient.

BATTERY

A nurse who has physical contact with a patient, even if that physical contact is no more than a slight or superficial touching of the patient, commits a battery if there is no consent.[4] A nurse who pushes a patient into an examining room, who force-feeds an unwilling elderly patient, or who restrains a psychiatric patient who is not dangerous but is considered difficult, commits a battery for which civil damages can be awarded. A nurse who obtains consent from a patient to hold the patient's arm for the purpose of taking a blood pressure, but goes beyond that procedure and administers an inoculation, commits a battery. The consent must relate to the particular procedure that is to be undertaken.[5]

If a patient orally communicates his or her consent to a particular form of treatment, but that consent was obtained through intimidation or un-

[3]   *Ibid.*, s. 11(1).
[4]   *Beausoleil v. Soeurs de la Charité* (1964), 53 D.L.R. (2d) 65 (Que. C.A.).
[5]   *Murray v. McMurchy*, [1949] 1 W.W.R. 989, [1949] 2 D.L.R. 442 (B.C.).

der duress, the consent is not valid and a battery occurs. It is even possible to commit a battery through an intermediary. A patient who is subjected to x-rays without having consented to the procedure is the subject of a battery. If a patient consents to receive one form of medication, but a nurse knowingly administers another medication, this constitutes a battery. Where consent is obtained by deceit, the consent is vitiated.

In some cases, the damages arising out of a battery will be minimal. For example, where a nurse takes a pulse against the patient's wishes, and no harm comes to the patient, damages will be nominal. However, if a court considers that the conduct of the nurse was malicious or reckless, the possibility of punitive damages arises. Even if no civil remedy is sought, this does not preclude professional discipline proceedings being brought against the nurse.

INFORMED CONSENT

A patient may consent to a particular kind of physical contact, but may do so on the basis of information that is inaccurate or incomplete. The inaccuracy or incompleteness of the information provided to the patient may be the result of carelessness on the part of the health care provider. In those circumstances, the courts have found that no battery occurs, but that there may be liability for the health care provider resulting from the negligent failure to obtain a truly informed consent from the patient.[6]

A health care provider must disclose the material risks of a particular procedure. The risks that must be disclosed depend upon the nature of the procedure. It should not be assumed that minor or unlikely adverse consequences will not factor into a patient's decision. On the other hand, serious risks that may lead to death or permanent injury should always be disclosed, even if the chance they will occur is remote. Ultimately, a court will make its determination of liability based upon whether or not the disclosure that took place in a particular case was reasonable. In Ontario, the test for what is reasonable is that before making a decision, the individual must be given information that a reasonable person in the same circumstances would require in order to come to a decision. This information includes:

1. The nature and expected benefits of the treatment;
2. Its material risks and side effects;
3. Alternative courses of action; and
4. Likely consequences of not having the treatment.[7]

---

6   *Reibl v. Hughes,* [1980] 2 S.C.R. 880, 14 C.C.L.T. 1, 33 N.R. 361, 114 D.L.R. (3d) 1.
7   HCCA, *supra*, note 2, s. 11(2)(a).

The Supreme Court of Canada has held:

> In deciding whether a risk is material and, therefore, one which
> should be explained to the patient, an objective approach should be
> taken. The crucial question in determining the issue is whether a rea-
> sonable person in the patient's position would want to know of the
> risk.[8]

As a nurse, you may occasionally encounter a patient who is highly
emotional, and the treatment itself may be compromised by complete
disclosure. It may be tempting to withhold or generalize information because it could be harmful to the patient. However, it is important to recognize the importance of individual autonomy. Modern rules governing
consent provide patients with the right to make their own health care
decisions.

A negligent failure to disclose material risks will not result automatically in liability. Liability arises only where the negligent conduct has
caused harm. Where a court concludes that the patient would have proceeded with the particular form of surgery, even if apprised of the material risks, there is no liability, as disclosure would not have prevented the
harm from occurring. Conversely, where a court concludes it is likely that
the patient would not have proceeded with the procedure if all material
risks had been disclosed, liability is likely to follow because the procedure, if properly explained to the patient, would not have been carried
out.

In *Petty v. MacKay*[9] an exotic dancer underwent cosmetic surgery to
have tissue removed from an area of the abdomen so that she could continue her exotic dancing. The surgery was not successful and the plaintiff
sustained permanent disfigurement as a result of the surgery. The trial
judge concluded, on the evidence, that the material risks of the surgery
were not explained by the surgeon to his patient. Nonetheless, the judge
dismissed the case. He found that even if the risk had been explained to
the patient, she would have accepted the risk and gone ahead with the
surgery. Consequently, the failure of the surgeon to disclose the material
risk of abdominal disfigurement did not place the plaintiff in a worse
position than she would have been in had the risk been disclosed to her.

In *Haughian v. Paine,*[10] a patient received a recommendation from a
neurosurgeon for surgery to correct the herniation of a cervical disc. The
surgery led to paralysis, which was later corrected, but nonetheless
caused significant harm to the patient. The patient alleged a lack of in-

---

[8]   *Ciarlariello v. Schacter*, [1993] 2 S.C.R. 119, 15 C.C.L.T. (2d) 209, at 222, 100 D.L.R. (4th)
      609.
[9]   (1979), 14 B.C.L.R. 382, 10 C.C.L.T. 85 (S.C.).
[10] [1987] 4 W.W.R. 97, 58 Sask. R. 232 (Q.B.).

formed consent. The court held that the diagnosis of the neurosurgeon was correct and that his recommendation for surgery, as opposed to more conservative treatment, met a reasonable standard of care. The court, however, also found that there had not been an adequate discussion of the risks involved in the surgery and that the patient, if informed of these risks and given the alternative of more conservative treatment, would not have consented to the surgery. The neurosurgeon was found liable for failing to obtain an informed consent, and damages were awarded.

Even where the communication of information may not have prevented the patient from undergoing the treatment, there may be liability for a failure to communicate risks which would have resulted in less stress for the patient. In *Snider v. Henninger*,[11] the patient underwent an emergency hysterectomy after the surgeon had made several attempts to suture a uterine artery and had not succeeded. Although the court found that the surgeon's care was not negligent and that the patient had no choice but to undergo the procedure, the physician was found negligent since he had failed to forewarn her of the possibility of a total hysterectomy. That information would have enabled her to obtain a second opinion and to prepare for the loss of childbearing capacity. In effect, the patient was not informed of the risks in a *timely manner*, with the result that her stress was increased and her recovery compromised. She was awarded damages in the amount of $12,000.

WITHDRAWAL OF CONSENT

A situation may occur in which a patient has agreed to undergo a procedure, but changes his or her mind and withdraws consent. A consent may be expressed in clear and unequivocal terms in the physician's office, but the patient may refuse to sign a consent form in the hospital prior to surgery. In other cases, the communication of the withdrawal may be in less forceful terms; the patient expresses reservations to a family member or asks questions a nurse is unable to answer. The Supreme Court of Canada has held that if there is any question about whether the patient is attempting to withdraw consent, it is incumbent upon the physician or health practitioner administering the procedure to ascertain whether the consent has in fact been withdrawn. If, during the course of a procedure, a patient withdraws his or her consent, the procedure must be halted.[12]

---

[11]   (1992), 96 D.L.R. (4th) 367 (B.C.S.C.).
[12]   *Supra*, note 8.

In *Nightingale v. Kaplovitch*,[13] the patient was undergoing a sigmoido-scopy. The examination, at one point, became extremely painful and the patient screamed, "Stop, I can't take this anymore." Nonetheless, the doctor proceeded with the examination. The patient made a sudden move caused by pain and sustained a punctured bowel. The trial judge concluded that the perforation had occurred after the patient's consent had been withdrawn. He held that it was a battery, and furthermore, that the physician had been negligent in continuing the procedure when the patient had asked him to stop.

Each case must be decided on its particular facts. In another case,[14] a patient suffering from acute muscular pain in her chest consented to re-ceive a cortisone injection into her chest muscle. At one point in the pro-cedure, the patient cried out, "For God's sake, stop." In that case, how-ever, the trial judge held that her exclamation did not constitute a with-drawal of consent, but rather, was an expression of pain and was not said for the purpose of having the procedure stopped.

EMERGENCY CARE

Where there is an urgent need for treatment and a valid consent is not possible, the caregiver may be exempt from obtaining the express and informed consent of the patient. A patient who has been rendered uncon-scious by an accident will be unable to consent to an emergency treat-ment. It is reasonable, however, for the caregiver, in the absence of evi-dence to the contrary, to infer that such a patient would want emergency treatment and would give the necessary consent if able to do so. An emergency does not exist, however, where the absence of intervention will not result in harm to the patient. If the patient's condition is not life-threatening and a delay in treatment will not harm the patient, the care-giver must wait until the patient is able to consent or until the appropri-ate substitute decision-maker is available to consent. Of course, if the condition of the patient begins to deteriorate, creating an urgent need for treatment, intervention without an express consent will be justified.

There may be situations in which the patient has given instructions, in advance, as to what treatment, if any, the patient should receive in an emergency. In *Malette v. Shulman*,[15] a physician was found to have com-mitted a battery when a blood transfusion was given to an unconscious patient. The patient had been brought into the emergency department of a hospital following a car accident. She required an urgent blood trans-

---

[13]   Unreported, April 20, 1989 (Ont. H.C.J.).
[14]   *Mitchell v. McDonald* (1987), 40 C.C.L.T. 266 (Alta. Q.B.).
[15]   (1990), 72 O.R. (2d) 417 (C.A.).

fusion. Her wallet contained a card identifying her as a Jehovah's Witness and stated that, for religious reasons, she did not want to receive a blood transfusion even in circumstances where her life was in danger. The physician, nonetheless, carried out the transfusion. The court held that the card in the patient's wallet constituted clear evidence of the patient's desire to refuse life-sustaining treatment. The physician's conduct, though intended to save the life of the patient, was held to be unlawful. Damages were awarded.

The *Malette* case has implications for other areas of health care in which a patient withholds consent. It confirms that, as a matter of common law, a competent patient has an absolute right to refuse life-sustaining treatment. A patient's express wish to abstain from treatment may be in the form of a document executed by the patient prior to admission to hospital, in a power of attorney or similar authorization to a substitute decision-maker or in a verbal agreement, between physician and patient, to a do-not-resuscitate order (commonly known as a DNR order). The patient's right to refuse treatment, even where there is no specific statutory authority for doing so, was upheld by a Quebec court which authorized a hospital to discontinue life-sustaining treatment when requested to do so by a patient who was suffering from an incurable disease.[16]

PREREQUISITES OF A VALID CONSENT

A thorough explanation of the material risks attached to a procedure is ineffective where the patient is incapable of understanding the nature of the procedure. Obviously, an unconscious patient cannot consent to a procedure. Similarly, a patient who has some form of emotional or intellectual disability may be incapable of understanding or appreciating the nature of the proposed treatment. However, it is inappropriate to assume that a patient who suffers from some form of emotional or mental disability is, by necessity, disqualified from consenting to a treatment or procedure. A patient who has a diminished level of intelligence or some other form of intellectual disability may be capable for certain purposes, but not others. He or she may be capable of understanding a relatively simple medical procedure or course of treatment. If the particular treatment is quite complex and the material risks inherent in the treatment are serious (although difficult to understand), one might then be compelled to obtain consent through some form of substitute consent mechanism.

---

[16] *Nancy B. v. Hôtel-Dieu de Quebec*, [1992] R.J.Q. 361 (C.S.).

Some health care providers assume that routine, non-invasive procedures, to which no reasonable patient is likely to object, can be performed without concern that a patient's legal rights are being violated. However, every health care provider must be alert to the wishes of the patient. If the patient objects, or is incapable of objecting or consenting to an invasive or complex treatment or procedure, it should not be undertaken. What if the situation does not constitute an emergency, but the patient's well-being will be threatened if the procedure is not performed? In that case, it may be necessary to seek legal advice, obtain a substitute consent, or in extreme cases, a court order.

Where an emergency arises and the patient is unable to consent, treatment can be administered. However, if there is clear evidence that the competent patient does not wish to have emergency treatment, even in a life-threatening situation, the patient's wish must prevail.[17]

TREATMENT OF A MINOR

Treatment of a minor may require the consent of a parent, guardian or next-of-kin. Some legal experts would argue that the performance of a procedure with parental consent, against the wishes of a minor, may be a violation of the minor patient's rights. Age is not the governing criterion for consent. It has been held that where a minor is capable of understanding and appreciating the nature and consequences of a particular procedure or treatment, the minor is capable of giving a valid consent.[18] In Ontario, barring a finding of incapacity by a health care practitioner or a court, a person of any age is presumed to be capable of making decisions relating to treatment, admission to a care facility, and personal assistance services.[19] This codifies the common law presumption that minors of any age can give or withhold informed consent to treatment.

In *Re Eve*,[20] the Supreme Court of Canada examined the related issue of minors and incapacity. In that case, the parents of a pubescent daughter who had Downs Syndrome sought to have her sterilized. The court concluded that the procedure was unnecessary and not in the daughter's best interests. The court also ruled that the public hospital regulation under which the authorization was sought was merely a procedural guide for obtaining written consent, and would provide the parents no sub-

---

[17] *Supra*, note 15.

[18] *Johnston v. Wellesley Hospital*, [1971] 2 O.R. 103, 17 D.L.R. (3d) 139 (H.C.J.).

[19] HCCA, *supra*, note 2, s. 4(2).

[20] *Re Eve*, [1986] 2 S.C.R. 388 (*sub nom. E. v. Eve*), 31 D.L.R. (4th) 1, 13 C.P.C. (3d) 6, 71 N.R. 1, 61 Nfld. & P.E.I.R. 273, 185 A.P.R. 273, 8 C.H.R.R. D/3773 (*sub nom. Eve v. E.*).

stantive authority than they would have under the common law or through other statutory authority.

In *Ney v. Canada (Attorney General)*,[21] a group of parents brought an application to set aside legislation that gave children under the age of legal majority the right to consent, in certain circumstances, to their own care and treatment. They argued that the legislation[22] infringed the rights of children and parents and was contrary to the *Charter of Rights and Freedoms*.[23] In rejecting their application, the judge held that the legislation created no new rights or obligations and was perfectly consistent with the common law in this area. The judge found that where a child has sufficient intelligence and maturity to understand and appreciate the nature and consequences of the proposed treatment, he or she is capable at common law of consenting to such treatment. If a child does not meet this test, and as a result is incapable of consenting, the consent of a parent or guardian will be required.

In *Walker (Litigation Guardian of) v. Region 2 Hospital Corp.*,[24] a 15-year old was diagnosed as suffering from acute myeloid leukemia. Although a treatment consisting of a blood or blood products transfusion was recommended, the child, who was a Jehovah's Witness, refused this treatment. The hospital applied for an order that the child be declared a "mature minor" capable of giving or withholding consent to any transfusion of blood or blood products as part of his treatment. The court initially rejected the application and issued an order that a blood transfusion be given if, in the opinion of his doctors, it was likely that he would die if he did not receive it. However, this decision was overturned by the New Brunswick Court of Appeal. New Brunswick's *Medical Consent of Minors Act*[25] provided that if two medical practitioners were satisfied that a minor was mature and able to consent to medical treatment, that the proposed treatment was in the best interests of the minor and the minor's continuing health and well-being, and the minor consented, then the consent process was legally acceptable. The Court of Appeal voted that, because all of these prerequisites were satisfied, there was no need for court intervention. In effect, it held that that the "mature" minor had a right to refuse treatment and that a child's wish not to receive blood or blood products transfused should be respected.

---

[21] (1993), 79 B.C.L.R. (2d) 47, 102 D.L.R. (4th) 136 (S.C.).

[22] *Infants Act*, R.S.B.C. 1979, c. 196, s. 16 (now R.S.B.C. 1996, c. 223, s. 17).

[23] *Canadian Charter of Rights and Freedoms*, Part I of the *Constitution Act, 1982*, being Sch. B of the *Canada Act, 1982* (U.K.), 1982, c. 11.

[24] (1994), 150 N.B.R. (2d) 366, 4 R.F.L. (4th) 321, 116 D.L.R. (4th) 477 (N.B.C.A.).

[25] *Medical Consent of Minors Act*, S.N.B. 1976, c. M-6.1.

SUBSTITUTE DECISION MAKING

Related to the question of parents attempting to make health care decisions for their children is the general issue of substitute decision makers.
A number of provinces have passed, or are in the process of passing,
legislation which provides a mechanism for obtaining patient consent in
circumstances where the patient is incapacitated. In Manitoba, where a
comprehensive legislative regime has been introduced for substitute decision making, patients are permitted to make advance decisions in relation to treatment or non-treatment[26] and to appoint proxies who will
make treatment decisions on the patient's behalf when the patient is no
longer able to do so: "[e]very person who has the capacity to make health
care decisions may make a health care directive".[27] If an individual can
demonstrate that he or she is capable of making the treatment decision,
the decision will be allowed to stand. "Capacity" is defined as the ability
"to understand the information that is relevant to making a decision and
... to appreciate the reasonably foreseeable consequences of a decision or
lack of decision".[28] The legislation also points out that a "person may
have capacity respecting some treatments and not others and respecting
a treatment at one time and not at another".[29] If the competent decision of
the patient is to refuse treatment, then treatment cannot be given. Likewise, if a valid advance directive is given by the patient, it must be followed, even where to do so means death for the patient.[30] A proxy, however, is not authorized to consent to treatment that is primarily for the
purpose of research or not for the protection of the patient's health unless
the directive expressly says so.[31] Although no action lies against a proxy
who acts "in good faith" or without knowledge of a directive or its contents, anyone who "willfully conceals, cancels, obliterates, damages, al-
ters, falsifies or forges a directive or a revocation of a directive" may be
punished by a fine of not more than $2,000, up to six months in prison, or
both.[32]

In Ontario, the *Health Care Consent Act, 1996* divides substitute decision makers into five categories:

---

[26] "Treatment" is defined as "anything that is done for a therapeutic, preventive, palliative, diagnostic, cosmetic or other health-related purpose, and includes a course of
treatment": *Health Care Directives Act*, S.M. 1992, c. 33, s. 1.

[27] *Ibid.*, s. 4(1).

[28] *Ibid.*, s. 2.

[29] *Ibid.*, s. 6(2).

[30] The activity of a health care provider is limited to the withdrawal or withholding of
treatment. The directive cannot authorize proactive measures which harm the patient
or accelerate death: *Rodgriguez v. British Columbia (Attorney General)*, [1993] 3 S.C.R. 519,
82 B.C.L.R. (2d) 273, 107 D.L.R. (4th) 342, [1993] 7 W.W.R. 641, 85 C.C.C. (3d) 15.

[31] *Supra*, note 26, s. 14.

[32] *Ibid.*, s. 27.

- court-appointed guardian;
- attorney with power of attorney for personal care;
- representative appointed by the Consent and Capacity Board;
- family members given authority by the HCCA; and
- Public Guardian and Trustee.[33]

This is a hierarchical list. The highest ranking person, who meets all of the requirements in the legislation, becomes the substitute decision maker. To qualify, the substitute decision maker must:

- Be capable of making decisions regarding treatment;
- Be at least 16 years old, unless the substitute decision maker is the incapable patient's parent;
- Not be prohibited by a court order from contacting the incapable patient;
- Be available to advise the health practitioner if the patient consents; and
- Be willing to become the substitute decision maker.[34]

The family members given statutory authority to become the substitute decision maker without prior authorization are also listed in hierarchical order in the Act as follows:

- Spouse or partner;[35]
- Child or parent;
- Non-custodial parent with rights of access only;
- Brother or sister; or
- Any other relative.[36]

All substitute decision makers must be guided by the following principles when making decisions on behalf of the incapable patient:

- Decisions must be based on wishes the substitute decision maker knows about, which were made when the patient was over 16 and was still capable; and
- If a wish is not known, or it is impossible to comply with the wish, the decision must be made in the capable person's best interests.

---

[33] *Health Care Consent Act, 1996*, S.O. 1996, c. 2, s. 20.
[34] *Ibid.*, s. 20(2).
[35] *Ibid.*, subss. 20(7), (8), (9).
[36] *Ibid.*, s. 20(10).

Best interests includes consideration of:

1. The values and beliefs that the patient held when capable;
2. Any prior wishes of the patient; and
3. The effects of the treatment including whether:
    (i)   treatment is likely to improve the condition, prevent the condition from worsening, reduce the rate at which the condition worsens,
    (ii) the expected benefit outweighs the risk, and
    (iii) this is the least intrusive course of effective treatment.[37]

Not all provinces have enacted this form of comprehensive legislation. Nonetheless, in the absence of such legislation, the courts are likely to apply many of the principles embodied in it. It is also likely that in provinces and territories in which there is no similar comprehensive regime, such legislation will be enacted in the future.

DELEGATION AND DOCUMENTATION OF CONSENT

It is the duty of the health care provider who will be performing the procedure or administering the treatment to obtain an informed consent from the patient. In most circumstances, the attending physician will be responsible for disclosing the material risks of a medical or surgical procedure. The obligation to do so should not be delegated. Consent forms may be required under certain statutes for certain forms of health care. In some jurisdictions, nurses who fail to obtain a patient's consent may be found guilty of professional misconduct.[38] Even where it is not legally required, a consent form may be a valuable precaution to show that a patient agreed to the treatment. The language employed is critical:

> For example, a form purporting to authorize a vast array of treatment or "all necessary treatments" while the patient is in the facility will carry little weight.[39]

---

[37] *Ibid.*, s. 21(2).

[38] O. Reg. 799/93 under the *Nursing Act, 1991*, S.O. 1991, c. 32 provides:
   The following are acts of professional misconduct for the purposes of clause 51(1)(c) of the Health Professions Procedural Code, [Sched. 2 to the *Regulated Health Professions Act*, S.O. 1991, c. 18]:
   9. Doing anything to a client for a therapeutic, preventative, palliative, diagnostic, cosmetic or other health related purpose in a situation in which a consent is required by law, without such a consent.

[39] J.J. Morris, *Law for Canadian Health Care Administrators* (Toronto: Butterworths, 1996), p. 125.

The informed consent of a patient obtained by a health care provider should not to be confused with the consent form that is executed by the patient. The consent form executed by the patient constitutes documentary "evidence" that an informed consent has been obtained, but is not the informed consent itself. The informed consent is the communication between the health care provider and patient about the material risks of the procedure for which consent is sought. The practice of having a consent form executed by the patient may be a requirement of hospital legislation in the various provinces. Within the hospital it is an administrative mechanism to ensure that patients are informed about the nature of their treatment, and where those procedures are invasive or bear a significant risk, that a valid consent was obtained. Although the consent document may be referred to as a consent, it is, in reality, only evidence of the consent.

Nurses are sometimes asked to have the consent form for a medical or surgical procedure executed by the patient. While there are no reported cases on this topic, this may be fraught with risks for the nurse. A patient, not surprisingly, may make the mistake of concluding that it is the nurse, by virtue of having provided the consent form for execution, who is obtaining the consent. The physician may have explained the procedure to the patient at some earlier point in time, without actually having the form executed. It is a better practice for the physician to have the consent form executed at the same time that the nature and risks of the procedure are explained to the patient.

In most cases, consent forms are to be signed by a witness. Nurses are often asked to witness the signature of the patient executing the consent form. It should be recognized that the nurse is only a witness to the signature of the individual. If required, the nurse should be able to substantiate that the signature is the signature of the patient and that the patient signed the document voluntarily in the presence of the nurse, and appeared competent to do so. The fact that the nurse witnessed the document is not intended to indicate that the nurse participated in some way in obtaining the informed consent of the patient.

If, upon being presented with the formal consent form for execution, the patient indicates that he or she has further questions or concerns about the proposed procedure, the appropriate response is to refer the patient's questions to the health care provider who will be performing the procedure. In circumstances where a patient has reservations about the procedure, even after having executed the consent form, it is the obligation of the nurse to bring this to the attention of the medical staff. Nurses must also be aware of their role in documenting the patient's consent (or lack thereof).

CURRENT ISSUES: CONSENT/EUTHANASIA

You are on duty late one night on the Palliative Care ward. Your patient's condition has been deteriorating over the past several hours. Although she is drifting in and out of consciousness, your patient has asked you on several occasions in the past several weeks to remove her from her respirator. On one occasion she asked you to give her an overdose of pain medication. As a health professional and a human being, you can see that she is suffering.

In spite of your training in palliative care, you are considering complying with her dying wish. You are confident that this is what she wants. Just this once, wouldn't it be the humanitarian thing to do?

She asks you again to help her. What do you do?

Consent is not a defence to euthanasia, which is an illegal act. In Canada, patients' rights are important, but they do not supersede the law.

Euthanasia (also known as assisted suicide or "mercy-killing"), has been widely debated in the past several years. It is controversial in any situation, and particularly when a health professional is involved. However, in spite of a patient's apparent pain and repeated wishes, health professionals must understand that moral justifications will not hold up in a court of law. A patient's consent to (or explicit request for) assistance in ending his or her life does not make it a legal act.

Criminal prosecution, civil liability and professional sanctions may all result in the case of a health professional who takes an active role in a patient's premature death.

Relevant Legislation

CANADA

Canadian Charter of Rights and Freedoms, Part I of the *Constitution Act, 1982,* being Sch. B of the *Canada Act, 1982* (U.K.), 1982, c. 11.

ALBERTA

Dependent Adults Act, R.S.A. 1980, c. D-32

BRITISH COLUMBIA

Health Care (Consent) and Care Facility (Admission) Act, R.S.B.C. 1996, c. 181

MANITOBA

Health Care Directives Act, S.M. 1992, c. 33

ONTARIO

Health Care Consent Act, 1996, S.O. 1996, c. 2, Sch. A

Mental Health Act, R.S.O. 1990, c. M.7

Nursing Act, 1991, S.O. 1991, c. 32

Substitute Decisions Act, 1992, S.O. 1992, c. 30

QUEBEC

Civil Code, L.Q. 1991, c. 64, ss. 10-25.

SASKATCHEWAN

Dependent Adults Act, S.A. 1989-90, c. D-25.1

CHAPTER 9

Nursing Malpractice

SYNOPSIS

This chapter addresses the elements of a nursing malpractice action, including a nurse's duty of care, the litigation process, what to expect at a malpractice trial, and an examination of case law relating to past lawsuits involving nurses.

INTRODUCTION

Patients expect that treatment by nurses and other health professionals will improve or remedy their disease or condition. When the result is unexpected, to the patients and family at any rate, the result may be a lawsuit against the health care providers and health care facility involved.

The findings of a federal task force appointed to conduct a review of liability and compensation issues in Canadian health care indicate a significant escalation in the liability of health care providers in Canada between the 1970s and early 1990s. The task force concluded that the rate of growth in the frequency and severity of claims over the previous decade equals the American rate of growth, and furthermore, that the increase in medical malpractice litigation has been more severe than the increase in litigation against lawyers, accountants, architects, dentists, engineers and other professionals in the same period. The study found that the increase in litigation frequency against doctors during the period in question had increased sixfold.[1]

Similar statistics are not available for nurses, but there is little doubt that nurses have experienced a similar increase in claims made against them by patients who claim that they have been provided with substandard or incompetent nursing care. Involvement in court proceedings, whether the claims can be proved or not, is an experience which is new and frightening to most nurses. The legal process that resolves civil

---

[1] *Report of the Federal/Provincial/Territorial Review on Liability and Compensation Issues in Health Care*, 1990, p. 3.

claims is perplexing. To a nurse who is found negligent and who must pay damages, the process may be shattering.

NURSING MALPRACTICE

Nursing malpractice consists of either negligence or (less commonly) an intentional tort by a nurse in the course of administering care and treatment to a patient. The party making the claim is usually the patient, or others (such as family members) who have suffered harm due to the alleged malpractice. If the patient is dead, the patient's estate may participate in bringing the claim. If the patient is a child, or an adult who is mentally incapable of bringing an action, a claim may be brought by the patient's litigation guardian.

INTENTIONAL TORTS

The bulk of this chapter deals with negligence, but it is important to note some acts of intentional malpractice. The law refers to this as an "intentional tort": a civil wrong done deliberately and which is compensable by a monetary award. In common law, a nurse who restrains a competent patient against the patient's wish, who confines an unruly patient to a room without lawful right or who injects a patient despite lack of consent, commits intentional torts.

There are numerous varieties of intentional torts in the health care context. Touching of any sort, without the patient's consent, is a "battery". It is not a battery if there is an emergency and an unconscious patient's consent cannot be obtained.

The intentional tort of false imprisonment may arise in health care issues. If a patient is detained in an area, contrary to his or her will, and there is no legal basis for the detention, this constitutes false imprisonment. To detain or restrain a patient for discourteous conduct, because a doctor insists on speaking to the patient before discharge, or because the patient wishes to leave the facility against medical advice, also constitutes false imprisonment.[2] It may, however, be acceptable to detain a patient if there is a risk that the patient will harm others or if a patient is engaged in conduct that gives rise to reasonable grounds for arrest and detention.

---

[2]   *Lebel v. Roe*, unreported, 20 May 1994, Whitehorse 64.89 (Y.T.S.C.).

Libel and slander are also intentional torts. If a nurse expresses, orally or in writing, information that is untrue and defames the patient's reputation, the nurse may be found liable.

NEGLIGENCE

In order to succeed in a negligence claim against a nurse, the party making the claim must demonstrate the four essential components discussed below.

1. Duty of Care

The patient must demonstrate a relationship between the patient and the nurse that gave rise to a duty of care. A nurse who took no part in the care of the patient or who was not working at the time the patient came to harm, had no obligation at the material time to care for the patient. Likewise, a patient who alleges incompetent care by a physician may have no claim to a duty of care by the nurse who happened to be present when the incompetent medical treatment was given. The nurse's duty is restricted to nursing. A patient cannot expect a nurse (unless the nurse improperly undertakes to provide care outside the scope of the nurse's training) to provide health care services which are in the domain of other health care professionals. It is not expected that a nurse will provide telephone advice to a prospective patient concerning the best method for being transported to hospital or that a hospital has a duty to call in a cardiologist for a patient with chest pain if the emergency department is staffed with qualified nurses and an emergency physician.[3]

Where a court concludes that there is a sufficient relationship between a nurse and patient to give rise to a duty of care, the nurse will be expected to provide nursing services that meet accepted nursing standards. A nurse will be required to provide services that a reasonable nurse with similar experience and qualifications would provide in similar circumstances.[4] A nurse will be taken, by a court, to have attained a reasonable standard of training. A nurse is not expected to have specialized training, unless the nurse undertakes to provide nursing services in a specialized area of practice. So, if a surgical nurse is in an emergency situation, caring for a patient who requires intensive care, that nurse will not be held to the standard of a nurse who has been trained to work in an intensive care unit. On the other hand, a nurse who agrees to work in the intensive

---

[3] *Bateman v. Doiron* (1991), 118 N.B.R. (2d) 20, 8 C.C.L.T. (2d) 284 at 288-91 (Q.B.); affd. (1993), 141 N.B.R. (2d) 321, 18 C.C.L.T. (2d) 1 (C.A.).

[4] *Dowey v. Rothwell*, [1974] 5 W.W.R. 311, 49 D.L.R. (3d) 82 (Alta. S.C.).

care unit will be held to the standard one would expect from trained intensive care nurses, even if that nurse has not had the requisite degree of
training.

A nurse is expected to remain abreast of current trends and developments in nursing practice. Nurses cannot use as an excuse the fact that
they were trained 10 or 20 years earlier. They are required to exercise a
level of nursing which is consistent with nursing standards at the time
the care is provided.[5]

The standard of care that a nurse will have to meet is an objective
standard, that is, the standard generally accepted by other nursing professionals. It cannot be a subjective standard: a standard based upon the
particular characteristics of a nurse whose conduct is under scrutiny.

A duty of care only exists in circumstances where the event giving rise
to the duty is reasonably foreseeable. In *Dowey v. Rothwell*,[6] the patient
advised a nurse that she was about to experience a seizure. The nurse
failed to put up the guard rails on the bed. The patient experienced a
grand mal seizure and fell to the floor breaking her arm. The court held
that the possibility of the patient falling off the examining table was reasonably foreseeable and the nurse was found negligent. Alternatively, if a
patient who has never had a seizure is placed upon an examining table
and there is no indication that a seizure is about to occur, the occurrence
of a seizure and a fall from the table is not likely to result in liability as
the occurrence was not reasonably foreseeable. This is illustrated in *University Hospital v. Lepine*,[7] where a patient with epilepsy who was admitted to hospital. He was put into a room on the fourth floor of the hospital. Suddenly and without warning, and in the presence of members of
the hospital staff, he jumped onto a chair, leaped through the window,
fell to the ground and sustained serious injuries. It was found at trial, and
again at the Alberta Court of Appeal, that the hospital was negligent because it had failed to provide constant supervision by keeping the patient
"under the care of a competent orderly or nurse at all times". The decision was overturned, however, by the Supreme Court of Canada, which
found that the conduct of the patient was not reasonably foreseeable by
the hospital or its staff.

2. Breach of Duty of Care

Once a patient in a malpractice action has demonstrated that a nurse had
a duty of care to provide a reasonable standard of nursing care, the patient must then prove that there was a breach of that duty of care. A pa-

---

[5]   *Ibid.*
[6]   *Ibid.*
[7]   [1966] S.C.R. 561, 57 W.W.R. 5.

tient may come to harm in a manner that is unanticipated. In hindsight, one may suggest modes of treatment or practice that may have prevented the harm. The fact that one can suggest improved or modified care of a patient in retrospect is not a sufficient ground upon which to advance an action for malpractice. Likewise, where the harm results from a material risk that is known to be associated with the procedure, it will not be a cause for complaint if the patient has been informed appropriately and in advance about the risk. Rather, the nurse's conduct will be judged upon the basis of whether or not the nurse breached an obligation to provide *reasonable* nursing care *under the particular circumstances*. The patient must produce evidence at trial to demonstrate that the nurse's conduct fell below accepted nursing standards.

In *Cavan v. Wilcox*[8] a registered nurse practising in New Brunswick was sued by a patient who had a part of his left hand amputated. Gangrene had developed following an injection by the nurse. The New Brunswick Court of Appeal overturned the trial judge's dismissal of the patient's action and found the nurse negligent for having improperly injected bicillin into the circumflex artery of the patient's left arm.

However, the Supreme Court of Canada, on reviewing the trial evidence, highlighted the evidence of nursing and medical experts who testified that nothing was taught to nurses, at that time, in regard to the presence of the circumflex artery in the deltoid muscle and the possibility of an injection going into that artery. The court concluded that there was ample medical evidence to support a finding that the injection was given "without any fault" on the part of the nurse. Because there was no evidence of a nursing standard having been breached (in fact, the evidence was the opposite) the court held that there was no evidence of "negligence" on the part of the nurse, even though it was clear that the patient had come to harm as a result of the injection.

A nurse may commit an error in judgment, but this does not lead to the conclusion that duty of care was breached by substandard nursing care.[9] In short, in order to prove malpractice, it is not sufficient for a court to find that a nurse might have done better or that another nurse would have done better. The court must find that there has been a breach of a standard of nursing practice.

---

[8] [1975] 2 S.C.R. 663, 9 N.B.R. (2d) 140, 2 N.R. 618, 50 D.L.R. (3d) 687 (*sub nom. Wilcox v. Cavan*), reversing 7 N.B.R. (2d) 192, 44 D.L.R. (3d) 42.

[9] *Elverson v. Doctors Hospital* (1974), 4 O.R. (2d) 748, 49 D.L.R. (3d) 196 (C.A.); affd. (1976), 17 N.R. 157, 65 D.L.R. (3d) 382n (S.C.C.).

3. The Breach of Duty Must Result in Damages

The purpose of a civil action is to request the court to order an award of monetary compensation for injury or harm. Unless the nurse's breach of duty of care to the patient has resulted in injury or harm, there can be no basis for a civil suit. For example, it has been held that a fetus is not a person,[10] and consequently, no action for damages can be advanced on behalf of a stillborn fetus, even if the stillbirth is the result of nursing negligence. Similarly, no damages can be recovered for sorrow, grief, embarrassment or hurt feelings. Therefore, if the loss can only be expressed in those terms, and there is no physical or economic impact from the malpractice, malpractice proceedings cannot be brought.[11]

If where a patient is unable to demonstrate entitlement to damages, and consequently, has no basis for a civil action for damages, the patient may be entitled nevertheless to initiate discipline proceedings where a nurse may be found guilty of professional misconduct or incompetence. However, without a claim for monetary damages, no action can be pursued.

4. Causation

It is possible to have a case in which a duty of care arises, the duty of care is breached by the nurse, and damages are sustained, but the particular breach did not *cause* the injury.[12] Where the losses or damages sustained by the plaintiff were not caused by the act of malpractice, a civil proceeding against the nurse cannot succeed.

In *MacDonald v. York County Hospital*,[13] a patient had been treated in hospital for a fractured dislocation of the ankle. The general surgeon had applied an unpadded cast over only two layers of cloth and did not carefully supervise the condition of the patient or issue special instructions concerning the supervision of the patient. The patient developed gangrene and was forced to undergo an amputation of his leg below the knee. The trial judge found that the nurses had been aware of the patient's deteriorating condition for an 18-hour period, but had done nothing more than record the apparent changes in the patient's condition and had failed to advise a physician of the drastic increase in the classic signs of circulatory impairment. Consequently, the trial judge found the hospi-

---

[10] *Mathison v. Hofer*, [1984] 3 W.W.R. 343, 27 Man. R. (2d) 41, 6 C.C.L.I. 58, 28 C.C.L.T. 196 (Q.B.).

[11] *Montgomery v. Murphy* (1982), 37 O.R. (2d) 631 (H.C.).

[12] *Barnett v. Chelsea and Kensington Hospital Management Committee*, [1969] 1 Q.B. 428.

[13] [1972] 3 O.R. 469, 28 D.L.R. (3d) 521; vard. (1973), 1 O.R. (2d) 653, 41 D.L.R. (3d) 321; affd. [1976] 2 S.C.R. 825 (*sub nom. Vail v. MacDonald*) 18 N.R. 155, 66 D.L.R. (3d) 530.

tal and its nursing staff partially responsible for the injuries sustained by the patient.

However, the hospital appealed the decision of the trial judge to the Ontario Court of Appeal. The Court of Appeal noted:

> [T]he symptoms observed that evening were those of change, indeed, serious change; but Dr. Vail was closely cross-examined by counsel for the respondent as to his probable course of conduct had he been notified of the changes which had occurred and, while he said that he would have attended at the hospital and examined the respondent's condition, he was very doubtful that he would have taken any action at that time. While it may be that the nurses were remiss in not calling the doctor and therefore negligent, there is, in view of the doctor's evidence, no reason to believe that the negligence was a contributory cause of the respondent's loss.[14]

In other words, although there was conclusive evidence that the nurses had failed to meet the appropriate standard of care, the evidence of the physician was that he would have failed to act even if the appropriate standard of care had been met by the nurses in reporting the serious changes to him. Consequently, the nurses' negligence did not cause any harm to the plaintiff.

It is also possible to have more than one breach of duty of care that causes the injury. When the injury arises from multiple causes, it is referred to as contributory negligence. Each province has legislation that permits a court to allocate responsibility among the parties who have breached their duty and contributed to the injury for which compensation is sought in the civil proceeding.[15] For example, in *MacDonald v. York County Hospital*,[16] the trial judge, who originally found the nurses to be liable along with the doctor (although this was overturned on appeal) found that the conduct of each had contributed equally to the patient's injuries. He found the physician to be 50 per cent responsible for the plaintiff's damages and the hospital and its nurses to be 50 per cent responsible.

Even where negligence exists, there may be statutory limitations on liability that preclude a nurse from being held responsible for a civil wrong. Such a circumstance arose in *Wowk v. Edmonton Board of Health*,[17] where the plaintiff suffered an injury because of a flu shot administered by a public health nurse. It was held that the nurse was not liable because s. 21(2) of Alberta's *Public Health Act*[18] provided for no liability

---

[14] *Ibid.*, at 679 O.R.
[15] For example, *Negligence Act*, R.S.O. 1990, c. N.1.
[16] *Supra*, note 13.
[17] (1994), 19 Alta. L.R. (2d) 232, 7 W.W.R. 78 (Q.B.).
[18] *Public Health Act*, S.A. 1984, P-27.1.

for an act done in good faith while performing services permitted by the regulations.

THE LITIGATION PROCESS

1. Statement of Claim

A civil suit is commenced by issuing an originating document which sets out the substance of the claim. This document, which in most provinces is referred to as a "statement of claim", may name as plaintiffs not only the patient who complains of the treatment which was given, but also family members who may have incurred losses as a result of the harm to the family member. If the patient has died, the administrator or executor of the estate will be made a party. The statement of claim may name as defendants any facility or any person who provided care to the patient. The named defendants will often include the hospital or health care facility where the patient's treatment was administered, physicians treating the patient, and sometimes nurses.

Generally speaking, hospitals are responsible for the conduct of nursing personnel employed by the facility. The hospital's responsibility is based upon the legal doctrine of vicarious liability.[19] This means that the hospital is legally responsible for the conduct of employees and agents who are negligent in the course of their duties. For that reason, it is not necessary that nurses be named as parties to an action for their conduct to be the subject of scrutiny in a lawsuit.

Under current Canadian law,[20] physicians who have privileges at hospitals are considered to be independent practitioners and there is no vicarious liability. Consequently, plaintiffs are more likely to name physicians personally as defendants in a lawsuit. However, it is not unusual to find nurses personally named as defendants in a lawsuit, and as such, they will be required to take the measures necessary to defend the allegations made against them.

The statement of claim, in addition to naming the parties to the lawsuit, will contain allegations of negligence against the defendants. The allegations advanced in the statement of claim are often broad and far-reaching. The plaintiff is required to plead all grounds upon which an eventual finding of malpractice may be made. Statements of claim are drafted and issued early in the proceedings, often before the issues in the

---

[19] *Cassidy v. Minister of Health*, [1951] 2 K.B. 343.
[20] *Yepremian v. Scarborough General Hospital* (1980), 28 O.R. (2d) 494, 110 D.L.R. (3d) 513, 3 L. Med. Q. 278, 13 C.C.L.T. 105; reversing (1978) 20 O.R. (2d) 510, 88 D.L.R. (3d) 161, 2 L. Med. Q. 216, 6 C.C.L.T. 81 (C.A.).

lawsuit have been well defined. In a statement of claim it is not unusual to find very broad allegations which, ultimately, cannot be supported. It is not necessary for a plaintiff to prove every allegation contained in the statement of claim. However, it is necessary to plead the particular allegation upon which a finding of malpractice is made. Consequently, most statements of claim contain a large catalogue of allegations, many of which will not be relevant to the ultimate decision at trial.

The statement of claim (or similar originating document) must be served *personally* upon the defendants to the lawsuit. Even if the document has been served upon the hospital administration, this does not automatically constitute effective service upon any employees of the hospital who are named as co-defendants.

2. Limitation Periods

In order to advance a civil claim, the court proceedings must be commenced within a stipulated period. This is to prevent claimants from coming forward many years after the events when records, witnesses and other evidence may no longer be available. Generally, in Canada the limitation period for claims in contract and negligence is six years. It should be noted that in the case of patients who are minors or mentally incompetent, the limitation period generally runs until the patient reaches the age of majority or becomes competent.[21]

Some provinces have passed legislation that sets out a limitation period in relation to nurses. Depending upon the law of the particular province, a patient usually has one or two years to sue a nurse for malpractice.

In Ontario, the Health Professions Procedural Code states:

> No person who is or was a member is liable to any action arising out of negligence or malpractice in respect of professional services requested of or rendered by the person unless the action is commenced within one year after the date when the person commencing the action knew or ought to have known the fact or facts upon which the negligence or malpractice is alleged.[22]

Whether or not a plaintiff "ought to have known" that grounds were present for a malpractice proceeding will be decided on the facts of each case. If a patient comes to harm in the hospital and it is or should be apparent to the patient and family that there is a question concern-

---

[21] *Swain Estate v. Lake of the Woods District Hospital* (1992), 9 O.R. (3d) 74, 93 D.L.R. (4th) 440 (C.A.); leave to appeal to S.C.C. refused (1993), 68 O.A.C. 320n; *Lawson v. Hospital for Sick Children* (1990), 74 O.R. (2d) 11, 71 D.L.R. (4th) 557 (Div. Ct.).

[22] *Regulated Health Professions Act, 1991*, S.O. 1991, c. 18, Sch. 2, s. 89(1).

ing the standard of care and treatment which was given, the limitation period is likely to run from the time the injury occurred. However, there may be other cases in which the possibility of malpractice is not immediately apparent. For example, the fact that a sponge has been left inside a patient during surgery may not be discovered until months, or even years afterwards. The plaintiff will only be required, in those circumstances where such a limitation period applies, to commence the action one year from the time when the possibility of malpractice was reasonably apparent.[23]

3. Statement of Defence

All provinces require that a defendant, who is served with a statement of claim in an action, deliver a statement of defence to the allegations contained in the statement of claim if the lawsuit is going to be defended. The rules of court usually will provide for a stipulated time period during which the statement of defence must be delivered. In practice, however, especially in more complicated malpractice proceedings, the lawyers for the various parties will be instructed to agree to extensions of time so that a proper investigation can be conducted by the defendants before delivery of the statement of defence.

Where there are multiple defendants, more than one statement of defence may be delivered. Where defendants are represented by a single lawyer, a single statement of defence will be delivered. If a lawsuit is commenced against a doctor, a nurse and a hospital, each may retain separate counsel and each may deliver a separate statement of defence. In practice, counsel retained by the hospital will represent the nurses' interests as well as the hospital's since the nurses are, in most cases, employees of the hospital for whom the hospital is vicariously liable. The physicians, if they are independent practitioners, will retain separate counsel and deliver a separate statement of defence.

4. Production of Documents

Once the statement of claim has been issued and served and a statement of defence delivered, the rules of court of each province require that the parties disclose and produce to one another any documents relevant to the civil proceedings. In a malpractice proceeding, the most important document is likely to be the health record. However, parties may also have in their possession, and be required to produce documents such as incident reports, nursing manuals, hospital policies, quality control material, employment records and internal memoranda. These documents,

---

[23]   *Law et al. v. Kingston General Hospital et al.* (1983), 42 O.R. (2d) 476 (H.C.).

however, must be produced only if they are relevant to the particular proceedings. Likewise, a plaintiff may be required to produce medical reports in relation to the plaintiff's current health condition, health care records relating to treatment which preceded or followed the treatment complained of, business or employment records which may help to substantiate the claim for damages and any notes or records compiled by the plaintiff or others in relation to the allegations made in the statement of claim.

Not all documentation that must be disclosed must also be shared with the other party. Inevitably, documentation will be created by the parties and their lawyers which relates to the actual conduct of the lawsuit. For example, where a hospital recognizes that a lawsuit has been commenced, or is likely to be commenced, it may call in its lawyer or insurer to conduct an investigation. Statements may be taken from nursing personnel, which will be used to assist the lawyer in the defence of the lawsuit. Correspondence may be exchanged among the hospital, the nurse, the insurer and the lawyer in relation to the defence of the lawsuit. Experts may be consulted to provide written opinions in respect of the standard of care to be expected of the various defendants.

While the parties may be required to disclose the existence of these documents, they may not be required to produce such documentation to the other parties. Such documentation is "privileged". The privilege exists so that lawyers and their clients will be able to conduct their cases in a confidential manner without having to disclose the entire basis for the defence or prosecution of the case to an adverse party in the civil suit.[24]

---

[24] There are two main grounds upon which privilege may attach to documents. The first is called "solicitor-client privilege". Documents which are exchanged between a party and his or her counsel, *e.g.*, letters of opinion, reports on the status of the case, written statements or memoranda from the client, are not subject to disclosure. Second, documents that are prepared in anticipation of, or for the purpose of litigation, need not be disclosed to the other parties in a lawsuit. For example, a report prepared by an investigator who has been asked to conduct an investigation in respect of an event that is likely to give rise to a lawsuit, need not be disclosed to another party. Both of these grounds of privilege allow the parties and their counsel to engage in frank and open discussions about legal matters and to have investigations conducted where litigation is anticipated.

There is also a third possible ground of privilege that is less frequently advanced. There are cases to suggest that certain documents may be privileged because it is in the interest of the public that they remain privileged. For example, in *Smith v. Royal Columbian Hospital* (1981), 29 B.C.L.R. 99, 123 D.L.R. (3d) 723 (S.C.), the court held that certain documents which were produced in the context of the peer review process in the hospital need not be disclosed in a lawsuit. The rationale is that the disclosure of such documents would prevent physicians from engaging in open discussion, and possibly criticism, of their peers which is, under a peer review system, designed to ameliorate services.

All provinces require parties to lawsuits to provide affidavits swearing that they have disclosed all documentation relevant to the lawsuit. Generally speaking, the affidavits will set out those documents which the party has in his or her possession, and does not object to producing, and those documents which the party has in his or her possession, but objects to producing on the ground of privilege.

5. Examinations for Discovery

Once pleadings have been exchanged and relevant documentation disclosed and produced, counsel for the various parties will arrange to conduct examinations for discovery. This process, as the name implies, permits each party to "discover" the merits and weaknesses of the opponent's case. It allows a party to obtain, if possible, admissions that will assist in narrowing the contentious issues for trial or that will assist the party on advancing his or her position at trial.

At an examination for discovery, a party's lawyer can ask questions of the other parties. Consequently, the patient's lawyer will be permitted to examine any nurse or physician who is named as a party to the action or a representative of the hospital if the hospital has been named as a party. In some jurisdictions it is possible to conduct an oral examination for discovery of a witness to the proceedings who is not a party. In other jurisdictions, witnesses are examined for discovery relatively infrequently and only by court order.

Although an examination for discovery is a part of the court process, and is authorized by the rules of court, it is not conducted in court. It is conducted in private offices, outside of court, with only the parties, their lawyers and a reporter present. Usually, each party will be examined separately with only the lawyers for the various parties present in the examination room. Testimony of the party being examined will be recorded and a transcript will be made of the examination. A party is required to answer all proper questions relating to the issues in the proceeding. If there is disagreement among the lawyers over what constitutes a proper question, it may be necessary to have the matter decided by a court later.

An examination for discovery can be a time-consuming and daunting procedure for the party being examined. Since the purpose of the examination is to "discover" the opposing party's case, the questioning is likely

---

Some statutes also contain provisions that confer a statutory privilege. For example, under the Ontario *Regulated Health Professions Act, 1991*, S.O. 1991, c. 18, s. 45(3). Information obtained in the course of an investigation or a proceeding is not to be disclosed apart from in the course of administering the RHPA, a health professions Act or the *Drug and Pharmacies Regulation Act*. Again, the rationale is that individuals who communicate with the disciplinary body will be reluctant to do so if their communications can later be made public in another.

to be wide-ranging and very detailed as lawyers attempt to bring to the surface any facts or information which may be of assistance to their own client's case. Nurses who are examined orally for discovery may be asked very detailed questions about their background and training, about the general operation of the hospital, about particular nursing practices and policies within the hospital, about their dealings with the patient whose treatment is the subject of the civil action, about their dealings with other patients in similar situations, about their relationships with their superiors, about the presence or absence of other health care personnel at the material time and their conduct and whatever other knowledge the nurse may have about the matters in issue.

It is difficult to overstate the impact which examinations for discovery can have upon the ultimate disposition of the civil action or to overemphasize the necessity of being well-prepared for discovery. A witness who testifies at an examination for discovery does so under oath and is sworn to tell the truth. Because the evidence of each party is recorded and transcribed, the answers given to questions at the examinations for discovery will be available for trial. They will be relied upon by the various parties to form conclusions about the evidence that will be heard at trial and about the likely success or failure of the case. Portions of the discovery transcript of one party, which assist another party, can be read into the record at trial and will constitute evidence against the party whose transcript is read.

Should the testimony of a nurse at trial deviate from his or her testimony at the examinations for discovery, a transcript of the nurse's discovery evidence can be used, in open court, to demonstrate the inconsistency in the nurse's testimony and to persuade the court that the nurse's evidence is inaccurate. In effect, the evidence given at examinations for discovery will set the tone for the entire lawsuit; any attempt to later modify evidence given at the examinations for discovery is likely to be challenged.

6. Pre-trial

The litigation process in all provinces provides for the holding of a pretrial. In some jurisdictions and at some levels of court, a pre-trial is mandatory. Alternatively, a pre-trial may be requested by the parties, or the court may direct that one be held in appropriate cases. As malpractice litigation often involves complicated medical issues and the testimony of numerous experts, a pre-trial is very common in those proceedings.

A pre-trial is presided over by a pre-trial judge and is attended by counsel for the various parties. Ordinarily, no parties or witnesses attend. The format is more like a meeting than a court proceeding. Memoranda may be filed by counsel outlining the evidence given at the examinations for discovery. Counsel may have statements from witnesses and may advise the pre-trial judge what evidence a witness is likely to give at trial. Transcripts from the examinations for discovery will be available. Often, reports will have been prepared by expert witnesses and these will be used at the pre-trial to demonstrate what the evidence of the experts will be concerning the relevant medical or nursing standards which will be under consideration at trial.

The main purpose of the pre-trial is to determine, with the assistance of a pre-trial judge, whether the action is capable of resolution through settlement. The pre-trial judge will not be the judge who tries the case. Accordingly, counsel for the various parties may feel free to disclose information at the pre-trial in a less adversarial manner than may occur at the actual trial. The pre-trial judge may provide the parties with the benefit of his or her views on liability. The pre-trial judge may suggest that certain facts are likely or unlikely to be proved at trial. There may be discussion in respect of any legal issues that will have to be decided at trial. The pre-trial judge may suggest possible compromises that may form the basis for a settlement.

Where a pre-trial settlement is not possible, the pre-trial judge may attempt to reach agreement on minor issues. For example, the parties may agree to certain facts at the pre-trial which can then be communicated to the judge presiding at trial so that the trial can be shortened. In some cases, it may be possible to formulate an agreement in respect of the damages that will be awarded if liability is found.

7. Alternative Dispute Resolution (ADR)

In recent years there has been a movement away from the traditional litigation process to "alternative dispute resolution" (hereinafter "ADR"). The traditional litigation process is expensive, time-consuming, and where the matter proceeds to trial, a gamble for all those involved. The legal formality associated with traditional litigation is often alienating to the parties. Litigation based upon an adversarial system of justice, complex rules of evidence, and in some unfortunate cases, posturing by parties or their counsel, will mean no resolution of the civil dispute for years. The sheer expense of the litigation process may defeat a valid claim. Financial stress on governments responsible for the administration of the civil litigation system has resulted in a shortage of courtrooms, fewer judges and lengthy waits for trial. It is not uncommon for a civil lawsuit, once declared ready for trial, to wait months, or even years, for the commencement of trial. Even where a matter does proceed to trial, a trial judge, after weeks of hearing evidence, may produce a result that surprises all of the parties and satisfies no one.

In this context, some parties to civil proceedings have begun to use ADR methods for resolving disputes. There are a number of methods. One is mediation, which may be as simple as a meeting among counsel and parties moderated by a mediator who will attempt to assist the parties in achieving a resolution of the dispute. The mediator may be a retired judge or some other individual whose experience and opinion is highly respected by the parties. That individual may be able to facilitate a resolution. Where, as in a malpractice case, the central issue in the case is the quality of care provided, it may be appropriate to invite experts having relevant expertise to comment upon the standard of care exercised by the health professional whose conduct is under scrutiny. A face-to-face meeting of experts, who may have opposing views, early on in the proceedings and long before trial, may correct misunderstandings and enlighten adversaries to the justice of the other side's position.

In some cases, the parties may choose to engage in binding or nonbinding arbitration. An arbitrator, or arbitration panel, may be appointed to consider the evidence and arrive at a decision. There may be an agreement to informalize the process to reduce the expense and accelerate a resolution.

8. Settlement

The vast majority of malpractice actions are settled prior to trial. Settlement may occur at any stage in the proceedings, although settlement is most likely to occur following the examinations for discovery or following pre-trial. Most settlements take place without any admission of liability. Often, a settlement will consist of the plaintiff withdrawing the claim prior to trial with no payment by the defendant. Where a plaintiff receives settlement proceeds as a condition of settlement, the plaintiff will be required to execute a release which contains a formal acknowledgment that the defendant or defendants, in settling the case, do not make any admission of liability, and furthermore, that in accepting the settlement proceeds, the plaintiff surrenders any right to bring any other proceeding in respect of the subject matter of the lawsuit.

In some instances, a significant component of the decision to settle the civil action will arise from economic considerations. The likelihood of a successful defence to a malpractice action must be weighed against the risks of an unsuccessful defence and the significant legal costs generated by such proceedings. To a certain extent, allegations of professional negligence against a nurse will be viewed as an attack on their reputation and prestige. In those circumstances, the defence may take a harder line and refuse to settle a case unless there is concrete evidence, by a qualified professional, that a reasonable standard of care has been breached.

In a complex malpractice proceeding where there are numerous parties and where there will be testimony from a number of experts, it is not unusual for a single party to incur costs in excess of $100,000 to prosecute or defend the matter through trial. Almost invariably, where a nurse or a hospital is sued, any award at trial will be paid by the hospital's or the nurse's insurer. Depending upon the amount of the settlement proposal, an insurer may be persuaded, from a strictly economic point of view, that settlement is advisable, even where there is a strong likelihood that the case can be defended successfully.

For example, if a plaintiff is prepared to accept the sum of $25,000 as a settlement and to execute a release which acknowledges that there has been no admission of liability and which renounces any claim to future proceedings, such a settlement may be attractive to an insurer where the cost of defending the proceeding is likely to exceed $25,000. Since it is impossible to predict the outcome of any litigation, the uncertainty of the ultimate result often engenders in parties a willingness to accept or pay a sum, in settlement, which represents only a fraction of the damages that would have been recovered if the action were successful at trial.

9. Trial

If an action is not settled, it will be placed upon a list of cases to be tried, and ultimately called to trial. Malpractice trials, because of their complex nature, tend to be lengthy. A malpractice trial is unlikely to take less than a week, and in most cases will take several weeks to try.

Because of the technical complexity of the issues arising in malpractice cases, they are most often tried by a judge alone. A malpractice trial may proceed with a jury, however, where the issues of liability are not overly intricate or complex.[25]

10. Assessment of Damages

An important aspect of every judicial decision in any case of civil litigation will be the assessment of damages. Usually, damages are assessed at trial regardless of whether or not liability is found. Damages must be assessed so that if, on appeal, liability is found, the appeal court will be in a position to give judgment for the plaintiff.

The assessment of damages, in more complex cases, can be very difficult. Often, the court must rely upon actuarial, economic, medical and rehabilitation experts in order to make the assessment.

---

[25] *Soldwisch v. Toronto Western Hospital* (1982), 39 O.R. (2d) 705, 139 D.L.R. (3d) 642, 30 C.P.C. 274 (H.C.).

ANATOMY OF A MALPRACTICE TRIAL

In *Khan et al. v. Salama et al.*[26] the patient, who was 20 years old, was admitted to hospital on September 3, 1980, to give birth to her first child. At approximately 1:30 a.m. on September 4, an anaesthetist administered an epidural anaesthetic to reduce the pain associated with giving birth. At about 4:35 a.m., an obstetrical nurse administered a "top-up" dose of anaesthetic. Shortly thereafter there was a drop in the patient's blood pressure and she went into a cardiac and respiratory arrest. Although the patient was resuscitated, she sustained irreversible brain damage and was described by the trial judge as being in a "persistent vegetative state". After caesarean section, the infant died.

After the events in hospital, an action was started in the Supreme Court of Ontario by the patient and her family to recover damages. The statement of claim named as defendants the anaesthetist, the hospital, several other doctors who assisted with the delivery and several nurses who were in attendance.

Counsel for the physicians delivered a statement of defence asserting that there was no negligence on the part of those physicians. In addition, the statement of defence of the physicians made cross-allegations against the hospital and its nurses that their conduct had caused or contributed to the harm sustained by the patient.

Counsel for the hospital and the nurses delivered a statement of defence denying liability on the part of those defendants, but making cross-allegations of negligence against the physicians.

Before trial, a settlement was reached with the plaintiffs and the defendants agreed to pay a fixed amount for damages. However, the settlement did not resolve the obligation, if any, of the respective defendants to contribute to the settlement. The issues which remained at trial were the negligence, if any, of the anaesthetist in carrying out the original epidural procedure and in setting up the catheter for the continuous epidural, and the negligence, if any, of the obstetrical nurse who was responsible for the patient at the time of the cardiac and respiratory arrest.

The court had the benefit of a number of experts on the technique used in locating the needle in the epidural space in order to administer anaesthesia, in his reasons for judgment the trial judge noted:

> [T]he method used in this case was the loss of resistance technique. After the skin has been swabbed with an antiseptic solution and the skin and subcutaneous tissue anaesthetized, a hollow needle, with the stylet inserted, is pushed through the supraspinous ligament and partly through the interspinous ligament. The stylet is then removed and the syringe filled with air or saline solution is attached to the

---

[26] Unreported, June 27, 1986, R. E. Holland J. (Ont. S.C.), summarized at (1986) D.R.S. 40.

needle. With a right-handed doctor the left hand holds the needle
steady against the skin and with the thumb of the right hand on the
plunger of the syringe, the needle is gently pushed through the liga-
mentum fiatum. As the tip of the needle reaches the epidural space
resistance ceases. The space has a negative pressure and the decrease
in resistance occurs suddenly. If the needle is pushed too far it pene-
trates the dura and the needle then enters the subarachnoid space.[27]

The theory of the plaintiffs' experts was that the needle had been inserted
into the subarachnoid space by the physician, beyond the dura. While the
amount of epidural anaesthesia administered by the nurse at 4:35 a.m.,
when the top-up dose was administered, would be a safe and acceptable
amount if injected into the dura, the same amount of anaesthetic pene-
trating beyond the dura and into the subarachnoid space would have
catastrophic results for the patient.

The theory of the experts who testified on behalf of the anaesthetist
was that there had been a migration of the catheter (which replaced the
original needle) from the dura into the subarachnoid space. It was suggested that such a migration was an unusual risk of the epidural anaesthetic procedure and can occur despite the best care of the physician. The
experts who testified on behalf of the anaesthetist expressed the opinion
that the administration of the epidural anaesthetic, by the anaesthetist,
was performed according to a reasonable standard of care for which no
negligence ought to be found.

The trial judge found, however, certain inconsistencies in the evidence
of the anaesthetist, which in turn prevented him from relying upon the
opinions of the anaesthetist's experts who had based their opinions on
his evidence. Two nurses, who had been present in the delivery room
when the epidural was administered, gave evidence at trial. The nurse
who had brought the patient to the delivery room for the epidural testified:

> [She] positioned the patient for the injection with Mrs. Khan's face
> towards her and her back to the doctor. She said that when the cathe-
> ter would not go in the doctor called for another catheter and rein-
> serted the needle, The second catheter went in smoothly. Dr. Salama
> then put the syringe into the catheter and the catheter was taped in
> place. The patient was turned on her back and the syringe was then
> labelled and put away in the pouch on the patient's chest. [The nurse]
> said that she did not see Dr. Salama make an injection through the
> catheter. She also testified that Dr. Salama left the delivery room be-
> fore Mrs. Khan was removed from the delivery room table back to her
> bed. She confirmed, however, that Mrs. Khan was able to move her-

---

[27]   *Ibid.* at pp. 5-6.

self over to the bed from the delivery room table and was able to move her legs.[28]

A second nurse also was present in the delivery room when the epidural anaesthetic was first administered. She had been out of the delivery room momentarily, but:

> [s]aid she returned to the room as Dr. Salama was giving the injection through the needle. She then saw him try to insert the first catheter without success. He pulled out the needle and she got another catheter for him. He re-inserted the needle with the stylet. She said that when he removed the stylet she saw some clear fluid dripping out of the end of the needle. Dr. Salama held his forearm under the dripping fluid and then inserted the catheter and removed the needle. The catheter was taped in place and the syringe inserted at the end of the catheter. Nurse Clark then put the syringe on the patient's chest.
>
> Nurse Thomas confirmed that Dr. Salama left the room before the patient was moved from the table back to her bed. She also confirmed that Mrs. Khan was able to move herself with minimum assistance.[29]

The trial judge found that there was conflict between the evidence of the anaesthetist and the nurses on two important points. The anaesthetist testified that following the administration of the epidural anaesthetic he had stayed with the patient while her blood pressure was checked and that he checked the level of the anaesthetic block by running his thumb up the side of the patient from her feet to her head. He testified that he wrote up the chart and left an order for top-ups. He said that he watched while the patient was moved from the operating room table to her own bed and that because of her ability to move herself he knew that there was no motor paralysis and that this proved to him that the injection had not occurred in the subarachnoid space. However, both nurses testified, as noted, that the anaesthetist left immediately after inserting the catheter.

The anaesthetist also testified that when he was unable to feed the catheter through the original insertion site of the needle, he had removed the needle and moved it one space higher to L1-2. He said that he repeated the process, and on that occasion, was able to insert the catheter. This contradicted the evidence of the two nurses that he had made a second injection, but through the catheter at the original location.

The trial judge accepted the evidence of the two nurses and stated, in his reasons for judgment:

> I can see no reason for the nurses to fabricate evidence in connection with the time at which Dr. Salama left the delivery room. On the other hand, it was clearly negligent for Dr. Salama to leave without observ-

---

[28] *Ibid.* at pp. 11-12.
[29] *Ibid.* at pp. 12-13.

ing for himself whether or not the patient could move her legs and there is good reason for him to say that he stayed in the room until after the patient had moved from the table to her bed. I accept the evidence of the nurses over his evidence in this connection. Dr. Salama's negligence in leaving the delivery room when he did, however, was not in any way causative of the problem that subsequently arose since it is clear from the evidence of the nurses that there was no paralysis of Mrs. Khan's legs or back at the time that she moved from the delivery room to her bed.

The question remains whether or not an injection was made through the catheter. It is clear from the facts that Mrs. Khan was able to move her legs and lower back after receiving the anaesthetic and that the anaesthetic that she did receive had been injected into the epidural space. She received about 8 c.c.'s of .5% marcaine. She either received this drug in one dose through the needle at the first site or in two doses — one through the needle at the first site and the second through the catheter at the second site, as Dr. Salama claims. If she received the second dose through the catheter and it went into the epidural space, then in some way the catheter must have migrated into the subarachnoid space by the time of the top-up dose because the effects of the administration of the anaesthetic top-up were so severe that in all probability the top-up injection was made into the subarachnoid space.

...

There was no cardiac or respiratory arrest when Mrs. Khan received the first 8 c.c.'s of .5% marcaine at about 1:30 in the morning and I can see no reason why there should have been such a severe reaction when she received 8 c.c.'s of .5% marcaine about 4:30 in the morning unless this injection had gone into the subarachnoid space. I find on a balance of probabilities that the top-up injection went into the subarachnoid space. I also find as a fact that Dr. Salama injected the first 8 c.c.'s through the needle into the epidural space at L2/3 and that there was no further injection through the catheter into L1/2. In this connection I again accept the evidence of Nurse Clark and Nurse Thomas over that of Dr. Salama. In inserting the needle the second time, Dr. Salama probably punctured the dura so that the catheter, when inserted, was placed in the subarachnoid space. This can be done even while exercising great care. The fluid that flowed back through the needle as observed by Nurse Thomas on the second insertion of the needle could well have been CSF.

There is no doubt, on the evidence of the experts, that to insert a catheter in this fashion without testing to ensure that the catheter is in the epidural space is negligent and fails below the standard of care to be expected from a reasonably competent anaesthetist.[30]

---

[30]   *Ibid.* at pp. 13-18 (emphasis added).

Having determined that the conduct of the anaesthetist was negligent and had resulted in the administration of marcaine directly into the subarachnoid space of the spinal column, the trial judge was required to make a further determination about the conduct of the obstetrical nurse who had administered the top-up and who had been present when the patient arrested. The anaesthetist alleged that if the nurse had acted properly when the arrest occurred, the harm to the patient would have been reduced or eliminated. The trial judge describes, in his reasons for judgment, the conduct of the obstetrical nurse both before and after the drop in blood pressure:

> On the night of the incident Nurse Santua was the team leader of two other nurses. She came on duty about 11:30 in the evening of September 3rd. She helped wheel Mrs. Khan's bed out at the time of the initial injection about 1:30 in the morning. However, she did not go to the delivery room with Mrs. Khan. Following the initial injection she checked on Mrs. Khan from time to time. Mrs. Khan's room was equipped with a call bell that registers at the Nurses' Station and an emergency bell, mainly used by the nurses, which sounds an alarm by a light and sounds outside the patient's door and also rings at the Nurses' Station. There is also an oxygen outlet in the wall with a tube attached to a face mask.
>
> Nurse Santua saw Mrs. Khan at about 3:30 in the morning. She checked the monitor which was recording the fetal heartbeat and contractions and took her blood pressure. Mrs. Khan was sleeping. At about 4:30 she looked in on her again while accompanied by Nurse Thomas. Mrs. Khan was sleeping when the two entered the room but she woke up and Nurse Santua told her that if she wanted another injection for pain she should call for it. As the two nurses were returning to the nurses' station the call bell sounded and they both returned to Mrs. Khan's room. Mrs. Khan said she would like a needle. She was on her back.
>
> Nurse Santua took the syringe out of the pouch and noted that it contained 10 c.c.'s of fluid. She then pulled back on the syringe and saw no return of blood or fluid. The patient's blood pressure was taken and was recorded at 110/70. Nurse Santua then injected 8 c.c.'s of the anaesthetic. The blood pressure was checked immediately afterwards and registered 100/70. Nurse Santua stayed in the room and Nurse Thomas went out to check on another patient. Nurse Santua checked the blood pressure again but this time got a reading of 50 systolic using her fingers on the inside of the patient's elbow. She thought that the reading must have been wrong and used her stethoscope to check the pressure again. She got another reading of 50/20. The patient was breathing. Her eyes were half-closed. Mrs. Khan comes from Guyana and has black skin. Nurse Santua saw no change in skin colour.
>
> Nurse Santua turned Mrs. Khan over onto her left side and strapped the oxygen mask to her face. She propped Mrs. Khan on her side with

a pillow and lowered her head, she turned up the flow of the intravenous and turned off the Pitocin, the medication which is fed intravenously to induce labour.

Nurse Santua checked the blood pressure again: this time there was no reading and at the same instant the patient stopped breathing. Nurse Santua took off the oxygen mask and noticed a change of skin colour around the mouth. She then reached for and pulled the emergency bell. She attempted to blow into the patient's mouth but the patient's jaw was locked and she blew into her nose instead. She then compressed Mrs. Khan's chest four or five times and at this point Dr. Salama entered the room and took charge. The cardiac arrest team arrived shortly thereafter. Mrs. Khan was revived but not in time to prevent irreversible brain damage.[31]

One nursing expert called on behalf of the anaesthetist testified that the obstetrical nurse had failed to meet a reasonable standard of care in her response to the dramatic drop in the patient's blood pressure. Her evidence was recorded at trial and is transcribed, in part, below:

Q. Before dealing with this particular case, I wanted to ask you, Ms. McParland, in 1980 with respect to the expected general average knowledge of a reasonably competent general duty nurse, non-specialized, for the moment, as to whether you can tell us what the expectation was with reference to that nurse dealing with a fall generally speaking in systolic-blood pressure, particularly the systolic record.

A. The average knowledge expectation of a general duty nurse in 1980 would have been that a fall of 20 points of blood pressure off the base line blood pressure in a normal individual would be considered the intermediate stage of shock and reportable to a physician.

Q. Ms. McParland, again dealing with our hypothetical general duty nurse in 1980, and assuming, with an assist from the back page of page 153 of Exhibit 14, a fall in blood pressure noted at 4:35 to be 110/70 — in other parts of the record it's referred to as 120/70 — a fall at 4:38 to 100/70, and then at 4:40, 50/20 and at 4:42 0/0, assuming that in relation to a patient similar to Mrs. Khan, are you able to express an opinion and advise His Lordship as to that which would be expected of a reasonably competent general duty nurse faced with that scenario in relation to medical assistance, if indeed that's appropriate?

A. My opinion would be that a fall from 120 or 110 to 100 would be cause for concern in the general duty nurse and a blood pressure at 50 would certainly cause her a great deal of alarm because that is a crisis situation and would have warranted an immediate call for help.

---

[31] *Ibid.* at pp. 20-23.

Q. To whom?

A. To a physician.

Q. Are you able to express an opinion, Ms. McParland, again with reference to 1980, as to whether a reasonably competent general duty nurse faced with the blood pressure readings that I have asked you to assume, whether that nurse acts in accordance with the standard of reasonable practice expected of a reasonably competent registered general duty nurse when calling for the medical help at the point of the blood pressure being recorded at 0/0?

A. *The nurse in my opinion failed to maintain the standards of practice at what would be anticipated in 1980 for a general duty nurse by waiting until the blood pressure reached 0.*

Q. And when, Ms. McParland, if you can help us, does the fall in blood pressure which you have described become a reportable event to the physician?

His Lordship: Just what do you mean by "reportable"? I would assume you mean that the physician should be called. I assume you don't mean just fill in the notes on the chart.

Mr. Forbes: Very much obliged, My Lord. My question is not clear.

Q. May I adopt His Lordship's observations. When do the events, the events that I have asked you to assume become a matter which in your opinion would require a reasonably competent nurse, general duty or obstetrical, to call a physician?

A. I *would expect that a reasonably competent nurse would notify the physician of the alteration from 120 to 100, and would consider that a reportable event given the patient's condition.* The absolute latest reporting to a physician would have occurred when the blood pressure fell below 80 millimetres of mercury.[32]

Conversely, evidence was called from nursing experts by the hospital, on behalf of its employee, the obstetrical nurse. They testified that her conduct, if it could be criticized at all, constituted no more than an error in judgment. One nursing expert called by counsel for the hospital was asked:

Q. Having regard to the information contained in the chart and on the graph, and assuming the nurses acted as stated by Nurse Santua in her evidence at trial, do you have an opinion as to whether or not the

---

[32] Emphasis added.

nursing care and the monitoring of the patient before the top-up accorded with acceptable standards for obstetrical nurses in 1980?

A. Yes, I do have an opinion, and I feel that the nursing care given prior to the top-up did meet with the acceptable standards of practice in 1980.

Q. Having regard to the information, assuming the information on the chart, and on the graph, and assuming Nurse Santua took the steps she stated in her evidence at trial, do you have an opinion as to whether or not the precautions she took before giving the top-up were in accordance with the acceptable standards of obstetrical nursing care in 1980?

A. Yes I do have an opinion. I felt Ms. Santua did adequately monitor the patient before receiving the epidural top-up. She did check the catheter to make sure the tape was intact and she did ask for aid to ... to verify that there was no cerebrospinal fluid or blood returned.

Q. Assuming the information contained on the chart and in the graph and assuming Ms. Santua acted as she stated in her evidence at trial, do you have an opinion as to whether or not her care for the patient and her monitoring of the patient after the top-up *were in accordance with acceptable standards for obstetrical nursing in 1980?*

A. Yes, I do have an opinion. I feel that Ms. Santua did respond in an appropriate manner to a sudden hypotensive episode following the administration of an epidural top-up. There are several reasons for this. One, she was given teaching that directed her to follow the steps that she took, and these are comparable to, say, for example, the teaching that I was given in 1980 at Mt. Sinai Hospital. Ms. Santua was certified in C.P.R. and this wasn't necessarily a standard in Toronto at that time, and that's actually a, a superior ... that's actually superior. She also followed the agency protocol, which again was comparable to what I was functioning under at Mt. Sinai Hospital at the same time. I feel that Ms. Santua recognized the ... the hypotension as being, as being a common occurrence in an obstetrical unit and therefore her actions were, were done ... in a manner that was based, on her assessments. I believe that she didn't miss a single step in what she was to do after a with a hypo-tensive episode. And in summary, *I feel that she did function within the acceptable standards of practice, of nursing practice in 1980.*[33]

The trial judge, having heard and weighed the evidence of the various expert witnesses, drew a conclusion in the nurse's favour. He found that while she may have committed an error in judgment, her conduct did not constitute negligence.

---

[33]	Emphasis added.

Certainly, in retrospect, Nurse Santua should have called for help as soon as the blood pressure fell to 70/20. Instead, she followed the protocol except that she took time to check and re-check the blood pressure before calling for help. In my opinion, her failure to call for help earlier than she did was a mere error in judgment. She had never experienced a case before where the blood pressure did not come back up after the protocol was followed.

Furthermore, the trial judge concluded that any delay attributable to the nurse was minimal, that it would be speculative to say that a delay of even one or two minutes would make any difference and that even if the nurse was negligent for failing to call for help earlier, her negligence was not "causative of the patient's present condition". In the result, the anaesthetist was found entirely liable for damages sustained by the plaintiff and her family and the action against the hospital and its nurses was dismissed.

REPORTED CASES INVOLVING NURSES

There are many reported cases that involve allegations of nursing malpractice. A sampling of Canadian cases from several general categories is set out below.

1. Failure to Monitor Patient

This is one of the most commonly litigated types of malpractice claim against nurses, with several subcategories that will be discussed in turn.

A. FAILURE TO MONITOR PATIENT: GENERAL

The general case of failure to monitor a patient is illustrated in the case of *Krujelis v. Esdale et al.*,[34] where an infant plaintiff suffered respiratory arrest in the recovery room following surgery. Experts testified, at trial, that patients in the recovery room following surgery should be closely watched and examined no less frequently than every five minutes. However, three of the nurses on duty in the recovery room were taking a coffee break. Only two nurses were left monitoring the recovery room, which contained seven patients at the material time. The plaintiff went unobserved for a period of approximately 20 minutes. The hospital was found liable for the negligent conduct of the nursing staff in leaving the patient unmonitored.

---

[34] [1972] 2 W.W.R. 495, 25 D.L.R. (3d) 557 (B.C.S.C.).

In *Laidlaw v. Lions Gate Hospital et al.*,[35] a patient sustained a permanent brain injury in similar circumstances. There were two duty nurses in the recovery room at the time. One went to have coffee, and at the same time, five patients were admitted to the recovery room. The court found that the remaining nurse on duty was unable to give the plaintiff the amount of attention required and that the plaintiff's respiratory difficulties went unnoticed until it was too late. The court found the other nurse negligent in leaving the room when there were patients present and when more arrivals might reasonably have been anticipated. Also, the nurse in the recovery room was held to be negligent for leaving the patient unattended for more than three or four minutes and in agreeing that her colleague could leave for coffee at a time when more patients were expected.

In *Traynor v. Vancott*[36] the plaintiff sustained a left radial nerve palsy due to pressure on the radial nerve. She was admitted to the hospital's recovery room following surgery. The patient remained anaesthetized and then deeply sedated for a lengthy period. The court, on inspection of the recovery room records, concluded that the patient had been "constantly supervised, checked and examined in the recovery room". However, on the ward, the court found a 10 hour gap in the nursing notes. The first notation, following the 10 hour gap, related to a complaint by the patient regarding her left arm. The court concluded that the injury must have occurred during this 10 hour interval and found negligence on the part of the nursing staff on the ward.

In *Bergen v. Sturgeon General Hospital*,[37] a patient was tentatively diagnosed as suffering from pelvic inflammatory disease. Over the course of several days the patient experienced abdominal swelling. There was "snapping" in her abdomen which left her perspiring, shaky and crying with pain. Ultimately, the patient was diagnosed as having suffered a ruptured appendix and transferred to a hospital in the city. She died, however, from septic shock. The court found that there was poor communication between the nursing staff and failure on the part of the nurses to secure the services of a physician when the plaintiff's condition deteriorated.

In *Dowey v. Rothwell*,[38] a patient who anticipated an epileptic seizure and communicated this to the nurse in attendance, fell from an examining table. The nurse had not put up the guardrails. The nurse was found to be negligent. Similarily, in *Foote v. Royal Columbian Hospital*,[39] a patient

---

35 (1969), 70 W.W.R. 727 (B.C.S.C.).
36 (1979), 3 L. Med. Q. 69 (Ont. H.C.).
37 (1984), 52 A.R. 161, 28 C.C.L.T. 155; additional reasons (*sub nom. Bergen v. Sturgeon (General Hospital District No. 100)*) at 63 A.R. 62 (Q.B.).
38 [1974] 5 W.W.R. 311, 49 D.L.R. (3d) 82 (Alta. S.C.).
39 (1982), 38 B.C.L.R. 222, 29 C.P.C. 94 (S.C.).

with epilepsy had experienced a seizure and almost drowned while taking an unsupervised bath. However, the treating physician had failed to tell the nursing staff of the patient's condition or to direct that the patient receive special nursing care. The physician was found negligent for failing to recognize that the patient was a high risk patient and not instructing the nursing staff. The action against the hospital and its nurses was dismissed.

In *Joseph Brant Memorial Hospital et al. v. Koziol et al.*,[40] the patient, who died in hospital, was injured in a motor vehicle accident. As a result of his injuries, he was placed on a Stryker frame. The trial judge found that the deceased patient had died as a result of the "regurgitation of gastric juices" occurring one to three hours before his death. The judge stated in his reasons that he did not have "the slightest doubt" that the patient had been given "inadequate nursing care", which resulted in his condition not being observed. The absence of entries by the nurses on the chart for a number of hours before the patient's death enhanced the conclusion that the patient had been poorly attended.

In *Robinson v. Annapolis General Hospital*,[41] the plaintiff had been admitted to hospital in a very weakened and irrational condition. The plaintiff was 69 years of age. She suffered from Parkinson's disease. Several days after being admitted to hospital she fell out of bed and fractured her left hip. The plaintiff alleged that the nurses ought to have provided sufficient supervision to prevent the accident and that sideboards or physical restraints should have been employed. The court held that the precautions taken by the nurses, in monitoring the patient frequently, in keeping the patient's door open at all times and in ensuring that the nursing staff could be summoned by a buzzer, were the standard approved practice and were competently carried out by the nursing staff. The court concluded that since the attending physician did not consider there was any risk of the patient deliberately trying to get up, it could not be expected that the nursing staff would anticipate this. The case against the hospital and its nurses was dismissed. A similar case was dismissed where an unattended patient fell out of bed.[42]

In *MacDonald v. York County Hospital*,[43] the patient's left foot became gangrenous and required amputation following surgery to the left ankle. On appeal, the Court of Appeal upheld the judge's finding of negligence on the part of the nurses, but overturned the finding of liability against

---

[40] [1978] 1 S.C.R. 491, 15 N.R. 302 (*sub nom. Kolesar v. Joseph Brant Memorial Hospital*), 77 D.L.R. (3d) 161, 2 C.C.L.T. 170.

[41] (1956), 4 D.L.R. (2d) 421 (N.S.S.C.).

[42] See *Beatty v. Sisters of Misericorde of Alberta*, [1935] 1 W.W.R. 651, [1935] 2 D.L.R. 804 (Alta. S.C.).

[43] [1972] 3 O.R. 469, 28 D.L.R. (3d) 521; vard. (1973), 1 O.R. (2d) 653, 41 D.L.R. (3d) 321; affd. [1976] 2 S.C.R. 825 (*sub nom. Vail v. MacDonald*), 8 N.R. 155, 66 D.L.R. (3d) 530.

them and the hospital on the ground that the surgeon, even if alerted to the condition of the plaintiff, would not have acted in any event, and therefore, the negligence of the nurses failing to monitor the patient's condition closely did not cause the injury to the plaintiff.

In *Child v. Vancouver General Hospital*[44] the plaintiff underwent serious abdominal surgery. Following surgery, his condition deteriorated and he was moved to a private room. The hospital directed three special nurses in eight-hour shifts to care for the plaintiff. The plaintiff was described as "confused" and "disturbed". He was unaware of his surroundings and suffered from hallucinations. One of the special duty nurses left for a coffee break while the patient was sleeping. When she returned 15 minutes later the patient had gotten out of bed, escaped through the window and fallen onto a canopy on a floor below. He suffered serious and permanent injuries. The trial judge concluded that there had been a course of conduct on previous days during which the patient had been left on six or eight occasions without incident. The verdict at trial, which was given by a jury, was that it was not within the bounds of reasonable probability that the patient would have a recurrence of one of his "confused states'" at which time he would do harm to himself. Rather, there appeared to have been an improvement in the patient's condition, and this was supported by the attending physician. The jury's verdict was upheld on appeal.

In *Serre v. De Tilly*,[45] the court held that there was no obligation on the part of the nursing staff to act independently or to call for other medical advice where they disagreed with the findings or directions of the physician unless there was clear and obvious evidence of neglect or incompetence on the part of the doctor.

In *Jinks v. Cardwell*,[46] the patient, who had been diagnosed as suffering from schizophrenia and was receiving medication for his condition, was discovered dead in a bathtub with the water running. The trial judge found that he had fainted and drowned. Hypotension was a well-recognized side effect of the drugs that the patient was taking and it was known that he was subject to fainting. The nurses were found negligent for failing to have checked the man's blood pressure before administering medication.

In *LaFrance v. Prince Rupert Regional*,[47] a patient suffered respiratory distress while in the intensive care unit as a result of a rare delayed swelling of his vocal cords. The nurse was negligent for failing to chart the dramatically significant changes in his breathing and failing to alert a

---

[44] [1970] S.C.R. 477, 71 W.W.R. 656, 10 D.L.R. (3d) 539.
[45] (1975), 8 O.R. (2d) 490, 58 D.L.R. (3d) 362 (H.C.).
[46] (1987), 39 C.C.L.T. 168 (Ont. H.C.J.).
[47] Unreported, July 6, 1993, Prince Rupert SC 5853 (B.C.S.C.)

doctor. Expert evidence indicated that when a patient has persistent stridor which is unrelenting with repositioning, suctioning or coughing, immediate physician assessment and treatment is required.[48]

In *Williams (Litigation Guardian of) v. North York General Hospital*,[49] a nurse administered codeine to a child who had just undergone a tonsillectomy. The child suffered respiratory arrest. The court found that the nurses were negligent in failing to properly monitor and diagnose the signs and symptoms of the patient. The major factor causing the respiratory arrest was the administration of codeine, which the nurses should have known might depress the ability to breathe.

In *Heidebrecht v. Fraser-Burrard Hospital Society*,[50] the plaintiff alleged that nurses failed to report signs and symptoms of meningitis to the doctor in a timely manner. There was no expert evidence on the standard of care expected of a registered nurse, and the court would not infer a standard from the expectations doctors hold of nurses. The court's opinion was that nursing is an independent profession with its own practices, procedures and standards of competence, and therefore it would be impossible to infer a standard from the doctors' opinions.

In *Thompson Estate v. Byrne*,[51] a patient was recovering in the intensive care unit from a quadruple bypass. She involuntarily extubated herself while a nurse assigned to her was helping another nurse and subsequently suffered brain damage. However, the court found that the procedure followed was adequate and that the combination of sequence of events which unfolded were rare and unforeseeable and there could be no assurance that the outcome would have been different if a trained and experienced anaesthetist had been in attendance at the time.

B. FAILURE TO MONITOR: OBSTETRICAL CASES

In *Meyer v. Gordon*,[52] a court found that the plaintiff mother had been left in an inappropriate supine position with no nurse or doctor attending her for a lengthy period prior to the birth of the infant child. It was only when the fetus presented, in the labour room, with no one present, that the husband alerted the nursing staff and assistance was then sought. The infant suffered hypoxia during birth and this resulted in permanent brain damage and cerebral palsy. A finding of negligence was made against the nurses.

---

48 See also *Mahovlich (Guardian litigation of) v. Bell* (18 February 1992), Vancouver A902944 (B.C.S.C.), affd. (1993), 27 B.C.A.C. 241 (C.A.).
49 Unreported, July 22, 1993, Toronto (Ont. C.J.).
50 Unreported, October 10, 1996, Vancouver C933456 (B.C.S.C.).
51 (1992), 114 N.S.R. (2d) 395, [1992] N.S.J. No. 327 (QL) (S.C.T.D.).
52 (1981), 17 C.C.L.T. 1 (B.C.S.C.).

In *Granger (Litigation Guardian of) v. Ottawa General Hospital*,[53] the attending nurse and nurse supervisor were negligent for failing to notify the obstetrician of decelerations in the fetal heartbeat of an infant who was then born with very severe disabilities. Although several physicians, including the patient's obstetrician, were parties to the action, they were exonerated on the basis that their treatment did not fall below the standard expected of normal, prudent practitioners with the same training. The staff obstetrician was entitled to rely on the information given to him by the nurse because nurses are professionals who possess special skills and knowledge and they have a duty to communicate their assessments to the physician. The judge stated "it seems to me that one of the hallmarks of the Canadian health system in a tertiary care hospital such as the Ottawa General with all of its attendant teaching responsibilities, is that those involved in obstetrics work as a team and that the interaction between members of that team is vitally important particularly in terms of reliance on one another for the provision of accurate information."

In *Look (Next Friend of) v. Himel*,[54] two physicians in obstetrics and gynecology and three obstetrical nurses were sued when a newborn suffered mental retardation following birth. The mother was given prostin to induce labour, and was not sufficiently monitored during a one-hour period. A nurse was found negligent for failing to monitor the patient but since the negligence did not cause the injury to the child, she avoided liability. A similar result occurred in *Kuan (Guardian ad litem of) v. Harrison*,[55] where although a nurse was found negligent for failing to act upon the information evident on the fetal monitor strip, there was no possible connection between the negligence and the infant's injury.[56]

C. FAILURE TO MONITOR SUICIDAL PATIENTS

In *Villemure v. Notre Dame Hospital*,[57] the trial judge found the hospital and its nursing staff negligent when a patient had been hospitalized following a suicide attempt and was left alone in a room. The patient commited suicide by throwing himself out of the window.

In *Ganger (Guardian ad litem of) v. St. Paul's Hospital*,[58] a patient was in the hospital for nasal surgery when he voiced suicidal thoughts. He was

---

[53] [1996] O.J. No. 2129 (Gen. Div.).
[54] Unreported, June 25, 1991, Toronto 23637/84, [1991] O.J. No. 1073 (QL) (Ont. Gen. Div.).
[55] Unreported, May 22, 1997, Vancouver C950264, [1997] B.C.J. No. 1215 (QL) (B.C.S.C.).
[56] See also *Marchand (Litigation Guardian) v. Public General Hospital Society of Chatham* (1998), 16 C.P.C. (4th) 201 (Ont. Gen. Div.).
[57] [1970] C.A. 538 (Que. C.A.); the appeal decision was overturned by the Supreme Court of Canada in [1973] S.C.R. 716 which reinstated the decision of the trial judge.
[58] Unreported, June 18, 1997, Vancouver CA019638, [1997] B.C.J. No. 1454 (QL)(B.C.C.A.).

transferred to an open, short stay crisis unit. After two days, he was discharged at his own request. A few days later he was readmitted with further suicidal thoughts. Three days later a nurse permitted the plaintiff to go unescorted to the hospital cafeteria. During his absence, he attempted to commit suicide by jumping out of an upper floor window of the hospital. It was alleged that the nurse failed to draw the plaintiff's wish to leave the ward to the doctor's attention and thereby created a risk of suicide when she gave the plaintiff permission to leave, when she knew that his ward privileges were to be re-evaluated by the treatment team later in the afternoon. The action was dismissed and the nurse was able to rely on the defence of clinical judgment.

In *DeJong (Litigation Guardian of) v. Owen Sound General & Marine Hospital*,[59] a patient with suicidal tendencies was placed in a room on the main floor in a psychiatric ward. The window in his room was of ordinary glass. He threw himself out the window and ran toward the road where he was hit by a car. The hospital was negligent for placing him in a room with easily breakable windows. Nurses were negligent in failing to increase the level of observation. Nurses were also negligent in failing to properly chart all relevant information concerning the plaintiff's condition.

In *Levesque v. The Health Sciences Centre*,[60] the plaintiff suffered injuries when he was escaping out of a window of a third floor seclusion room. He loosened and removed the metal parameter of the window, which was designed to be opened only with a key. This was the first escape from a seclusion room. He was not suicidal. The staff made regular visual checks every 10 to 15 minutes. The policy required checks every five minutes in cases where the patient was suicidal. The claim against the hospital was dismissed because the staff was entitled to rely on the fact that no previous suicides had occurred in that room, that the patient was not suicidal and that the five minute check policy was not applicable.

D. FAILURE TO MONITOR OUT-PATIENTS

In *Molnar v. Coates*,[61] the plaintiff was injured when stabbed by her brother, an out-patient of a mental health centre. Calls had been made by the family to the Mental Health Centre, indicating a serious concern that the patient's condition was deteriorating. There was an allegation that the Centre failed to monitor the patient's condition following adjustment of medication prescribed by the physician. The Court of Appeal ordered

---

[59]   (1991), 31 O.R. (3d) 594, [1996] O.J. No. 809 (QL) (Gen. Div.).
[60]   (19 February 1996), Winnipeg CI 91-07571, [1996] M.J. No. 99 (Q.L.)(Man.Q.B.), aff'd (13 February 1997) AI 96-30-02743, [1997] M.J. No. 71 (QL)(C.A.).
[61]   (1991), 5 C.C.L.T. (2d) 236 (B.C.C.A.).

a new trial against the Crown-operated facility. The Court of Appeal held that the staff of the Centre owed a duty of care to the plaintiff because the Centre was in a position to exercise pharmaceutical control over the patient. Also, the fact that the patient was residing in the plaintiff's home placed the plaintiff at a much greater risk than members of the community at large.

2. Medication or Injection Errors

In *Barker v. Lockhart*,[62] the head nurse of a hospital instilled an excessively strong solution of silver nitrate into a newborn baby's eyes without first ascertaining the strength or purity of the solution. This resulted in the total destruction of one of the child's eyes. The court found that the nurse was negligent for failing to take any precautions to ascertain the strength or purity of the solution. The nurse's employer, the hospital, was found vicariously liable for her conduct.

In *Cavan v. Wilcox*,[63] the nurse had injected two c.c.s of bicillin. The patient had refused to allow an administration of the injection to his buttock, and instead, the nurse elected to give the injection into the deltoid muscle of the upper left arm. Subsequently, the condition of the patient deteriorated to such an extent that amputation of a portion of his left hand was necessary. The trial judge found that the bicillin had been injected improperly into the circumflex artery. However, on the facts of the case, and based upon the expert evidence given at trial, the trial judge concluded that the unfortunate incident was not the result of a breach of nursing standard, a decision ultimately upheld by the Supreme Court of Canada.

In *Bugden v. Harbour View Hospital*,[64] a patient was admitted to hospital for the treatment of a dislocated thumb. The doctor who was setting the thumb asked a nurse to provide him with some novocaine. The nurse asked a second nurse, who was in charge of drugs in the hospital at that time, for the novocaine dosage. The second nurse gave the first nurse a bottle and the physician injected the patient's thumb with 4 c.c.s of its contents. However, the bottle contained adrenalin. The patient died. The bottle was labelled as adrenalin, but neither of the two nurses nor the doctor had noticed this. The court held that the physician was entitled to rely upon the nursing staff to provide him with the correct medication and that he was not negligent for not having checked the label on the

---

[62]   [1940] 3 D.L.R. 427, 14 M.P.R. 546 (N.B.C.A.).
[63]   [1975] 2 S.C.R. 663, 9 N.B.R. (2d) 140, 2 N.R. 618, 50 D.L.R. (3d) 687 (*sub nom. Wilcox v. Cavan*).
[64]   [1947] 2 D.L.R. 338 (N.S.S.C.).

bottle. However, both nurses were found liable for having failed to observe, by checking the label, that the bottle contained adrenalin.

In *Fiege v. Cornwall General Hospital et al.*,[65] the defendant nurse injected the plaintiff's buttock with talwin. The nurse maintained, at trial, that she injected the upper, outer quadrant of the patient's right buttock and not the left buttock as was alleged by the patient. However, on the evidence, the trial judge concluded that the nurse had injected the left buttock of the patient and injured the sciatic nerve. The nurse was found negligent for having made an injection over the sciatic nerve. The court found that the nurse had breached an accepted nursing standard in her performance of the intramuscular injection.

In *Huber v. Burnaby General Hospital*,[66] negligence was found where the sciatic nerve was injured in the course of an injection to the buttock. The injection had been given in darkness and the nurse testified that she had used a flashlight. Another patient testified however, that there was no flashlight and that the plaintiff had cried out when the injection was given. In *Laughlin v. Royal Columbian Hospital*,[67] the negligent administration of an intramuscular injection into the sciatic nerve had caused the plaintiff to suffer a permanent "foot drop".

In *Sisters of St. Joseph v. Villeneuve*,[68] a child had been injected with sodium pentothal which had entered and damaged the brachial artery and resulted in serious circulatory problems which necessitated amputation of the child's right hand. There was evidence that the child was disturbed and terrified at the time that the injection was administered, that two nurses assisted the physician by restraining the child, but that at the moment of injection the patient had "lurched" causing the needle to pierce the brachial artery and the sodium pentothal to be injected into it. At trial, the judge held the physician entirely liable for going ahead with the injection in those circumstances. On appeal, the Ontario Court of Appeal found negligence on the part of one of the nurses for her failure to control the patient's movements. Ultimately, on appeal to the Supreme Court of Canada, the majority of the court concluded that the decision of the trial judge ought to be reinstated as there was no evidence of negligence on the part of the nursing staff who had been "doing their best" to control the patient.

---

[65]   (1980), 30 O.R. (2d) 691, 117 D.L.R. (3d) 152, 4 L. Med. Q. 124 (H.C.).
[66]   (1973), 73 D.R.S. 90-904 (B.C.S.C.).
[67]   (1971), 71 D.R.S. 90-676 (B.C.C.A.).
[68]   [1971] 2 O.R. 593, 18 D.L.R. (3d) 537; vard. [1972] 2 O.R. 119, 25 D.L.R. (3d) 35; affd. [1975] 1 S.C.R. 285, 47 D.L.R. (3d) 391, 2 N.R. 37 (*sub nom. Villeneuve v. St. Joseph's Hospital*).

Gibson v. Henniger,[69] involved a case where a plaintiff was not warned of the risks associated with a drug and was injected without specifically consenting to the injection. The plaintiff developed tremors hours after the second injection, and continued to suffer them ever since. Although there was no evidence that the doctor or the nurse gave a warning about the tremors, the judge held that they could not have given a warning because these tremors had not been previously known to them, and therefore there was no duty to disclose. With respect to consent, there was a general consent to treatment form signed by the plaintiff on admission.

3. Surgical Cases

Numerous malpractice cases arise out of surgery. In most cases, the allegations are directed towards the physicians performing the surgery. However, occasionally, the nurses are also implicated. In the Quebec case of *Hôpital Général de la Région de l'Amiante v. Perron,*[70] a patient had sustained devastating and permanent brain damage as a result of the improper administration of anaesthesia during surgery. The court found that it was an "abnormal event" and that the anaesthetist had demonstrated, through his evidence, that he had followed the generally-recognized practice of an ordinary, reasonably competent anaesthetist. In addition, no fault was imputed to the nursing staff despite allegations by plaintiff's counsel that the nurses had failed to notice the patient's condition and to summon assistance as soon as the emergency became apparent.

In *Savoie v. Bouchard,*[71] the plaintiff was a surgeon who had performed an operation on a patient who was known to be a highly contagious carrier of hepatitis B. Because of the patient's contaminated condition, extra precautions were taken by all health care personnel in the operating room, including double masks, gowns and gloves. In the course of the operation, the surgeon pricked himself on the hand with a syringe as he was reaching back for a sponge. The surgeon contracted a very serious case of hepatitis several months later and commenced an action against one of the operating room nurses. The judge concluded that the surgeon had not followed the proper practice of returning the syringe to the scrub nurse so that she could clear the operating field. On the other hand, the judge concluded that the scrub nurse fell below a reasonable standard of care when she failed to retrieve the syringe as quickly as possible when it was laid down by the surgeon. The judge found the surgeon to be 50 per

---

[69] Unreported, March 11, 1997, Vancouver CA021234, [1997] B.C.J. No. 779 (QL) (B.C.C.A.).

[70] (1979), 3 A.C.W.S. 409 (Que. C.A.).

[71] (1982), 43 N.B.R. (2d) 271, 113 A.P.R. 271, 23 C.C.L.T. 83 (Q.B.); vard. (1983), 49 N.B.R. (2d) 424, 129 A.P.R. 424, 26 C.C.L.T. 173 (*sub nom. Bouchard v. Savoie*) (C.A.).

cent responsible for his own injury and the nurse to be responsible for the remaining 50 per cent.

In *Thomson v. Barry*,[72] a tube had been left in a closed incision following surgery. The court concluded that there was no negligence on the part of the surgeon, but that the nurse in attendance at the surgery had been negligent. Similarly, in *Jewison v. Hassard*,[73] a sponge was left in the patient's abdomen. The surgeon checked the operation site before closing, but also asked the nurse if all the sponges were accounted for and the nurse advised that they were. The nurse was found negligent for failure to keep a correct count of the sponges. In *Frandle v. MacKenzie*,[74] the patient underwent surgery in 1982 during which a bone graft was taken from his hip. In the ensuing months, the hip became painful with a "puffy" lesion at the bone-graft site. An x-ray and subsequent surgery located a swab or sponge which had resulted in an abscess and necessitated several further operations. The trial judge found that the nurse who had been "keeping a mental count of the sponges" was negligent for failing to do so correctly, but found a "greater degree of fault" with the surgeon who had failed to ask for a formal sponge count.

In *Cosgrove v. Gaudreau*,[75] a surgical sponge was left in the plaintiff's abdomen and had to be removed by surgery. The court held that there was contributory negligence as between the surgeon and the scrub nurse with each being found 50 per cent liable.

4. Heat-Related Injuries

There are a number of early cases which deal with injuries sustained due to improper application of heat. In *Lavere v. Smith's Falls Public Hospital*,[76] a nurse placed an "over-heated brick" against the foot of an anaesthetized and unconscious patient resulting in a burn injury. In *Nyberg v. Provost Municipal Hospital Board*,[77] an unconscious patient sustained severe burns to the ankle when two hot water bottles were found lying next to his skin. In *Vuchar v. Toronto General Hospital Trustees*,[78] a patient was burned as the result of an excessive application of heat supplied by an electric heat cradle placed over the patient's body. In all of these cases, the nursing staff was found to be negligent.

---

[72] [1932] 2 D.L.R. 814, 41 O.W.N. 138 (C.A.).
[73] (1916), 26 Man. R. 571, 10 W.W.R. 1088, 28 D.L.R. 584 (C.A.).
[74] (1988), 47 C.C.L.T. 30 (B.C.S.C.).
[75] (1981), 33 N.B.R. (2d) 523, 80 A.P.R. 523 (Q.B.).
[76] (1935), 35 O.L.R. 98, 26 D.L.R. 346 (C.A.).
[77] [1927] S.C.R. 226, [1927] 1 D.L.R. 969.
[78] [1937] O.R. 71, [1937] 1 D.L.R. 298 (C.A.).

In *Sisters of St. Joseph v. Fleming*,[79] a nurse was found negligent for burns sustained by the patient during the administration of diathermic treatment. In *Harkies v. Lord Dufferin Hospital*,[80] a three-year-old boy was scalded and burned by a steam inhalation device used to treat pneumonia. The nurse was absent from the room at the time and was only alerted to what occurred by the child's screams.[81] In another case, the patient sustained burns to both feet from hot water bottles.[82]

5. Failure to Properly Position a Patient

In *Moore v. Castlegar and District Hospital*,[83] the plaintiff was treated following a motor vehicle accident. The court concluded that the plaintiff's complete spinal cord injury was sustained in the motor vehicle accident and it was not necessary to address allegations relating to a nurse's failure to conduct a neurological assessment or to take spinal precautions.

In *Farrell v. Cant*,[84] nurses were negligent in the post-operative care of the patient, including the positioning of the patient, which caused ulnar neuropathy (nerve damage). The court concluded that there was a "high probability" that the injury happened during a time period when a nursing intern took over the care of the patient. The court concluded based on medical evidence that ulnar neuropathy could occur without hospital negligence.

In *Horbal Estate v. Smith*,[85] a man with manic depression died of suffocation during his stay in a psychiatric ward of a hospital. It was alleged that nurses failed to observe that the deceased was suffering from an upper airway obstruction and that simply placing the patient in a recovery position would have prevented his death. It was also alleged that they failed to report this condition to a medical doctor. The evidence did not establish that the nurses failed to carry out their duties in accordance with accepted nursing practices.

---

[79]   [1938] S.C.R. 172, [1938] 2 D.L.R. 417.
[80]   66 O.L.R. 572, [1931] 2 D.L.R. 440 (S.C.).
[81]   See also *Bernier v. Sisters of Service (St. John's Hospital, Edson)*, [1948] 1 W.W.R. 113, [1948] 2 D.L.R. 468 (Alta. S.C.).
[82]   *Eek v. High River Municipal Hospital*, [1926] 1 W.W.R. 36, [1926] 1 D.L.R. 91 (Alta. S.C.) (burns to both feet from hot water bottle); see also *Logan v. Colchester County Hospital Trust* (1928), 60 N.S.R. 62, [1928] 1 D.L.R. 1129 (C.A.) (patient burned); *Sinclair v. Victoria Hospital*, [1943] 1 W.W.R. 30, 50 Man. R. 297, [1943] 1 D.L.R. 302 (C.A.) (child spilled boiling water from inhalator on top of himself); *Farrell v. Regina*, [1949] 1 W.W.R. 429 (Sask. K.B.) (infant patient rolled off a scale onto a hot radiator).
[83]   Unreported, May 31, 1996, Vancouver C918107, [1996] B.C.J. No. 1209 (QL) (B.C.S.C.).
[84]   (1992), 104 Nfld. & P.E.I.R. 9 (Nfld. S.C.T.D.).
[85]   (1992), 75 Man. R. (2d) 258, 6 W.A.C. 253 (C.A.).

6. Failure to Obtain Information From a Caller

In *Poole Estate v. Mills Memorial Hospital*,[86] the plaintiff's wife died from an overdose of anti-depressants. The plaintiff had called Poison Control to find out what to do after noticing that her behaviour was abnormal after taking six pills. The defendant nurse took the call, and after consulting with the defendant doctor, informed the plaintiff that six pills was a dosage within the therapeutic range. The nurse and doctor were each held to be 15 per cent liable. The nurse's liability stemmed from not pursuing the matter further. The nurse ought to have known from her training that when suicide is a possibility, it is important to obtain information from a caller as to the condition of the person who ingested the medication.

In *Cranwill (Next friend of) v. James*,[87] the infant plaintiff was born with congenital heart defects. He was released from hospital once his condition had stabilized. After about a week, his condition took a turn for the worse. His mother phoned the clinic and spoke to the nurse, who told the mother the baby was likely fussy, and to call the clinic back if difficulties continued. Three hours later, after continued deterioration, the mother phoned the clinic back and was told to bring the child in. It was held that the nurse acted appropriately on the phone.

7. Negligent Pre-operative Procedures

In *Crandell-Stroud v. Adams*,[88] the deceased patient did his own shaving prior to surgery, causing scratches on his abdomen. Nursing protocol for skin preparation was not followed because it was not the practice to allow the patient to perform his own pre-operative skin care. The scratches were not noticed by the nurses. The patient suffered from a skin condition, and he developed sepsis, which caused his death. The nurses were found negligent, but the surgeon was not liable because he was free to rely on pre-operative protocol.

8. Miscellaneous

In *Elverson v. Doctors Hospital*,[89] two nurses were attempting to lift the foot of a bed containing a patient who was experiencing hemorrhage during labour. When the nurses had difficulty in achieving their purpose, the patient's husband assisted them by lifting the bed for the purpose of placing blocks under it. In doing so, he aggravated a pre-existing back

---

[86] (11 March 1994), Kamloops No. 17664 (B.C.S.C.).
[87] (1994), 164 A.R. 241 (Q.B.); affd. (1997), 193 A.R. 204 (C.A.).
[88] (1993) 110 Nfld. & P.E.I.R. 22 (Nfld. S.C.T.D.).
[89] (1974), 4 O.R. (2d) 748, 49 D.L.R. (3d) 196 (C.A.); affd. (1976), 17 N.R. 157, 65 D.L.R. (3d) 382n (S.C.C.).

condition. The husband sued the hospital, a nurse and the attending physician. The plaintiff alleged that the nurse was negligent for failing to summon an orderly to assist them and that this caused the plaintiff's injury. It was held at trial, and on appeal, that even "in the most unfavorable light" the action of the nurse was no more than an "error of judgment".[90] Moreover, the court concluded that even if there was negligence, the injury to the husband was not reasonably foreseeable.

In *Kielly v. General Hospital Corp.*,[91] the plaintiff suffered a massive heart attack while under observation on a cardiac floor. The nurses were held to be negligent for filing to make proper progress notes detailing his condition. They did not have the resident doctor attend to him when his pain persisted. They were found negligent at trial, and the Court of Appeal dismissed their appeal.

In *Brown v. University of Alberta Hospital*,[92] a hospital policy required reporting suspected child abuse to the authorities. A physician was held liable for failing to communicate a diagnosis of possible shaken baby syndrome. The child was discharged, and four days later was readmitted. During those four days, the child had been further abused by the father. The physician was liable of the injuries caused by the vigorous shaking. It was also alleged that the nurses ought to have suspected child abuse and ought to have reported it to the mother, physicians and child welfare authorities, but the action against them was dismissed.

CURRENT ISSUES: MULTIPLE PROCEEDINGS

Q. You are a registered nurse who is being investigated by your provincial nursing regulatory body for professional misconduct (a disciplinary offence) arising out of an incident in which a patient died. Your hospital administrator then brings you a statement of claim naming you as one of several defendants in a civil action being brought by the patient's estate and his wife and children. Can you be investigated in two separate hearings?

A. Yes, and in fact it is possible that in these circumstances your conduct could be examined in a criminal investigation (if there was reason to believe that a crime, like practising euthanasia, had been committed). It could also be examined in an inquest. However, it is important to note that the proceedings of your discipline hearing may not be used in evidence at your civil trial, depending on the confidentiality provisions within the provincial legislation that governs the disciplinary body.

---

[90] *Ibid.*, at 750 O.R.
[91] (1994) 125 Nfld. & P.E.I.R. 236, [1994] N.J. No. 398 (QL) (Nfld. S.C.T.D.), affd. unreported, May 30, 1997, 95/106, [1997] N.J. No. 123 (QL) (Nfld. S.C.C.A.).
[92] (1997) 145 D.L.R. (4th) 63, 33 C.C.L.T. (2d) 113 (Alta. Q.B.).

CHAPTER 10

Inquests and Inquiries

SYNOPSIS

This chapter introduces the coroner and medical examiner systems, and walks nurses through the inquest process (including seeking standing, appearing as a witness, role of the coroner's jury, jury recommendations and judicial review). It also explains the function of public inquiries.

INTRODUCTION

What if a patient dies unexpectedly? On occasion, the death will be investigated, leading to one of three types of legal proceedings: criminal prosecutions, malpractice actions and disciplinary hearings. These proceedings are adversarial in nature; the parties do not share a common goal. In an adversarial process, one party is usually called upon to prove that a law or professional standard has been breached. It is possible that as a nurse who was part of the health care team, you could be called upon to defend your conduct. In the event that you are unsuccessful, you may be required to pay damages or face professional sanctions.

A fourth type of legal proceeding is the inquest or inquiry. It is not intended to be an adversarial process, but is instead inquisitorial.[1] It involves the investigation (usually by a coroner), of an unexplained or suspicious death.[2] Inquests may involve investigating the conduct of nurses and other health care professionals, the management of health care facilities, and the treatment and care of patients. Inquests are not designed to establish criminal or civil liability, or to exercise a discipli-

---

[1]   See R.C. Bennett, "The Ontario Coroners' System" (1986-87), 7 *Advocates Quarterly* 53 at p. 62. "There are no parties, no plaintiff, and no defendant, since no one is on trial and no one is accused. The procedure is inquisitorial rather than accusatorial and the jury is a finder of facts. An inquest is, therefore, a search for the truth and not an exercise to present enough evidence to prove or disprove that someone was responsible. The less adversarial the approach, the better the inquest, and the more successful the results." Excerpts reproduced with permission of the author and of Canada Law Book Inc., 240 Edward Street, Aurora, Ontario L4G 3S9.

[2]   C. Granger, *Canadian Coroner Law* (Toronto: Carswell, 1984), p. 64.

nary function; in fact, the tribunal conducting the inquest may be barred from making any finding of fault.[3]

It is not unusual for health care professionals to become involved in such investigations, and possibly, in inquests. The Chief Coroner of Ontario has reported:

> Deaths following treatment in hospital where the family alleges malpractice are an increasing problem in Ontario ... probably the most volatile and potentially hazardous area of a hospital is the Emergency Department. Emergency Departments are generally overcrowded and require decisions as to whether or not hospital admission is necessary. The most common complaints regarding emergencies are that the diagnosis was missed, that patients were required to spend long periods of time in Emergency waiting for a bed in hospital and did not receive adequate care, or cases such as overdoses that are diagnosed late and treated too lightly. Nursing home deaths are commonly disputed by the family, and the major issue usually centres on the level of treatment that is received. In addition, coroners hear from families dissatisfied with psychiatric care, whether it is a wrong diagnosis resulting in the release of the patient prior to his or her suicide, or placement in housing that leads to problems and ultimately death.[4]

PROVINCIAL LEGISLATION

All provinces have passed legislation codifying the common law office of coroner and giving those empowered by law the capacity to investigate unexplained or suspicious deaths, and where appropriate, to conduct inquests.

The nature and number of inquests have changed dramatically in recent years. At one time, inquests were more frequent, but they were relatively short hearings which focused on the particular questions formulated by the relevant legislation. It was unusual for an inquest to take more than one or two days.

In more recent years, inquests have become lengthy proceedings that have more in common with wide-ranging public inquiries than with the traditional inquest. Inquests have also become increasingly adversarial. At one time, inquests were called only when there was a "mysterious death". Today, inquests involving nurses practising in health facilities rarely involve a mystery. It is relatively clear from the health record who

[3] For a brief history of the role of coroners, see T.D. Marshall, *Canadian Law of Inquests* (Toronto: Carswell, 1980), Chapter 2. Excerpts reproduced with permission of Carswell, a division of Thomson, Canada.

[4] J. Young, "An Overview of the Ontario Coroners' System" in *Inside Inquests* (Toronto: Law Society of Upper Canada, Department of Continuing Legal Education, 1993), p. A-1. Reproduced with the permission of Dr. James G. Young.

the patient was and how, when, where and by what means the death occurred. An inquest is more likely to occur where there is criticism by family or friends or where the coroner or medical examiner, in the course of the investigation, has uncovered an area of concern or criticism and has concluded that it should be dealt with in the context of a public hearing.

The changing nature of inquests was confirmed by the Ontario Divisional Court in a case involving an inquest into the circumstances surrounding the deaths of disabled patients at two residential health facilities.[5] The inquest related to the deaths of four young adults at one institution and 17 children at the other. Applications for judicial review were brought during the course of the inquest to determine certain jurisdictional and procedural issues that had arisen. In the course of its reasons, the court stated:

> The public interest in Ontario inquests has become more and more important in recent years. The traditional investigative function of the inquest to determine how, when, where, and by what means the deceased came to her death, is no longer the predominant feature of every inquest. That narrow investigative function, to lay out the essential facts surrounding an individual death, is still vital to the families of the deceased and to those who are directly involved in the death.
>
> A separate and wider function is becoming increasingly significant; the vindication of the public interest in the prevention of death by the public exposure of conditions that threaten life. The separate role of the jury in recommending systemic changes to prevent death has become more and more important. The social and preventive function of the inquest which focuses on the public interest has become, in some cases, just as important as the distinctly separate function of investigating the individual facts of individual deaths and the personal roles of individuals involved in the death.[6]

A less frequent but not unusual form of inquisitorial proceeding is the public inquiry. In contrast to inquests, inquiries do not necessarily involve death. Instead, they may involve a broad range of issues from specific occurrences to government policy. Again, all Canadian provinces have passed legislation providing for the government appointment of individuals to carry out investigations and to inquire, sometimes by way of hearing, into certain issues or events. One of the best-known public inquiries, and one that garnered the attention of the nursing profession,

---

5   *People First of Ontario v. Porter, Regional Coroner, Niagara* (1991), 5 O.R. (3d) 609, 50 O.A.C. 90, 85 D.L.R. (4th) 174 (Div. Ct.); revd. (1992), 6 O.R. (3d) 289, 87 D.L.R. (4th) 765 (C.A.).

6   *Ibid.*, at 619 (O.R.).

was the inquiry following the deaths of numerous infant patients at the Hospital for Sick Children in Toronto.[7]

THE CORONER SYSTEM VS. THE MEDICAL EXAMINER SYSTEM

The majority of provinces in Canada have passed legislation that calls for the investigation of violent or unnatural deaths by a coroner.[8] Three provinces — Alberta, Manitoba and Nova Scotia — have passed legislation which establishes the office of "medical examiner".[9]

In the coroner system, which is most closely aligned with the traditional common law institution, the coroner is empowered to investigate, and where appropriate, hold inquests into violent or unnatural deaths. In most cases, the coroner is a medical doctor, although this may not be a specific requirement under provincial legislation. In many cases, a chief coroner is responsible for regional coroners acting under his or her supervision.[10] Often, regional coroners carry out their duties on a part-time basis. In Ontario, in 1993, the Chief Coroner was assisted by the Deputy Chief Coroner and eight full-time Regional Coroners. Initial investigations were carried out by one of approximately 400 investigating coroners, most of whom were experienced family physicians.[11] Under the coroner system, the coroner not only investigates a death, but where he or she deems it necessary to conduct an inquest, presides over the inquest as well.

Where the legislation establishes the role of a medical examiner, the medical examiner conducts the initial investigation in much the same manner as a coroner. He or she interviews witnesses, police, forensic experts and others. As well, the medical examiner ordinarily carries out an autopsy and prepares an autopsy report and a record of the investigation.

The decision of whether or not an inquest will be held, however, is not within the jurisdiction of the medical examiner. In the medical examiner system, a board or agency is appointed under the governing legislation

---

[7] Ontario, *Report of the Royal Commission of Inquiry into Certain Deaths at the Hospital for Sick Children and Related Matters* (Toronto: Ministry of the Attorney General, 1984) (Commissioner: Samuel Grange).

[8] British Columbia: *Coroners Act*, R.S.B.C. 1996, c. 72; New Brunswick: *Coroners Act*, R.S.N.B. 1973, c. C-23; Ontario: *Coroners Act*, R.S.O. 1990, c. C.37; Prince Edward Island: *Coroners Act*, R.S.P.E.I. 1988, c. C-25; Quebec: *Causes and Circumstances of Death Act*, R.S.Q. 1977, c.R-0.2; and Saskatchewan: *Coroners Act*, R.S.S. 1978, c. C-38.

[9] *Fatality Inquiries Act*, R.S.A. 1980, c. F-6; *Fatality Inquiries Act*, S.M. 1989-90, c. 30; Nova Scotia *Fatality Inquiries Act*, R.S.N.S. 1989, c. 164.

[10] For example, *Coroners Act*, R.S.B.C. 1996, c. 72, s.3.

[11] J. Young, *supra*, note 4, at A-5.

to review the findings and report of the medical examiner in order to determine whether or not a public inquiry, similar to the traditional inquest, will be held. When the determination is made to hold a public inquiry, it is usually conducted by a judge. Depending on the governing legislation, the inquiry may proceed before a jury.

INITIAL INVESTIGATION

When does the duty to report an unusual death arise? Generally, the provincial legislation provides for the mandatory reporting of unusual or unexplained deaths to the local coroner or medical examiner. A number of provincial statutes set out in detail the types of death that are considered to be reportable. For example, under the Alberta *Fatality Inquiries Act* "any person having knowledge" is required to report the following:

(a) deaths that occur unexplainedly;
(b) deaths that occur unexpectedly when the deceased was in apparent good health;
(c) deaths that occur as the result of violence, accident or suicide;
(d) maternal deaths that occur during or following pregnancy and that might reasonably be related to pregnancy;
(e) deaths that may have occurred as the result of improper or negligent treatment by any person;
(f) deaths that occur
   (i) during an operative procedure;
   (ii) within 10 days of an operative procedure;
   (iii) while under anaesthesia; or
   (iv) [repealed 1991, c. 21, s. 9]
   (v) any time after anaesthesia and that may reasonably be attributed to that anaesthesia;
(g) deaths that are the result of poisoning;
(h) deaths that occur while the deceased person was not under the care of a physician;
(i) deaths that occur while the deceased person was in the custody of a peace officer;
(j) deaths that are due to
   (i) any disease or ill-health contracted or incurred by the deceased;
   (ii) any injury sustained by the deceased; or
   (iii) any toxic substance introduced into the deceased,
   as a direct result of the deceased's employment or occupation or in the course of one or more of his former employments or occupations.[12]

---

[12] R.S.A. 1980, c. F-6, s. 10(2) [am. 1991, c. 21, s. 9].

In addition, the legislation may require notification of the coroner or medical examiner if the deceased was a prisoner, a patient of a psychiatric facility, or where the deceased was an infant or child.

Where a coroner or medical examiner is notified of a reportable death, he or she carries out investigations to establish the following five elements:

1.   the identity of the deceased;
2.   the date, time and place of death;
3.   the circumstances under which the death occurred;
4.   the cause of death; and
5.   the manner of death.

The coroner or medical examiner has the authority to take possession of the body of the deceased. As well, he or she may take possession of any items that appear pertinent to the investigation, such as clothing, weapons, medication, and documents. For example, the following rules apply in Ontario:

> A coroner may,
> (a) view or take possession of any dead body, or both; and
> (b) enter and inspect any place where a dead body is and any place from which the coroner has reasonable grounds for believing the body was removed.
> (2) A coroner who believes on reasonable and probable grounds that to do so is necessary for the purposes of the investigation may,
> (a) inspect any place in which the deceased person was, or in which the coroner has reasonable grounds to believe the deceased person was, prior to his or her death;
> (b) inspect and extract information from any records or writings relating to the deceased or his or her circumstances and reproduce such copies therefrom as the coroner believes necessary;
> (c) seize anything that the coroner has reasonable grounds to believe is material to the purpose of the investigation.[13]

In some jurisdictions, it is an offence to interfere with a body or physical evidence pertinent to the investigation. In Ontario, it is an offence to knowingly hinder or obstruct the work of a coroner. Similarly, it is an offence to withhold information from, or furnish false information to a coroner.[14]

The coroner or medical examiner examines the body of the deceased and may conduct an autopsy. The autopsy may be conducted by a trained pathologist under the supervision of the coroner or medical ex-

---

[13]   Ontario *Coroners Act, supra*, note 8, s. 16.
[14]   *Ibid.*, note 8, s. 16(6)(a) and (b).

aminer. The autopsy usually includes an external examination of the body, as well as the possibility of

> dissection, removal and gross examination of the internal organs, weighing and measuring, study and testing of tissue samples, recovery of bullets and other foreign objects, photographing and x-raying, and study of the surrounding physical context. These may lead into further scientific procedures such as ballistic tests, fingerprint tests and so forth.[15]

In addition to examining the physical scene of the death and conducting an autopsy, some provinces specifically provide that the medical examiner or coroner has "specific statutory powers of entry, inspection, search and seizure ... to facilitate effective investigation."[16] A coroner or medical examiner sometimes requires the assistance of other physicians, experts or police in order to carry out the investigation.

Upon completion of an investigation into a death, the coroner or medical examiner prepares a report for review by the appropriate authorities. Depending on his or her findings, further steps may be taken at this stage to investigate the death. Occasionally, the findings (and possibly the report or excerpts from the report) are disclosed to the deceased's family, the media, and other members of the public. The Ontario *Coroners Act* provides:

> 18(2) Every coroner shall keep a record of the cases reported in which an inquest has been determined to be unnecessary, showing for each case the identity of the deceased and the coroner's findings of the facts as to how, when, where and by what means the deceased came by his or her death, including the relevant findings of the *post mortem* examination and of any other examinations or analyses of the body carried out, and such information shall be available to the spouse, parents, children, brothers and sisters of the deceased and to his or her personal representative, upon request.[17]

Even where an inquest is not held, the coroner's investigation may lead to recommendations in a less formal setting than is usually the case with an inquest. For example, where the death has occurred in a "hospital, nursing home or psychiatric facility" a request for an inquest or further investigation can result in intense scrutiny of the institution. Cooperation may avoid the expense and publicity of an inquest:

> Often the coroner or Regional Coroner will ask the complainant to detail his/her concerns in writing. The investigating coroner reviews

---

15 C. Granger, *supra*, note 2, p. 158.
16 *Ibid.*, p. 170.
17 Ontario *Coroner's Act, supra*, note 8, s. 18(2).

the complaint along with the written record from the institution and any other available information, such as a police report. Detailed reviews are often necessary in medical cases involving operative procedures, children's deaths and institutional care in settings, such as nursing homes, homes for the aged and rest homes. For this reason, specific standing committees of experts have been established and sit regularly, such as the Anaesthesia Review Committee, Long Term Care Review Committee and the Paediatric Review Committee. These medical experts are from both academic and non-academic medical settings and review cases at the request of the Chief Coroner. The full medical chart, along with the autopsy results and the coroner's investigation to date, are supplied to the committee. Generally the committee assigns a particular member to conduct the initial review. That physician then discusses the case following review with the committee at large and preliminary opinion and set of concerns is formulated. These are passed on to the Regional Coroner and investigation coroner. This information often forms a useful basis to decide the next course of action. Commonly the Regional Coroner and the local coroner will organize a meeting with the affected institution and medical staff. This Regional Coroner's review will discuss the case in detail in an informal way and hopefully result in a set of recommendations to help prevent similar deaths in the future. The family is then informed of the results of this review.[18]

INQUESTS AND PUBLIC INQUIRIES INTO DEATHS

At common law, where a coroner's investigation did not establish a satisfactory explanation for a violent or unexplained death, an inquest was held. In the coroner system, that determination is usually made by the investigating coroner. As noted above, in the medical examiner system, that decision is made by some other person or agency based upon the findings of the medical examiner. It is important to note that although coroners and medical examiners conduct many investigations, very few of these result in an inquest or public inquiry. Ontario's Chief Coroner has reported that the number of inquests held annually in Ontario has dropped significantly. Twenty years ago, there were 1,200 inquests annually. That figure is now approximately 150.

> At present, most of the 150 inquests per year are selected because there is an obvious need for the public to understand the circumstances and there are recommendations that will protect the public in future. This decreased number of inquests is by design. The office of the Chief Coroner feels that it is a better use of limited resources to do fewer inquests but cover topics in more detail. Such inquests receive

---

[18] J. Young, *supra*, note 4, at A-11-A-13.

more coverage and seem to result in more implementation of recommendations.[19]

The criteria for holding an inquest or inquiry into a death are ordinarily set out in the governing legislation. An inquest or inquiry may be necessary in order to complete an investigation. It may also be necessary in order to "satisfy curiosity or suspicion, to eliminate speculation, or to publicize a hazard or a danger and obtain recommendations or measures to avoid such deaths in the future".[20] The Ontario *Coroners Act* provides as follows:

> 20. When making a determination whether an inquest is necessary or unnecessary, the coroner shall have regard to whether the holding of an inquest would serve the public interest and, without restricting the generality of the foregoing, shall consider,
> (a) whether the matters described in clauses 31(1)(a) to (e) are known;[21]
> (b) the desirability of the public being fully informed of the circumstances of the death through an inquest; and
> (c) the likelihood that the jury on an inquest might make useful recommendations directed to the avoidance of death in similar circumstances.[22]

In most provinces, the legislation gives the coroner or agency responsible for deciding whether to hold an inquest a great deal of discretion in making that decision. In some cases, the decision to hold an inquest or inquiry may be the result of considerable pressure from family, friends or interest groups. In fact, the Chief Coroner of Ontario has made it clear that input from these parties can have a considerable influence:

> On occasion, special interest groups, the press or a ministry of government may call for an inquest. The true facts of the investigation must then be compared with the claims that are being made to see whether an inquest would be useful. If the facts being written or discussed publicly vary too much from the facts the investigation is revealing, then it may be necessary to hold the inquest simply to set the record straight and correctly inform the public.[23]

---

[19]   *Ibid.*, at A-13.
[20]   C. Granger, *supra*, note 2, at p. 195.
[21]   For example, who the deceased was; how, when, where, and by what means the deceased came to his or her death.
[22]   Ontario *Coroner's Act, supra*, note 8, s. 20.
[23]   *Supra*, note 4, at A-13.

An inquest or public inquiry into a death usually takes the form of a hearing. In most instances, the hearing will be open to the public.[24] However, the legislation may state that an inquest can be held in private.[25]

The coroner (or tribunal conducting the public inquiry) has broad powers to regulate the proceedings. In Ontario, the coroner has jurisdiction over:

1. Administering oaths and affirmations for all purposes of the inquiry (s 49);
2. Adjourning proceedings when and for however long as is appropriate (s. 46);
3. Preventing irrelevant or unreasonable cross-examination of witnesses and improper arguments (s. 50(2));
4. Determining what is admissible in evidence (s. 44(2));
5. Making rulings and give such directions as may be necessary to preserve order and prevent abuse of process (s. 50); and,
6. Calling for the assistance of police officers to enforce directives (and either punish those who contravene them for contempt or, if he or she lacks sufficient power to do this, apply to other authorities to impose such penalties) (s. 47)[26].

WHO ATTENDS?

1. Witnesses
2. Crown Attorneys
3. Coroner / Judge
4. Parties with Standing
5. Counsel
6. Family Members of the Deceased

---

[24] For example, the British Columbia legislation provides:
    An inquest must be open to the public but the coroner may hold all or part of the hearing closed to the public
    (a) if the coroner is of the opinion that national security might be endangered, or
    (b) if a person is charged with an indictable offence under the *Criminal Code*, and relevant evidence about that person's conduct may be given at the inquest. (*Coroners Act*, R.S.B.C. 1996, c. 72, s. 28).

[25] Arguably, such a broad privacy provision contravenes the *Charter of Rights and Freedoms*. In *Edmonton Journal v. Canada (A.G.)*, [1985] 4 W.W.R. 575, 37 Alta. L.R. (2d) 287, 13 D.L.R. (4th) 479 (*sub nom. Re Edmonton Journal and Alberta (A.G.)*), 17 C.R.R. 100 (C.A.); leave to appeal to S.C.C. refused (1984), 17 C.R.R. 100, the Alberta Court of Appeal upheld the reasoning of the lower court judge who concluded that a coroner's inquest or a fatality inquiry was not a court proceeding to which the *Charter of Rights* applied.

[26] *Coroners Act*, R.S.O. 1990, c. C.37.

An inquest or public hearing into a violent or unnatural death proceeds in a manner similar to a court proceeding. Initially, witnesses are called by a Crown attorney, who conducts an examination-in-chief to elicit their testimony. Following the examination-in-chief, parties with standing (or their counsel) are given the opportunity to cross-examine the witness. The coroner or judge exercises a judicial function to oversee the general management of the inquest, to determine what evidence will be admissible, place restraints upon cross-examination if necessary, and make determinations as to standing.

STANDING

In Ontario, the coroner must give standing to any person who a "is substantially and directly interested in the inquest".[27] In British Columbia, a person is given standing if he or she "may be affected by evidence likely to be adduced at an inquest".[28] Generally, persons given standing at an inquest are entitled to appear personally and be represented by counsel. They may also call evidence and cross-examine witnesses. If the evidence in question is relevant, a party who has standing may issue a summons to have any other person testify, as long as the latter's testimony is seen to be relevant to the issues being considered at the inquest.

When a death occurs in a health care setting, nurses, doctors and other health practitioners who cared for the patient may be called upon to testify. These witnesses will be examined and cross-examined. It is not unusual for a Crown attorney, or possibly other parties, to call expert evidence to assist the jury in understanding the health care issues involved. An expert witness may also comment upon the performance of the nurses and other health care practitioners involved. The jury, upon hearing the evidence, may make recommendations that imply weakness or fault, despite the fact that no specific finding of fault was made.

The secondary use of a nurse's testimony at an inquest or public inquiry may be limited. It may be protected in subsequent civil or criminal proceedings to which they are a party. For example, under the *Fatality Inquiries Act* of Alberta, "no answer given by a witness at a public fatality inquiry shall be used or be receivable in evidence against him in any trial or other proceeding ... other than a prosecution for perjury ... ."[29] It is not clear, however, that the testimony of a witness at an inquest, who is *not* a

---

[27] *Coroners Act*, R.S.O. 1990, c. C.37, s. 41(1) [am. 1993, c. 27, sched.]; see also *Booth v. Ontario (Coroner)* (1994), 16 O.R. (3d) 528; *Stanford v. Regional Coroner, Eastern Ontario* (1989) 38 Admin. L.R. 141, 33 O.A.C. 241, 38 CP.C. (2d) 161.

[28] *Coroners Act*, R.S.B.C. 1996, c. 72, s. 36.

[29] R.S.A. 1980, c. F-6, s. 42(1) [am. 1998, c. 23, s. 7].

party to the subsequent proceeding, cannot be used in evidence. For example, if a nurse who testified at an inquest were called subsequently to
testify at a civil proceeding to which the nurse is not a party, it is not clear
whether the earlier testimony can be used to cross-examine the nurse as
evidence in the civil proceeding. A witness may be entitled to retain and
have counsel present at an inquest or inquiry, although the right of counsel to participate may be severely limited.[30]

The governing provincial legislation may require the coroner to hold
an inquest even where a decision has been made not to hold one. In *Re
Gregoire and Thompson et al.*,[31] a decision was made not to hold an inquest
after a patient died in hospital, although a physician had questioned
whether the patient's care, or lack thereof, contributed to the death. On
application to the court, an inquest was ordered on the basis of uncertainty about the cause of death.

In *Lawson v. British Columbia (Solicitor General)*,[32] the British Columbia
Court of Appeal upheld an order of the Solicitor General that an inquest
be held about the circumstances in which a patient died after refusing
blood transfusions following a Caesarian section. Questions had been
raised about the possible influence of others of the same faith, posing as
family members, in the patient's refusal.

In *Saxell v. Campbell*,[33] it was held that the coroner had no jurisdiction
to order that an inquest be held when an "inquiry" under the British
Columbia *Coroners Act* had already been held. In that case there had been
a stillbirth at a delivery attended by a midwife. There was a suggestion
of cover-up at the hospital to where the mother had been taken when
fetal distress developed. The inquiry had already concluded that the
midwife had "assisted in [the mother's] rapid expedient admission to the
hospital when she recognized fetal distress", and therefore, no formal
inquest was required.

JURIES

Traditionally, juries are employed as fact-finders in coroner's inquests.[34]
In some jurisdictions, this is still the practice. In a number of jurisdictions
the employment of a jury at an inquest or public inquiry is optional.

---

[30]　See *Coroners Act*, R.S.O. 1990, c. C.37, s. 43: "A witness at an inquest is entitled to be
advised by his or her counsel or agent as to his or her rights but such counsel or agent
may take no other part in the inquest without leave of the coroner".

[31]　(1988), 51 D.L.R. (4th) 131 (N.B.Q.B.).

[32]　(1992), 63 B.C.L.R. (2d) 334, 88 D.L.R. (4th) 533 (C.A.); leave to appeal to S.C.C. refused
(1992), 70 B.C.L.R. (2d) xxxiii*n*.

[33]　(1987), 21 B.C.L.R. (2d) 44 (S.C.).

[34]　C. Granger, *Canadian Coroner Law* (Toronto: Carswell, 1984), p. 230.

Once all of the evidence has been heard, the coroner or officer conducting the inquest or inquiry may permit parties with standing (or through counsel) to make arguments and submissions to the coroner or officer (and where applicable, to the jury). Their arguments and submissions may suggest what findings should be made in relation to the circumstances of death, and also, what recommendations the coroner, officer or jury may choose to make. The coroner or officer normally sums up the evidence and issues a charge to the jury relating to the findings it must make.

The role of the jury is to make findings in regard to the circumstances of death.[35] Traditionally, juries were empowered to name individuals responsible for the death if they came to the conclusion that the death occurred as a result of a criminal act. In some provinces, the jury is prohibited from making a finding of legal responsibility. If the jury comments inappropriately, the verdict may be set aside.

In *MacKenzie v. MacArthur*[36] the deceased had been brought to the Vancouver General Hospital. The examining physician concluded that he was suffering from a personality disorder. He was taken from the hospital to jail where he was examined by a second physician. He was then sent to another hospital where he was refused admission when it was learned that he had already been seen at Vancouver General Hospital. He was returned to Vancouver General Hospital, where the previous diagnosis of a personality disorder was reconfirmed. Plans were made for a psychiatric assessment. However, before the further testing could occur, the patient died.

An inquest was held. The evidence of the health care professionals was heard. The coroner instructed the jury not to make any finding of legal responsibility or reach any conclusion of law. However, in reviewing the evidence, the coroner suggested to the jury that it should consider that one of the treating physicians had treated the deceased in a careless fashion. The coroner then supplied to the jury a typewritten sheet containing possible findings, including the suggestion in regard to the treating physician. Subsequently, the jury returned a verdict that mirrored the language of the coroner: it concluded that the physician had treated the deceased in a careless fashion, failed to conduct an adequate examination and did not keep adequate records of the examination performed.

The British Columbia Supreme Court concluded that the verdict reached by the jury was a finding of legal responsibility, which was improper and contrary to the provisions of the *Coroners Act*, per Callaghan J.:

---

[35] This is the traditional determination of "who the deceased was and how, where and by what means the deceased died": T.D. Marshall, *Canadian Law of Inquests* (Toronto: Carswell, 1980), p. 101.

[36] (1980), 25 B.C.L.R. 303, 119 D.L.R. (3d) 529, 57 C.C.C. (2d) 130 (S.C.).

> Clearly, the coroner exceeded his jurisdiction when he, contrary to s.
> 28(2) of the *Coroners Act*, advising the jury in writing that it could find
> that Dr. MacKenzie acted in a careless fashion. He compounded the
> error when he accepted that portion of the verdict wherein the jury
> found that Dr. MacKenzie assessed and treated the deceased Landry
> in a careless fashion. As the verdict in part was contrary to s. 28(4) of
> the *Coroners Act*, the verdict as returned cannot stand.[37]

The decision of the court in this case is consistent with the general principle that coroners' inquests and public inquiries into deaths must remain
inquiries, rather than proceedings to determine civil or criminal liability.

The coroner, in the course of instructing the jury, may express a view
on matters of evidence in order to assist the jury in arriving at a verdict.
Generally, coroners have considerable leeway in charging a jury and their
comments can have a significant impact upon the jury's verdict, as well
as any recommendations the jury might make. Where the coroner's instruction involves a forceful statement of opinion that may amount to a
direction to the jury, however, the verdict will be set aside.[38]

RECOMMENDATIONS

One of the major functions of the inquest or public inquiry is to present
recommendations to the proper authorities. These recommendations aim
to avoid or reduce the risk of future deaths occurring in similar circumstances. It is the practice of the Ontario Coroner's Office to send verdicts
and recommendations to appropriate groups including safety associations, sporting associations, medical and other scientific associations or
regulating bodies who are interested in receiving verdicts and recommendations. It is also the practice of the Ontario Coroner's Office to follow up with recipients of recommendations where no reply is received.[39]

A report of the Ontario Law Reform Commission recommends that the
Chief Coroner be required to inquire as to the implementation of the jury
recommendations, or the reasons why implementation has been post-
poned or rejected. The Commission also recommends that the Chief
Coroner's office compile and publish an annual report, which should
including specific responses of individuals or agencies affected by the

---

[37] *Ibid.*, at 312-13 (B.C.L.R.).
[38] *Re Beckon* (1992), 9 O.R. (3d) 256, 57 O.A.C. 21 (*sub. nom. Beckon v. Deputy Chief Coroner (Ont.)*, 93 D.L.R. (4th) 161 (C.A.).
[39] E. P. King, "How to Use the Findings: Is There Life After an Inquest?"in *Inquests and the General Practitioner* (Toronto: Law Society of Upper Canada, Department of Education, 1987), pp. C-1&2.

recommendations. It further recommends that the annual report be reported in the Ontario legislature.

Juries commonly make broad and detailed recommendations that can have a significant impact on nursing practice and health care:

- Where an infant patient died as a result of acute gastoenteritis with dehydration and hypovelmic shock, the jury recommended that back-up resources be readily available and be called by a "triage" nurse as urgency dictates. It also recommended that emergency nursing staff be allowed to initiate I.V. procedures. These recommendations suggest a move to less "physician-driven" procedures.[40]

- In another case, the jury concluded that where a patient died of hypothermia in extreme winter temperatures after going missing from a hospital, observation rounds during a shift change should be performed by both charge nurses together. It also recommended putting in place hospital search procedures for missing patients, with appropriate co-ordination between hospital and police searches.[41]

- Another inquest involved a suicidal patient who died of asphyxiation after he was found hanging by a bedsheet in a seclusion room at a provincial psychiatric hospital, some five minutes after he had last been seen by nursing staff. The jury recommended that individual nursing staff be assigned to an individual patient's primary care for the duration of their stay, with a shift matrix to be drawn up. This would result in the most responsible nurse being more likely to make appropriate decisions.[42]

- Where the patient died as a result of an intracerebral hemorrhage after being assessed by a triage nurse as a "possible overdose", it was recommended that health care professionals be reminded of the importance of not being unduly influenced by a patient's past history and/or diagnoses, such as a psychiatric condition.[43]

- Where a Jehovah's Witness patient died as a result of massive post partum blood loss after refusing a blood transfusion, the jury recommended that the Ontario Antenatal record be revised to include a declaration of the patient's willingness to accept or refuse blood products. It was also recommended that nurses employed in Ontario hospitals (in any capacity) be required to periodically review

---

[40]   *Re Brandon Breen*, Verdict of Coroners' Jury of Ontario dated December 6, 1995.
[41]   *Re Luigia Baratto*, Verdict of the Coroners' Jury of Ontario dated September 13, 1995.
[42]   *Re Glenn Hawryluk*, Verdict of Coroners' Jury of Ontario dated February 10, 1998.
[43]   *Re Silvia Marchese*, Verdict of Coroners' Jury of Ontario dated Mary 17, 1995.

relevant nursing manual of the particular unit of employment, completed by dated signature.[44]

- It has been recommended that all quiet rooms, intensive observation and treatment units in psychiatric facilities be equipped with non-breakable glass. This recommendation arose after a patient suffering from excited delirium threw a ceramic toilet tank top through a window into the nursing station, putting himself and the nursing staff at considerable risk.[45]

- In another case the infant patient died accidentally as a result of an adult dosage of digoxin being administered. The jury recommended that hospital procedures for recording written communications be reviewed for compliance, and that nursing entries on paediatric flowsheets should accurately reflect time and dates of all events, including drug administration.[46]

As previously discussed, the main purpose of an inquest or a public inquiry is to make findings and recommendations which will avoid or reduce the risk of a death occurring in similar circumstances in the future. However, in many instances, the participants at an inquest or public inquiry may have a somewhat different agenda. One lawyer has suggested that the primary rule of counsel for the family of the deceased at an inquest may involve "the assembling of evidence for anticipated litigation", and that in those situations, "the verdict of the jury is of secondary importance".[47] In a similar vein, and probably in response to activities by prospective plaintiffs at inquests and public inquiries, "individuals and entities whose conduct may be perceived as having caused or contributed to the death have increasingly found it necessary to retain counsel to represent their interests at the inquest."[48]

Consequently, inquests and public inquiries into deaths frequently involve proceedings which appear more adversarial than inquisitorial and at which the activities and conduct of nurses and other health care practitioners, may be closely scrutinized. There may be an underlying intention in the minds of some parties to build a case for future civil proceedings and an award of compensation. Nurses who become involved in

[44] *Re Cathy Grenci*, Verdict of Coroners' Jury of Ontario dated May 14, 1996.
[45] *Re Zdrovko Pukec*, Verdict of Coroners' Jury of Ontario dated November 27, 1996.
[46] *Re Anthony Pescarino*, Verdict of Coroners' Jury of Ontario dated March 16, 1996.
[47] D. W. Scott, "Representing The Family At The Hearing," in *Inquests and the General Practitioner, supra*, note 39, p. E-1.
[48] M. E. Royce, "Tactical and Practical Considerations for Counsel Acting For a Potential Defendant in Civil Proceedings," in *Inquests and the General Practitioner, supra*, note 39, p. 1-2.

inquests should consider seeking legal advice, and possibly obtaining representation at the inquest or public inquiry. In some instances, nurses, physicians and the health care facility will be entitled to, or seek to retain, separate counsel. Nonetheless, if this occurs, it is advisable from a tactical point of view to consult and cooperate with one another in preparing to examine and cross-examine witnesses and to formulate arguments and submissions.

JUDICIAL REVIEW

Can the verdict be appealed? Generally, the verdict of a coroner, jury or officer conducting a public inquiry cannot be appealed. However, a party or person affected by the verdict may apply for judicial review in limited circumstances, for example, where the conduct of the inquest or public inquiry exceeds its jurisdiction or breaches the governing legislation. Applications for judicial review have been entertained by the court in circumstances where the coroner refused standing to someone at an inquest,[49] where it was alleged that there was bias or a reasonable apprehension of bias on the part of the coroner,[50] where the inquest verdict involved a finding of legal responsibility,[51] where it was alleged that an inquest could not be held in the circumstances of a "still birth",[52] where it was alleged that the coroner lacked jurisdiction to seize privileged documents,[53] where it was alleged that summonses to witnesses who were judicial officers should be quashed,[54] and where it was alleged that the public was being improperly excluded from an inquest.[55]

However, the court hearing an application for judicial review will ordinarily exercise considerable deference and may be reluctant to overturn it. In fact, the court's power to intervene has been characterized by one court as "a very scrawny power" which is unlikely to be exercised unless

---

[49] See Booth and Stanford, *supra*, note 27.
[50] *Evans v. Milton* (1979), 24 O.R. (2d) 181, 9 C.P.C. 83, 46 C.C.C. (2d) 129, 97 D.L.R. (3d) 687 (C.A.). Leave to appeal to S.C.C. refused 24 O.R. (2d) 181n; *Re Reid and Wigle* (1980), 29 O.R. (2d) 633, 114 D.L.R. (3d) 669 (H.C.).
[51] *MacKenzie v. MacArthur*, *supra*, note 36.
[52] *Bassett v. Saskatchewan (A.G.)* (1983), 23 Sask. R. 11, 5 C.C.C. (3d) 518, 149 D.L.R. (3d) 721 (C.A.).
[53] *Re Scottish & York Ins. Co. and Harpur* (1983), 42 O.R. (2d) 201 (H.C.); *Mrazek v. Rolf* (1983), 27 Alta. L.R. (2d) 91 (Q.B.).
[54] *Re Reinking* (1984), 3 O.A.C. 137 (Div. Ct.); *Re Allan and Ontario (A.G.)* (1984), 47 O.R. (2d) 164, 14 C.C.C. (3d) 178, 11 D.L.R. (4th) 537 (Div. Ct.).
[55] *Edmonton Journal v. Canada (A.G.)*, *supra*, note 25.

there has been a clear breach of substantive rights by an excess of statutory jurisdiction or failure to adhere to the principles of natural justice.[56]

A court will interfere only in cases of jurisdictional error. It will be only in rare cases that an inquest will be interrupted for the purpose of seeking a review by the court.

> The public interest requires that the coroner be able to go about his/her job without intermittent interference by the courts, particularly on issues within the specialized medical and curial expertise of the coroner.
>
> If inquests were conducted by judges or lawyers or royal commissioners, they would have a more legalistic or policy focus. One unique value of an inquest is that it is conducted by men and women with a medical orientation who bring to their task their medical experience and their situation-sense of patients, families, illnesses, medical record confidentiality, medical institutions, and medical care.[57]

PUBLIC INQUIRIES

In addition to inquests, there is another legal procedure designed to be inquisitorial as opposed to adversarial in nature. This procedure may be employed, on occasion, to conduct an investigation in the field of health care. The federal government and each province have enacted legislation which allows the Lieutenant-Governor in Council to authorize the appointment of a commissioner (or commissioners) to conduct a public inquiry concerning any matter connected with the good government of the country or province.[58] Once appointed, a commissioner has many of the same powers that a coroner or judge presiding over an inquest has. He or she may hold hearings, summon witnesses, grant standing, control cross-examination and make recommendations. Commissioners may be ordered by the government to conduct inquiries in a wide spectrum of areas. On a number of occasions federal and provincial inquiries have been given terms of reference which relate directly to health care.[59]

---

[56]   *Re Reid and Wigle, supra*, note 50, at 637 O.R.

[57]   *People First of Ontario v. Porter, Regional Coroner, Niagara* (1991), 5 O.R. (3d) 609 at 645-46.

[58]   See the pertinent legislation, listed at the end of the chapter, for the precise wording employed in each statute.

[59]   For example, *Royal Commission on Health Services, 1964-65*, (under R.S.C. 1952, c. 154), The Honourable Justice Mr. Emmett Hall, Commissioner; *Commission of Inquiry into the Non-Medical Use of Drugs, Final Report 1973* (under R.S.C. 1970, c. I-13), The Honourable Justice Gerard Ledain, Commissioner; *Commission of Inquiry of the Pharmaceutical Industry, Report 1985*, (under R.S.C. 1985, c. I-13) Dr. H.C. Eastman, Commissioner; *Commission of Inquiry into the Confidentiality of Health Records in Ontario, Report 1980*, (under R.S.O. 1971, c. 49), The Honourable Justice Horace Krever, Commissioner; *Royal Commission of Inquiry into Certain Deaths at the Hospital for Sick Children, 1984*, (under R.S.O.

One of the most complex, and perhaps notorious commissions of inquiry was the Royal Commission of Inquiry into Certain Deaths at the Hospital for Sick Children in 1984.[60] That inquiry arose out of circumstances that continue to be both mysterious and peculiar. Between June 30, 1980 and March 22, 1981, 32 infants and three older children died on two adjacent cardiac wards at the Hospital for Sick Children in Toronto. By the time of the last death, March 22, 1981, suspicions had been aroused that some of the infants had died from overdoses of digoxin, a drug used for the control of congestive heart failure. Investigation of these mysterious deaths led to a belief on the part of police that overdoses of digoxin had been administered by someone on the ward and shortly thereafter one of the nurses, Susan Nelles, was arrested and charged with the murder of four of the infants.

However, at the conclusion of a preliminary hearing into the charges, Nelles was discharged and no further criminal proceedings were taken on the ground that there was not sufficient evidence upon which a reasonable jury could convict Nelles. The preliminary hearing led to no immediate resolution of the mystery and toxicological evidence suggested that many of the infants who died, beyond those Susan Nelles was charged for, had been victims of digoxin overdoses. The Province of Ontario appointed a Commissioner to conduct a public inquiry into the deaths at the Hospital for Sick Children.

The public inquiry heightened the awareness of the nursing profession to legal implications related to nursing practice and exposed nurses to the emotional and professional trauma they may be subjected to when their nursing conduct becomes the subject of police or judicial scrutiny. Ultimately, Nelles was exonerated, but the lengthy process she was submitted to caused her substantial legal costs and enormous anxiety.

Moreover, the public inquiry conducted by Commissioner Grange and the treatment of Ms. Nelles by police and prosecution, suggest an ironic conundrum. A nurse whose conduct or activity is questioned, and who attempts to obtain legal advice or counselling, risks enhancing the suspicions of investigators. This is not to suggest that nurses should refrain from seeking legal advice in situations where their nursing practice may be the subject of criticism. However, the nurses and counsel ought to be aware of the adverse interpretation that may be drawn from such behaviour.

1980, c. 411) The Honourable Justice Mr. Grange, Commissioner; *Royal Commission on New Reproductive Technologies* (under R.S.C. 1985, c. I-13); *Royal Commission on the Blood System in Canada* (under R.S.C. 1985, c. I-13) The Honourable Justice H.J. Krever, Commissioner.

[60] Ontario, *Report of the Royal Commission of Inquiry into Certain Deaths at the Hospital for Sick Children and Related Matters* (Toronto: Ministry of the Attorney General, 1984) (Commissioner: Samuel Grange).

CURRENT ISSUES: NURSE AS WITNESS

You are served with a subpoena to appear as a witness at an inquest. You are very nervous about being a witness, in part because you dislike being the center of attention, and also because you do not remember all the details of what happened and why the patient died. You are worried that if you say too much at the inquest, you might be implicated in the patient's death.

The first step is to familiarize yourself with the subject matter of the inquest. You should review all available documentation, including the health record and specifically, your own entries. At the time of the death, did you make a statement to the police? If so, review that document carefully, since it may be shown to you at the inquest to "refresh your memory" of the events of the day in question. You may be asked whether, prior to the patient's death, you were aware of specific policies or procedures in your workplace. If you were, try to recall how and when they were brought to your attention (*e.g.*, posted on a bulletin board, delivered by inter-office mail).

It would be wise to meet with the lawyer who has requested your testimony, or with your own lawyer if you have retained one. He or she will brief you on inquest procedures, and what will be expected of you. Make sure that you take his or her phone number, and get specific details about where the inquest will be held. The lawyer should be able to give you a rough idea of when your testimony will be heard, although this may change once the inquest has begun. You should also ensure that your present employer is aware of the fact that you will be attending the inquest.

On the day you are to appear at the inquest, show up early and dress professionally. Listen to the questions that are being asked, and answer carefully. No one will mind if you ask for clarification of a question.

Above all, try to relax. You are not on trial, you are merely being asked to recount a series of events to your best knowledge. You are not being asked for your opinion, and the best you can do is answer truthfully, even if the only answer is, "I don't know".

RELEVANT LEGISLATION

CANADA

Inquiries Act, R.S.C. 1985, c. I-11

ALBERTA

Fatality Inquiries Act, R.S.A. 1980, c. F-6

Public Inquiries Act, R.S.A. 1980, c. P-29

BRITISH COLUMBIA

Coroners Act, R.S.B.C. 1996, c. 72

Inquiry Act, R.S.B.C. 1996, c. 224

MANITOBA

Fatality Inquiries Act, S.M. 1989-90, c. 30

NEW BRUNSWICK

Coroners Act, R.S.N.B. 1973, c. C-23

Inquiries Act, R.S.N.B. 1973, c. I-11

NEWFOUNDLAND

The Public Inquiries Act, R.S.N. 1990, c. P-38

NORTHWEST TERRITORIES

Coroners Act, R.S.N.W.T. 1988, c. C-20

Public Inquiries Act, R.S.N.W.T. 1988, c. P-14

NOVA SCOTIA

Fatality Inquiries Act, R.S.N.S. 1989, c. 164

Public Inquiries Act, R.S.N.S. 1989, c. 372

ONTARIO

Coroners Act, R.S.O. 1990, c. C.37

Public Inquiries Act, R.S.O. 1990, c. P.41

PRINCE EDWARD ISLAND

Coroners Act, R.S.P.E.I. 1988, c. C-25

Public Inquiries Act, R.S.P.E.I. 1988, c. P-31

QUEBEC

Causes and Circumstances of Death Act, R.S.Q. 1977, c. R-0.2

Public Inquiry Commissions Act, R.S.Q. 1977, c. C-37

SASKATCHEWAN

The Coroners Act, R.S.S. 1978, c. C-38

The Public Inquiries Act, R.S.S. 1978, c. P-38

YUKON

Coroners Act, R.S.Y. 1986, c. 35

Public Inquiries Act, R.S.Y. 1986, c. 137

CHAPTER 11

Employment Law

SYNOPSIS

This chapter sets out information that may assist a nurse in dealing with various situations arising in the workplace. It discusses minimum employment standards, wrongful dismissal, collective bargaining, the right to organize, arbitration, discipline matters, unfair labour practices, the right to strike, occupational health and safety, and professional responsibility relating to the duty of care toward patients.

INTRODUCTION

Before modern labour relations came into existence, workers were liable to have their wages altered, their duties changed, or their employment terminated at the whim of their employers. If workers in a particular field were in plentiful supply, an employer could lower wages or demand that workers perform dangerous work on threat of dismissal. There were no employment benefits such as paid vacations, overtime pay, workers' compensation benefits, medical and dental plans, or pensions. There were almost no health and safety standards. Equal pay for women performing equal work was out of the question. Union activity was illegal and often met with violence. Over the last hundred years, however, the courts and legislatures have developed laws and standards that provide employees with a larger measure of protection and support in employment.

UNIONIZED OR NON-UNIONIZED WORKPLACE?

A major distinction one must be familiar with is whether the nurses in a given workplace (hospital, nursing home, or other facility), are represented by a union. The answer to this question will lead to very different legal considerations in most cases. Employees who join a union gain certain legal rights, such as the ability to enter into collective bargaining with the employer, and give up others, such as the right to sue if they are wrongfully dismissed (though they can take a grievance to their union, which will proceed on their behalf). Other legal rights, such as the minimum employment standards set by legislation, exist for most employees regardless of whether they are represented by a union. Employees in non-unionized and unionized workplaces alike may negotiate benefits in excess of the minimum standards.

MINIMUM EMPLOYMENT STANDARDS

Federal and provincial governments in Canada have passed legislation that ensures minimum employment standards to employees in their respective jurisdictions.[1] There are minimum age requirements for full-time employment. Individuals who have not reached a certain age, ranging from age 14[2] to 17,[3] are prohibited from engaging in full-time employment, employment that would interfere with school work, employment that is considered to be unwholesome or harmful,[4] or that would require them to work at certain late hours.[5] Employers are required to keep basic personnel records, which include such information as the name, age, and address of the employee, as well as the employee's wage rate, hours of work, vacation periods and pay, leaves of absence, date of lay-off or discharge, and corresponding notices. In most jurisdictions, full-time employment is limited to an eight-hour day and 40 hours of work per week (with exceptions for certain types of workers and with provisions for overtime).

Minimum wage legislation was originally conceived in the 1920s, as a means of ensuring that women in the workforce received a "living wage"[6] (legislative support for the idea that women should be paid the same wage as men performing the same work was still over a half-century away). Minimum wages are still set by employment standards legislation, and are raised from time to time. This legislation also regulates the amount of overtime employees may work and the obligation to be paid extra for it. Employers are obliged to allow each employee to take vacation each year (the length of which may depend upon the duration of employment), and to pay them for it. Employees are entitled to take time off on statutory holidays, or, in the alternative, to receive additional compensation when they are required to work on the statutory holiday.

---

[1] See the list of relevant legislation at the end of the chapter.
[2] *Labour Standards Code*, R.S.N.S. 1989, c. 246, s. 68.
[3] *Canada Labour Code*, R.S.C. 1985, c. L-2, s. 179.
[4] *Employment Standards Act*, S.N.B. 1982, c. E-7.2, s. 39 [am. S.N.B. 1984, c. 42, s. 22].
[5] *The Labour Standards Act*, R.S.N. 1990, c. L-2, s. 46.
[6] *Canadian Master Labour Guide*, 5th edition (Don Mills: CCH Canadian Ltd., 1990), p. 73.

Employees may take a leave of absence for pregnancy, adoption, bereavement, sickness, education, voting and jury duty. All Canadian jurisdictions provide for unpaid maternity leave of 17 or 18 weeks, depending upon the jurisdiction. Employment continues throughout the period of leave and the employer must take the employee back in the same position she held prior to the leave of absence, or to another position of similar nature. Some jurisdictions also provide for parental leave, which may be taken by either mothers or fathers upon the birth or adoption of a child.[7]

If the workplace is not unionized and no collective agreement exists which provides otherwise, an employer is not required to maintain the services of an employee, no matter how satisfactory the employee's services may be. In common law, which is the system underlying all legislation in Canada outside Quebec, and which operates to fill any gaps in legislation, an employer may dismiss an employee "at will". However, an employer may not dismiss an employee without reasonable notice unless there is "just cause" such as disobedience, misconduct or neglect of duties on the part of the employee. When an employer dismisses an employee without reasonable notice and without just cause, it is termed "wrongful dismissal". The employee is entitled to be compensated for the lack of reasonable notice, but not to be reinstated. The period of "reasonable notice" is conceived as a period during which the employee can make alternative employment arrangements. Again, the employee will not be entitled to reasonable notice if the employee has acted in a manner which justifies immediate termination of the employment contract, giving the employer "just cause" for termination. "Reasonable notice", as regulated by employment standards legislation, depends upon length of service, but as discussed in the following section on "Wrongful Dismissal", if a wrongful dismissal case goes to court, there are other considerations such as the position held, duties and responsibilities, likelihood of finding similar employment, and job market conditions, which will enter into the calculation of "reasonable notice". Therefore, the notice periods set by legislation (from one week to eight weeks depending upon the length of employment) should be viewed as minimum guidelines. The employee may or may not be required by the employer to continue to work during the notice period. If an employer terminates an employee and asks the employee to leave his or her employment immediately, this does not affect the employer's obligation to continue to pay

---

[7] See *Canada Labour Code*, R.S.C. 1985, c. L-2, s. 206.1(1); Manitoba *Employment Standards Act*, R.S.M. 1987, c. E110, s. 37; New Brunswick *Employment Standards Act*, S.N.B. 1982, c. E-7.2, ss. 43-44.02 [am. 1984, c. 42, s. 24; 1988, c. 59, ss. 17-18; 1991, c. 52]; Quebec *Act respecting labour standards*, R.S.Q. 1977, c. N-1.1, s.81.10-81.13; Saskatchewan *Labour Standards Act*, R.S.S. 1978, c.L-1, s. 29.1.

the employee throughout the notice period. On the other hand, if an employee is given working notice and does not continue to work during the notice period, though expected to do so by the employer, the right to be paid throughout the notice period is forfeited.

WRONGFUL DISMISSAL

Legislation guaranteeing minimum employment standards does not prevent an employer and an employee from entering employment contracts that provide benefits exceeding the minimum standards. In some cases the employment contract will be in writing and will contain provisions expressly agreed upon by the parties. Without any formal agreement, oral or written, certain common law terms will be implied automatically by the employment relationship. Employment contracts are considered to be contracts of "personal service" and for that reason courts will not require either party to honour the contract by specific performance. In other words, the court will not force an employer to hire the person, nor will they force the person to work for the employer. The only remedy available to the employee is monetary damages for the employer's failure to give reasonable notice. A contract of service between an employer and employee entitles the employee to seek compensation for wrongful dismissal.[8] It is important, however, to note that unionized employees must pursue the grievance procedure in their collective agreement rather than commencing a civil action against their employer. In *Zakerson v. Jubilee Residences Inc.*,[9] a nurse brought an action for wrongful dismissal after being dismissed from her employment in September, 1984. The employer argued that the nurses' employment contract was governed by a collective agreement entered into by the union on her behalf and that she had no right to bring a civil action. The court agreed that the plaintiff's common law right to bring a civil action for damages for wrongful dismissal was precluded by the fact that she belonged to a bargaining unit which had reached a collective agreement with the employer governing termination of employment. The nurses' rights had to be determined by an arbitrator as set out in the collective agreement.

The amount of compensation for wrongful dismissal is based upon the court's assessment of what constitutes a reasonable period of notice that an employee will require to seek alternative employment. The award of damages will be based upon the amount that the employee would have earned during such notice period. Where the employer gives a period of

---

[8] *Barton v. Agincourt Football Enterprises Ltd.* (1982), 134 D.L.R. (3d) 1, 82 C.L.L.C. 14,197, 42 N.R. 97, 18 B.L.R. 27 (S.C.C.).

[9] [1987] 1 W.W.R. 346, 52 Sask. R. 198, 32 D.L.R. (4th) 371 (Q.B.).

notice that is later judged to be too short, the employee will be entitled to the amount of wages he or she would have earned during the additional period the court deems to be reasonable. Also, if the employee is able to mitigate and find a new employment, the income earned from the other employment will be subtracted from the award. In calculating the period of reasonable notice, the court will look at such factors as the age and educational background of the employee, the length of service, the level of seniority and, to a certain extent, the availability of alternative employment.[10] The Supreme Court of Canada has recognized that bad faith conduct in the manner of dismissal is another factor that is properly compensated for by an addition to the notice period.[10a]

An employee will not be entitled to reasonable notice of termination in circumstances where the employer is justified in treating the employment contract as at an end. This is generally referred to as "termination for just cause". Minor acts that are inconsistent with an employee's duties will not be considered of sufficient weight to warrant immediate dismissal. However, serious breaches of duty that are in direct violation of the employer's interests will be sufficient. In circumstances where an employer has known of earlier breaches without giving a warning or another indication of disapproval, a court may conclude that the employer condoned the employee's misconduct and this may disentitle the employer from terminating the employment contract without notice.

In *Harrop v. Markham Stouffville Hospital*[11] the defendant employed the plaintiff as a psychiatric nurse for two and one-half years. She was dismissed after forming a close social relationship with a recently discharged psychiatric patient. She had been very involved in the patient's treatment. At the time of her dismissal, she had 21 years' experience in the profession. The defendant hospital did not have a written policy limiting social interaction between nurses and patients, but the plaintiff knew that the therapeutic relationship was incompatible with a social relationship. In fact, she had attempted to keep the relationship a secret from the other members of the therapy unit. The plaintiff sued for wrongful dismissal. Her action was dismissed; the court found that she was aware of how central the therapeutic relationship was to her position and of the vulnerability of the patient, making a social relationship incompatible with her duties. This breach of her duties was too serious and the court found the hospital acted reasonably in dismissing her.

---

[10]   Ellen E. Mole, *Wrongful Dismissal Practice Manual* (Toronto: Butterworths, 1984) Chapter 5, "Reasonable Notice".
[10a] *Wallace v. United Grain Growers Ltd.*, [1997] 3 S.C.R. 701.
[11]   (1995), 16 C.C.E.L. (2d) 214 (Ont. Gen. Div.).

In *Meaney v. Agnes Pratt Home,*[12] a registered nurse had begun working for a nursing home in 1980 as a part-time nurse on the night shift. Two days before she was dismissed she was given a new job description with more hours of work per week at the same rate of pay. She was reclassified as a temporary, full-time worker. She was terminated two days after her change in position for "cause". The employer alleged that she had violated the nursing home's policy of failing to require a resident to take medication in the presence of a nurse. It was alleged that the plaintiff left medication with the residents, administered incorrect doses and had given the wrong medication in one instance. There had been earlier reprimands for not following the home's policy. Upon termination, the employer offered the nurse two weeks' salary in lieu of notice. The court held that the employer was entitled to summarily dismiss the nurse where the nurse was seriously or grossly incompetent in the performance of her duties. It found that the plaintiff was well aware of the standard of competence expected of her and that her failure to offer a reasonable explanation for her carelessness justified the employer in summarily dismissing her. Furthermore, the court found that the payment of two weeks' salary was merely an act of generosity by the employer.

In *Edwards v. Royal Alexandra Hospitals,*[13] the plaintiff had worked for the defendant for 37 years when her mid-management position was eliminated due to economic cutbacks. The plaintiff was offered a posting as a general duty nurse if one came up, but she was physically unable to perform the duties. The plaintiff was also given the option of having the defendant purchase back some of her pensionable service, which would have forced her to retire, and which she was not prepared to do. She sued for wrongful dismissal and was awarded a notice period of 21 months. The court ruled that in more affluent times, the plaintiff would have received a greater notice period, but under the current economic circumstances that were not the defendant's fault, the notice period was decreased. Conversely, in *Trudeau-Linley v. Plummer Memorial Public Hospital,*[14] the fact that the health-care industry was depressed and employment opportunities were limited was seen as a reason to give a more generous notice period of 22 months to an employee with nearly 21 years of service.

In *Robinson v. vanWalraven,*[15] the plaintiff worked as a nurse in the defendant's office for twelve and one-half years. Her employment was cut from full-time to three days per week, and her employment was eventually terminated when another physician left the office. She received

---

[12] (1989), 74 Nfld. & P.E.I.R. 18, 231 A.P.R. 18 (Nfld. S.C.T.D.).
[13] (1994), 19 Alta. L.R. (3d) 277, 154 A.R. 226, 5 C.C.E.L. (2d) 196 (Q.B.).
[14] (1993), 1 C.C.E.L. (2d) 114 (Ont. Gen. Div.).
[15] Unreported, Jan. 31, 1997, Docket no. 474/96, Searle Deputy J. (Ont. Gen. Div.).

two months' notice. She sued for wrongful dismissal, and immediately found alternate employment at a lower hourly rate but as a full-time employee, therefore earning a larger income than when she had worked for the defendant. The court ruled in her favour, awarding her seven months' notice, less the employment income she actually earned during the notice period. The court held that the plaintiff had to expend extra time and trouble by having to work 16 extra hours per week to replace her lost income and although her losses decreased with each raise she obtained at her new job, her loss during the notice period was $2,595.60 and she was entitled to this amount.

In *Wells v. Newfoundland & Labrador Nurses Union*,[16] the plaintiff had been employed for one year as the Newfoundland and Labrador Nurses Union's business manager. The business manager's contract provided that he not be involved in a "related business or occupation". The plaintiff accepted a position as a commissioner with the Royal Commission on Employment, a body with which the union had philosophical differences. The plaintiff was dismissed without notice on the basis that his appointment was contrary to union policy, was in opposition to the terms of this contract and constituted a conflict of interest. The court upheld the dismissal, and it found that there was no conflict of interest between his duties to the union and his duties to the Employment Commission. However, the court held that the union reasonably anticipated that the Commission's work would draw the plaintiff away from his normal office hours which he was required to spend on behalf of the union, and that this in itself constituted grounds for a dismissal without notice.

In *Rocmaura Inc. v. McLeod-Allen*,[17] the plaintiff, a head nurse, had been absent from work due to illness. On returning she was asked to sign a report which criticized her nursing treatment when a patient had fallen. She refused to sign the document, and instead, resigned. She was awarded damages on the basis that the employer's conduct had constituted a "constructive dismissal," without notice, of the nurse.

DAMAGES FOR MENTAL DISTRESS AND PUNITIVE AND AGGRAVATED DAMAGES

Termination, whether for just cause or not, is likely to be a traumatic experience for the employee. In recent years, employees have recovered damages not only for the failure of the employer to give reasonable notice of termination, but also for damages where the circumstances of the dismissal have resulted in significant mental suffering to the employee.

---

[16] (1986), 57 Nfld. & P.E.I.R. 67, 170 A.P.R. 67 (Nfld. S.C.T.D.).
[17] (1989), 27 C.C.E.L. 47 (N.B.C.A.).

In *Speck v. Greater Niagara General Hospital*,[18] a senior nurse commenced an action for wrongful dismissal against her employer after being dismissed on the ground that she was unable to perform her managerial duties satisfactorily. In addition to advancing a claim for damages resulting from the employer's alleged failure to give reasonable notice, the nurse claimed damages for mental suffering caused by the dismissal.

The plaintiff, who had been employed by the hospital for 13 years (and employed at other hospitals for 20 years before that), testified at trial that she was "stunned by her sudden dismissal".[19] She became "distraught and full of anxiety". She suffered from sleeplessness and loss of appetite. She lost 15 pounds. She returned to the care of her psychiatrist who increased her medication. She testified that the firing "wiped her out". At the time of trial, the depression had continued and the plaintiff was bitter about the destruction of her career in nursing and felt hopeless about her professional future and financial position.

The trial judge commented that although all of the individual defendants who gave evidence on behalf of the hospital had not intended to cause suffering to the plaintiff, they acted, nonetheless, without any thought to the consequences of the termination to the plaintiff, and in doing so, they engaged in a "reckless breach" of the hospital's employment contract with the plaintiff. The court concluded that at the time Nurse Speck was dismissed:

> [t]he defendant hospital had virtually no complaint about her clinical nursing skills, and it is clear from the evidence that her skills of this type were good. The dissatisfaction of the hospital was entirely with her performance as a supervisor, that is, in her ability to direct junior nurses and other staff in an effective and harmonious way. If the hospital had given her reasonable notice, and permitted or encouraged her to carry on in a face-saving way while she tried to find employment in another hospital as a staff nurse (*i.e.*, not as a supervisor), I think the plaintiff probably would have found work in another hospital that would have been acceptable to her.

> By dismissing her for cause, the hospital crushed the plaintiff and led her to fear that she could never get employment in another hospital because of the unfavourable references that would be given by the hospital ...

> I have decided on the balance of probabilities that virtually all of the mental suffering experienced by the plaintiff was caused by the defendant's breach of contract, that is, by the way in which she was

---

[18] (1983), 43 O.R. (2d) 611, 2 D.L.R. (4th) 84, 2 C.C.E.L. 21 (H.C.).
[19] *Ibid.*, at 619 O.R.

terminated; without notice because of cause, rather than by the termination itself.[20]

The judge concluded that the plaintiff should have been given nine months' notice of termination and that her income during this period would have been $20,253.13. In addition, he awarded to the plaintiff the cost of drugs and transportation in connection with medical treatment for her depression caused by the wrongful dismissal and the sum of $15,000.00 to compensate her for the suffering and loss of enjoyment of life which she sustained as a result of the mental distress negligently inflicted by the hospital.

By way of contrast, in *Buchanan v. Hilton Canada Ltd.,*[21] the plaintiff was a head nurse with 11 years of service at a hotel medical department. Following a heated argument over the poor salaries of nurses working for the hotel, the plaintiff was terminated without notice. She had been a member of the management staff of the hospital since 1970. Her record as a head nurse was described as "faultless" and "admirable". She claimed damages for loss of income resulting from the failure of the employer to give notice, and as well, damages for impairment of her health due to a nervous breakdown caused by the dismissal. The court concluded that she was entitled to six months notice. However, the court also concluded that the defendants could not have foreseen that the dismissal would lead to a nervous breakdown and that there had been no evidence of malice. Furthermore, the plaintiff had found employment that was more remunerative in the following year. Accordingly, no damages were awarded for any impairment of her health condition.

In *Wallace v. United Grain Growers Ltd.*[22] the Supreme Court of Canada stated that while bad faith conduct might be compensable by increasing the notice entitlement, it was not prepared to imply a requirement of "good faith" reasons of dismissal as a general rule. The extent to which *Wallace* will affect future wrongful dismissal decisions is still unclear.

COLLECTIVE BARGAINING

The traditional legal relationship between employer and employee is that of a private employment contract. Nurse managers, nurses working as private duty nurses, and many nurses employed by private hospitals and institutions will have their employment relationship governed by private contract and the common law. However, the majority of nurses in Can-

---

[20]   *Ibid.*, at 620-21 O.R.
[21]   [1982] C.S. 825 (Que. S.C.).
[22]   *Supra*, note 10a.

ada now belong to unions or associations that engage in collective bargaining with the employer on behalf of a group. Collective bargaining has been described as "bargaining between a group of employees (the collective) who bargain through a recognized bargaining agent (the union) and an employer with respect to common terms and conditions of employment."[23]

Collective bargaining gives nurses greater strength as a group than they have as individuals. An individual nurse who demands higher pay or better working conditions from an employer, unless that nurse possesses extraordinary abilities valued highly by the employer, has relatively little bargaining power. A nurse who withdraws her labour or pickets an employer's premises alone will have minimal impact. Conversely, the use of a union as the instrument for negotiating allows nurses to bargain from a position of collective strength.

The right of employees to engage in collective bargaining has not always been well received by business or government. Only in the last 50 or 60 years has it been possible for employees to engage, without restriction, in the "three freedoms" of labour relations: the right to form unions, the right to appoint a union as the bargaining agent for a group of employees, and the right to employ negotiating tools such as strikes, pickets or boycotts.

In the early days of trade union activity, some governments concluded that trade unionism restrained free trade and was harmful to the overall economic interests of society.[24] However, in recent times an accommodation, sometimes uneasy, among government, business and labour, has been reached. Collective bargaining is a well-recognized and legitimate form of negotiating employment contracts in the health care field, although there are restrictions and guidelines imposed by government to ensure that the process is fair and, should there be a failure of the parties to reach a bargain, to ensure that such failure does not have damaging consequences for third parties.

The withdrawal of labour by employees of a television manufacturer may inconvenience consumers, but may be an inconvenience that our society is prepared to countenance in order to allow labour and management to negotiate freely. However, where the withdrawal of services or the use of other types of economic sanctions can have serious consequences for the consumer, limits may be imposed. For example, nurses may wish to withdraw their labour as a bargaining tool in the negotiating process, but such activity can have grave consequences for patients who require nursing care. Canadian labour relations statutes have tried to

---

[23] W.B. Rayner, *The Law of Collective Bargaining* (Scarborough: Carswell, 1995), p. 2-2.
[24] The English *Combination Act*, 39 and 40 George III, c. 106, declared all agreements and combinations affecting wages, hours of work and working conditions to be illegal.

achieve a balance in this situation, sometimes to the satisfaction of no one, in order to allow nurses to engage freely in collective bargaining, but without compromising patient care. This topic will be addressed in the "Right to Strike" section later in this chapter.

THE RIGHT TO ORGANIZE

All provinces have passed legislation that provides a framework for collective bargaining. It is a basic right of employees to form a union and engage in collective bargaining. Not every employee, however, is entitled to join a union and negotiate pay and working conditions collectively. Employees who perform managerial functions or who act in a confidential capacity for the employer in matters relating to labour relations cannot be members of the union. There is a bar in most jurisdictions to members of certain professions — medical, dental, architectural, engineering, and legal — forming a union. Groups who are considered to provide essential services, such as firefighters or police, may have restrictions on their rights to engage in collective bargaining.

BARGAINING UNITS

Employees who wish to arrive at a collective agreement with their employer are identified as members of a particular "bargaining unit". The labour relations board of each jurisdiction will determine the appropriate unit of employees for which a union is to be recognized as the exclusive bargaining agent. Once the appropriate bargaining unit has been determined, a union may apply for "certification" as the union that will represent the bargaining unit in negotiations with the employer. Bargaining units may be small or large. Determination of the appropriate bargaining unit is flexible. As one board has held:

> [T]he established practices in the industry, local conditions and considerations, and special circumstances relating to the manner in which the work is organized and carried on in the employer's establishment are all factors which may enter into the conclusion ...[25]

In some instances, negotiations on behalf of nurses by the union will be with the particular facility or institution, in other instances the bargaining will be more broadly-based. For example, in Alberta, the union engages

---

[25] *Re Transport Drivers, Warehousemen and Helpers' Union and Carwil Transport Ltd.*, (1952) 52 C.L.L.C. 16, 617.

in province-wide bargaining on behalf of all members. Employers may appoint their own representatives and once agreement is reached, it binds all employers and union members.

Unionized nurses are required to pay dues which will be used to finance the union's activities, and in some cases, to fund professional activities which may be organized by the union on behalf of its members. Officers of the union are elected to their positions and every union member has an opportunity to participate in what the legislation requires be a democratic process. Before a union can be certified to act on behalf of a particular bargaining unit, there must be a vote of the employees which approves the union and its activities on behalf of the employees. Unless a majority of employees is in favour of the union, the union will not be permitted to act on behalf of the employees.

COLLECTIVE AGREEMENTS

Once a union is certified to act on behalf of a particular bargaining group it will enter into negotiations with the employer. This will result in the first collective agreement. That collective agreement will form the basis for discussion and amendment in future years when it comes time for contract renewal. A union contract is likely to enhance employment benefits beyond what is guaranteed under minimum employment standards legislation. Collective agreements governing the employment relationship of unionized nurses and their employers in Canada may contain provisions in the following areas:

1.   The definition of various kinds of nurses, *i.e.*, full-time, regular part-time, limited part-time, *etc.*;
2.   The obligatory payment of dues by each member and permission of the employer to allow the union to interview and receive applications from new employees;
3.   The establishment of various committees such as the bargaining committee, the grievance committee and the accident prevention committee;
4.   The establishment of a grievance procedure which will serve as a process to resolve differences which arise between the parties under the collective agreement;
5.   A professional responsibility clause which may give an individual nurse or a group of nurses the right to protest the assignment of work which may, in the view of the nurse or nurses' group, compromise patient care;

6.   Access to the nurse's own personnel file and any documentation which may be created in respect of a complaint, reprimand, suspension or other sanction;

7.   The relative seniority among nurses;

8.   Leaves of absence including a leave of absence for particular union duties, bereavement, jury and witness duty, maternity, adoption, and education leave;

9.   Sick leave and long term disability;

10.   Hours of work;

11.   Regular rate of pay and rate of pay for holidays, vacation, and over-time work;

12.   The length of the collective agreement and the time at which negotiations for renewal may take place.

ARBITRATION

Labour arbitration is a procedure used to interpret and to enforce the collective agreement. The power to arbitrate is limited to those disputes arising out of disagreements over interpretation of the collective agreement. Aspects of employment that do not touch upon provisions of the collective agreement are not arbitrable.[26] Collective agreements provide a mechanism to resolve disagreements privately without recourse to a court. Parties to the agreement may bring a grievance that will be decided by arbitration. While arbitration may be less formal than a court proceeding, it is not unusual to have representation by lawyers or union officers. Testimony will be heard under oath, cross-examination will be permitted and the parties will be permitted to make final submissions to the board of arbitration before a decision will be issued. There may be a single arbitrator, or depending upon the collective agreement and the wishes of the parties, a panel of three arbitrators.

Arbitrators interpret the employment relationship based upon the contents of the collective agreement and whatever common law rights have not been altered by the collective agreement. An arbitrator may be asked to decide whether an employee's conduct constitutes "just cause" for immediate dismissal, whether dismissal is an appropriate penalty or whether some lesser form of penalty such as suspension, reduction in seniority rights, demotion or a fine may be more appropriate. An arbitrator may be asked to decide whether an employee who has "quit", has in reality been "discharged", whether management has assigned work to non-union employees contrary to the collective agreement, whether the

---

[26]   *Re New Orchard Lodge/Extendicare Ltd., Ottawa v. O.N.A.* (1983), 12 L.A.C. (3d) 221 (Ont.).

conduct of a group of employees amounts to a "strike" (or the conduct of the employer to "a lockout"), and whether a union, through its own organizing conduct, has caused or contributed to illegal strike action by the employees.

The decision of the arbitrator is binding upon the employer, the employee and the union. Collective agreements provide no right of appeal to a court and most labour relations statutes specifically stipulate that no arbitrator's decision is reviewable by a court. Courts may intervene, in rare cases, where they conclude that there has been clear injustice that justifies their intervention.

In *Balanyk and Greater Niagara General Hospital*,[27] a nurse sought judicial review of an arbitrator's order. The nurse had been suspended indefinitely from her employment with the hospital following complaints about her performance by several nurses. The hospital wished the nurse to undergo a psychiatric assessment, but she refused. She brought a grievance under the collective agreement. At the arbitration hearing she presented a letter from her doctor stating that she was free from any physical or mental disease that would preclude her from working as a registered nurse. The arbitrator did not decide whether the grievance was justified. Instead the nurse was ordered to undergo a psychiatric assessment. The court held that the arbitrator had erred by failing to deal with the issues raised by the grievance, namely, whether there was just cause and whether the penalty was appropriate. The arbitrator's decision was quashed by the court and the grievance was referred back to him for a proper hearing.

In *N.S.N.U., Local Grace Maternity Hospital v. Grace Maternity Hospital*,[28] the Nova Scotia Court of Appeal overturned a decision of the lower court and set aside the decision of an arbitrator. The Court of Appeal held that the lower court had arrived at its own interpretation of the collective agreement instead of determining whether the arbitration board's interpretation was one that it could reasonably bear. The court reaffirmed the principle that an arbitration board's decision ought not to be quashed or set aside by a court except in exceptional circumstances. In that case, a part-time nurse brought a grievance on the basis that she was entitled to the same increments on the salary scale at each anniversary of her employment as those given to full-time nurses. The arbitrator, in construing the particular collective agreement, disagreed that part-time nurses were so entitled.

---

[27] (1988), 64 O.R. (2d) 102, 25 O.A.C. 212, 49 D.L.R. (4th) 132 (Div. Ct.).

[28] *N.S.N.U., Local Grace Maternity Hospital v. Grace Maternity Hospital* (1986), 78 N.S.R. (2d) 178, 193 A.P.R. 178 (*sub nom. Grace Maternity Hospital v. N.S.N.U., Local Grace Maternity Hospital*) (C.A.); leave to appeal to S.C.C. refused (1987), 79 N.S.R. (2d) 355*n*, 176 A.P.R. 355*n*, 80 N.R. 317*n* (S.C.C.).

MANAGEMENT RULES AND DECISIONS

Collective agreements usually contain provisions supporting the right of the employer to manage the workplace. Management rights may include responsibility for maintaining order, discipline and efficiency; hiring, assigning, classifying and discharging staff; determining hours of work and methods of working; and identifying services to be performed and the equipment to be used. Although broad, the exercise of management rights must be consistent with the terms of the collective agreement. A management rule or policy must be reasonable, and it must be considerate of special circumstances that may arise in an individual case. Where there is a dispute whether management is acting within the scope of the collective agreement, or in a manner that conflicts with the terms of the agreement, a party to the collective agreement may resort to arbitration. Generally, an employee is required to comply with a management rule, even where there is a disagreement, until the dispute has been resolved by arbitration. This principle has given rise to the colloquialism: "work now, grieve later".

REASONABLENESS

Whether a management rule or policy is reasonable will be evaluated in the context of the collective agreement and the "business purpose" of the enterprise. The main business purpose of a health facility is the care and treatment of patients.

Where a new no-smoking policy was implemented at a facility that provided care for cancer out-patients, an arbitrator ruled that the ban was consistent with the health facility's desire to show leadership in cancer prevention, and therefore it was reasonable.[29] The same decision sets out general principles to be followed where management decides to initiate new rules or policies in the workplace. The rule or policy must be consistent with the collective agreement, be clear and unequivocal and be enforced consistently, and the consequences of non-compliance must be brought to the attention of employees before any disciplinary action is taken.

In *Greater Niagara General Hospital v. Ontario Nurses' Association*,[30] a part-time nurse applied for a full-time position, but was denied the position because she failed a physical examination. She grieved on the basis that her hypertension would not affect her ability to do the job. She also

---

[29] *Thameswood Lodge v. London & District Service Workers' Union, Local 220* (1984), 15 L.A.C. (3d) 228 (Ont.).
[30] (1987), 32 L.A.C. (3d) 140 (Ont.).

grieved on the basis that other job transfers had not required a physical examination. The grievance was denied. The board of arbitration held that the physical examination was a condition of employment that arose in the hiring process and was not a term of the collective agreement that could be grieved. It confirmed that the hospital had a legitimate business purpose in ensuring that its employees were fit to perform the work required without undue risk to the employee, the hospital or its patients.

Even where management is able to demonstrate a business purpose for its decision, there must be a reasonable relationship between the intended objective and the means chosen to attain it. In a case where surgical nurses called in to assist in off-hours were required to scrub stretchers as part of their duties, it was held that the hospital's interest in the "efficient deployment of nursing personnel during a time period to justify the costs incurred by the call-in" was not sufficient to justify the assignment of non-nursing tasks. The board of arbitration ruled that, in the absence of evidence that scrubbing stretchers was an urgent requirement, which could not be handled in some other way, it was unreasonable to require nurses to engage in duties they did not perform ordinarily.[31]

A management decision that does not take into account the circumstances of an individual case may be judged arbitrary, and, consequently, unreasonable. In *Sherbrooke Community Society v. S.U.N., Local 22*,[32] a nurse asked for an eight-day leave of absence during July and August. The hospital refused because of its rule that no leaves would be granted during those two months. The nurse filed a grievance through her union, stating that she had made the request four months ahead of time and that the administration could easily have found someone to replace her in that time. She also stated that the hospital had refused to listen to, or to consider, the reasons why a leave of absence was necessary. The board of arbitration ruled that the hospital had acted unreasonably because it gave no consideration to the nurse's specific request: "Discretion cannot properly be reduced to a mechanical exercise by the administrator of any legal regime."[33]

"WORK NOW; GRIEVE LATER"

An employee's refusal to carry out an order or direction from a supervisor may be detrimental to patient care. Where an employee has refused to comply with a direction or request of management, the employee may be subject to discipline, even in circumstances where management's con-

---

[31] *Lennox and Addington County General Hospital v. O.N.A.* (1986), 25 L.A.C. (3d) 97 (Ont.).
[32] (1981), 2 L.A.C. (3d) 97 (Sask.).
[33] *Ibid.*, at 102.

duct was unjustified. This principle has particular application to the health-care setting in which a worker's refusal to carry out a direction or order may be detrimental to patients.

In *Abbie J. Lane Memorial Hospital v. N.S.N.U.*,[34] a nurse was hired on the condition that she was not posted to a particular floor where her husband worked. On being requested to "float" to that floor, the nurse objected. She was then sent home for the day without pay. She grieved the suspension. The arbitrator ruled that even if she did consider an assignment on the particular floor a breach of her employment contract, she was not entitled to disobey a direct order: she should have carried out her assignment as requested and grieved later.

Although the general rule is that an employee must obey management pending resolution of a dispute through the grievance process, there are exceptions to the rule. Employees are entitled to disobey management where obedience would result in:

1. the performance of an illegal act;
2. harm to the health or safety of the employee or others; and
3. a situation in which a successful grievance of an unjustified order would not give adequate redress to the employee.[35]

DISCIPLINE

While management has the authority to evaluate, critique and oversee unionized employees, it can discipline or dismiss employees only when there is just cause. When a collective agreement is in force, an employee may dispute or grieve an employer's disciplinary action before an arbitration board if he or she believes that the disciplinary action taken by the employer is unwarranted.

A threshold issue is whether management's conduct constitutes discipline. Negative comments, warnings or unfavourable evaluations may not constitute disciplinary conduct. This is justified on the rationale that:

> Common sense dictates, however, that there should be some latitude in an employer to make negative comments respecting an employee's performance without necessarily incurring the risk of a grievance with the full panoply of procedures that might ensue.[36]

---

[34] (1981), 2 L.A.C. (3d) 126 (N.S.).
[35] See *Riverdale Hospital v. C.U.P.E., Local 79* (1985), 19 L.A.C. (3d) 396, at 403 (Ont.).
[36] *City of Toronto v. C.U.P.E., Local 79* (1984), 16 L.A.C. (3d) 384, at 391 (Ont.).

Employer conduct amounting to discipline must "involve or result in a change in status or monetary loss to the employee".[37] A poor reference letter may not be considered a matter of discipline where the letter is written "in good faith and without malice" and its purpose is not to "punish or penalize", but only to evaluate for future employers.[38] Similarly, routine performance evaluations that contain negative comments are not a matter of discipline if no practical result follows. A form setting out a negative evaluation may allow the employee to make his or her own written comments and this information may be considered in the future by an arbitrator should the unfavourable evaluation become a matter of discipline. An employer will not be answerable to the grievance process for "every utterance which expresses less than complete approval of an employee's job performance and which might at some point be taken into account in a way that affects the employee's career."[39] A performance evaluation may be an act of discipline, however, if it is accompanied by a warning that continued poor performance could result in suspension or discharge and if the evaluation will be used to demonstrate a pattern of poor performance that may culminate in suspension or discharge. Factors determining whether an evaluation constitutes a matter of discipline include whether it was in writing and forms part of the employee record, whether it was communicated to the employee and the union, whether it contains some sanction (such as a warning or caution), whether it was reviewable through the grievance procedure and whether it would be relevant in showing a pattern of conduct in a future disciplinary proceeding.[40]

PROGRESSIVE DISCIPLINE

Generally, before disciplinary action can be taken, an employee must be made aware of the employer's dissatisfaction and must be given an opportunity to remedy substandard performance. A series of informal meetings, imprecise performance evaluations and verbal reprimands will make it difficult to establish that "progressive discipline" has been employed. The employer must tell the employee, in specific terms, that job performance has not been satisfactory and must be improved, and that, if it is not, it will lead to demotion, suspension or termination.

---

[37] *Edmonton and Rural Auxiliary Hospital and Nursing Home, District 24 and Alberta Association of Registered Nurses*, [1981] 3 W.L.A.C. 301, at 304 (Alta.).
[38] *Supra*, note 26 at 228.
[39] *Children's Hospital of Eastern Ontario v. O.N.A.* (1987), 30 L.A.C. (3d) 238, at 245 (Ont.).
[40] *Calgary General Hospital v. C.U.P.E., Local 8* (1986), 23 L.A.C. (3d) 25 (Alta.).

RIGHT TO UNION REPRESENTATION

Most collective agreements contain provisions requiring that employees be afforded protection or representation where disciplinary action is taken. Consequently, where an employee is the subject of some form of discipline, a union representative may be invited to a meeting between the employer and the employee, or the union may receive a copy of a negative evaluation. In *St. Joseph's Hospital (Brantford) v. O.N.A.*,[41] a collective agreement entitled a nurse to be represented by a union representative whenever steps were taken to impose discipline. A nurse involved in a medication error was suspended by the hospital without a union representative being notified or present. An arbitration panel held that the suspension was improper; if the employee had been represented, the hospital might have been persuaded to modify the form of discipline it proposed to take or to make some other arrangements that would ensure patient safety.

PENALTIES

Arbitrators have considerable scope in deciding what penalties are appropriate. Unless the parties specify in the collective agreement that a particular penalty will be imposed summarily for a particular offence, all aggrieved dismissals are open to review to see whether the disciplinary measure "seems just and reasonable in all the circumstances".[42] The arbitrator will want to know if the disciplinary standard was applied discriminatorily, if there were mitigating circumstances and if the employee is capable of rehabilitation.[43] When a decision to dismiss is overturned, the employer may be required to pay a sizeable compensation package or to reinstate the employee.

The employer bears the onus of demonstrating that there was just cause for dismissal.[44] The employer must show that the employee committed a serious infraction, which he or she knew, or should have known, would lead to serious disciplinary measures, including dismissal, or in the alternative, must show that there is a well-documented record of progressive discipline in the case of non-culpable deficiency in work performance.

A refusal by an employee to perform essential aspects of the employment position is likely to constitute just cause for dismissal. One excep-

---

[41] (1987), 28 L.A.C. (3d) 408 (Ont.).
[42] *Belleville General Hospital v. S.E.I.U., Local 183* (1985), 18 L.A.C. (3d) 161 at 163 (Ont.).
[43] *Ibid.*
[44] *Oshawa General Hospital v. O.N.A.* (1981), 2 L.A.C. (3d) 201 (Ont.).

tion to this general rule is where performance of the job would result in violation of the non-discrimination clause found in most collective agreements. In *Peterborough Civic Hospital v. O.N.A.*,[45] an I.C.U. nurse, because of her religious beliefs, refused to commence blood transfusions, and was dismissed as a result. The arbitration board held that the hospital had violated the non-discrimination clause of the collective agreement. Although the board agreed that it was an essential duty for a nurse in I.C.U. to "hang blood", it was not an essential duty for a nurse on a regular floor. The nurse's religious beliefs could have been accommodated by transferring her to a different floor. On the issue of accommodation of religious beliefs, the panel stated (at p. 34):

> An employer who can accommodate without significant cost to itself or to its other employees the inability for serious reasons of an individual employee to comply with one of its rules but chooses instead to terminate that employee cannot in our view be said to have terminated for just cause.

The arbitration board ordered that the nurse be reinstated without loss of seniority or benefits on the condition that she accept work in another hospital unit.

DISCIPLINE CASES

In some cases, the employee may disagree that there has been any cause for discipline. In other instances, the employee may argue that the penalty imposed by the employer is excessive and ought to be reduced. Arbitrators have been asked on a number of occasions to review disciplinary action taken by employers against nurses. It has been ruled that:

- a discharge was inappropriate and a three-day suspension substituted where a nurse had recorded that she had started her shift at 7:00 a.m. when actually she had started at 7:45 a.m. and was witnessed by her supervisor. She claimed an earlier starting time based on a history of early starts. While she acted defiantly, it was not with intent to defraud the employer;[46]
- a nurse was entitled to have a record of her earlier suspension removed from her employment record where no further discipline had occurred for a 16-month period;[47]

---

[45]   (1981), 3 L.A.C. (3d) 21 (Ont.).
[46]   *Leisureworld Inc., Scarborough Nursing Home v. O.N.A.* (1994), 36 C.L.A.S. 303.
[47]   *Parkwood Hospital v. O.N.A. (Tiahur)* (1989), 7 L.A.C. (4th) 141 (Ont.).

- a five-day suspension was appropriate for a nurse who refused to provide assistance to an elderly resident whom she mistakenly believed to be capable of walking on her own;[48]
- it was not appropriate to discharge a nurse who stole inexpensive foam mattresses from the hospital where the nurse immediately admitted her actions and did not premeditate the theft. It was still possible for the hospital to trust the nurse despite her actions;[49]
- where the only evidence of abuse of a nursing home resident by a nurse were hearsay statements made by the resident and the resident's spouse, discharge was unjustified;[50]
- a ten-day suspension was unjustified where the employer alleged that the responses given by an in-charge nurse were deceitful. The panel found that the nurse had given truthful information in response and could not be blamed for providing limited information when that was all that was requested and she did not know the details of the incident;[51]
- a conditional reinstatement was justified for a nurse who had misappropriated drugs due to his own addiction where the prognosis for recovery was good;[52]
- a two-day suspension ought to be substituted for a five-day suspension in circumstances where the grieving nurse had admitted a medication error and had altered a medical profile where there was already a hostile relationship between the grieving nurse and the nurse who had made the allegations;[53]
- a two-week suspension ought to be substituted for a dismissal in circumstances where it was concluded that a nurse's failure to follow correct procedure in administering treatment during an emergency was an isolated incident and occurred in circumstances where the employer had failed to warn the grievor about earlier dissatisfaction with her overall job performance.[54]

UNFAIR LABOUR PRACTICES

To ensure free collective bargaining to participants, labour relations boards in the various jurisdictions have a mandate to protect employees

---

[48] *Cove Guest Home v. N.S.N.U.* (1990) 14 L.A.C. (4th) 48 (N.S.).
[49] *Scarborough General Hospital v. O.N.A.* (1994), 35 L.A.C. (4th) 119 (Ont.).
[50] *Alberta Healthcare Association v. Canadian Health Care Guild* (1993), 37 L.A.C. (4th) 215 (Alta.).
[51] *Big River Union Hospital and S.U.N. (Saskatchewan)* (1994), 35 C.L.A.S. 264.
[52] *Castlegar & District Hospital Society v. B.C.N.U.* (1997), 64 L.A.C. (4th) 107 (B.C.).
[53] *Ottawa General Hospital v. O.N.A.* (1988), 9 C.L.A.S. 41.
[54] *Braddan Private Hospital v. C.U.P.E., Local 2209* (1987), 9 C.L.A.S. 19.

and employers from activities that may distort or impair the ability of the parties to engage in collective bargaining. If it is to fairly represent the employees, the union must be free of any influence from the employer. Employers cannot interfere in the formation or administration of a trade union nor contribute support to the union.[55] Generally, union representatives are permitted to enter an employer's premises for the purpose of soliciting union membership. While an employer may not be prevented from expressing views about the union and if the introduction of collective bargaining in the workplace will be constructive to the employer-employee relationship, the employer will not be permitted to use "coercion, intimidation, threats, promises or undue influence".[56] A refusal by an employer to hire an applicant because of union-related activity, or similarly, a decision to terminate an employee because of union-related activity, is an unfair labour practice. Employers cannot oblige employees to agree, as a pre-condition of employment, not to join a union or engage in union activities. Once a union has been certified to act on behalf of a bargaining group, the employer is obliged by law to bargain "in good faith" with the union. The parties are obliged by law to "make every reasonable effort to enter into a collective agreement".[57]

It is possible for employees to be harmed by unfair activities of the unions. Some employees may not welcome a union in the workplace. Others may support a union other than the one that has been selected to represent the bargaining group. It is an unfair labour practice for a union to take retaliatory action against an employee who opposed the introduction of the union into the employment setting. The union has an obligation to represent fairly the interests of the individual employee even in circumstances where the interests of the individual may be in conflict with the overall interests of the majority of union members.[58]

Labour relations statutes in Canada also seek to protect the employer from certain types of union and employee conduct.[59] No employee is permitted to strike while the collective agreement is in place. There are certain obligations for bargaining and notice that must be fulfilled before a legal strike can take place. A work slow-down or "work to rule" campaign may be the equivalent of an illegal strike. Court action, injunctions, back-to-work orders and fines may be sought by parties who are subjected to unfair labour practices.

---

[55] W.B. Rayner, *The Law of Collective Bargaining* (Scarborough: Carswell, 1995), p. 10-7.

[56] For example, *Ontario Labour Relations Act*, S.O. 1995, c.1, s. 70.

[57] *Canada Labour Code*, R.S.C. 1985, c. L-2, s. 50(a)(ii). There is similar language in provincial labour relations statutes.

[58] *Collective Bargaining Law in Canada*, 2nd ed. (Toronto: Butterworths, 1986) p. 295.

[59] *Ibid.*, p. 297.

THE RIGHT TO STRIKE

The most powerful weapon available to employees in the negotiating process is the ability to withdraw labour, on a collective basis, until the employer agrees to employment terms which are satisfactory to the employees. The right to strike exists in all Canadian jurisdictions, subject to certain procedural requirements before a strike can take place, and also, to the exclusion of certain employee groups. In British Columbia, a "strike includes a cessation of work, a refusal to work or to continue to work by employees ... in concert, or ... with a common understanding, or a slowdown or other concerted activity ... that is designed to or does restrict or limit production or services." This definition does not include a cessation of work required for the health or safety of employees.[60]

In most Canadian jurisdictions nurses have the right to strike, although this right may be circumscribed. Many jurisdictions have enacted legislation to deal with emergency disputes or other special circumstances where normal collective bargaining mechanisms prove ineffective.[61] In British Columbia, there are laws that govern the resolution of disputes where a serious danger to life or health is likely, or is continuing, to occur.[62]

In Ontario, hospital nurses or nurses who work in nursing homes and homes for the aged are not permitted to strike. In Alberta, public hospital employees are prohibited from striking. The Alberta legislation[63] was enacted following strikes in 1980 and 1982. In 1980, 6,400 Alberta nurses walked out of 81 hospitals. After four days of a legal strike, a public emergency was declared by the government and the nurses were ordered back to work. The nurses defied the back to work order for six days, following which the nurses gained a 39 per cent increase in pay over two years. In 1982, another strike took place and it lasted for 23 days. On January 25, 1988, approximately 11,000 nurses walked out of hospitals in Alberta in direct contravention of the legislation barring strikes by hospital employees. Civil contempt charges were launched and this resulted in fines of several hundred thousand dollars to the union.

The withdrawal of labour by nurses raises difficult ethical questions. Does a profession have a different level of responsibility to society and to the patients it serves than other employees who engage in strike action? Should there be any restriction on a profession's right to strike? Does the nature of nursing make it an "essential service" which cannot be withdrawn in any circumstance? Are limitations upon the nursing profes-

---

[60] *Labour Relations Code*, R.S.B.C. 1996, c. 244, s. 1(1).
[61] *The Law of Collective Bargaining, supra*, note 22, p. 22-1.
[62] *Labour Relations Code*, R.S.B.C. 1996, c. 244, s. 137(2).
[63] *Labour Statutes Amendment Act, 1983*, S.A. 1983, c. 34, s. 2(28) [creating new s. 117.1(1)(b), *Labour Relations Act*].

sion's right to strike discriminatory? Do they offend the *Charter of Rights and Freedoms*? Are alternatives to the right to strike, such as binding arbitration on both the employer and employee, equitable substitutes?

The government of each jurisdiction (provincial or federal) determines how the rights of the workforce and the rights of the public should be balanced against each other, and as a result, there are different schemes across Canada to deal with this issue. For example, in Alberta the right to strike is denied to large parts of the public and parapublic sectors,[64] in Saskatchewan there is a general right to strike, but *ad hoc* legislation is used to prohibit or end strikes,[65] and in British Columbia an adjudicative tribunal regulates essential service stoppages.[66]

There are also distinctions within jurisdictions between how different services that could be "essential" are addressed. In Ontario, the *Hospital Labour Dispute Arbitration Act*[67] (or HLDAA) prevents striking by all hospital employees. Therefore, all nursing and other hospital care is considered essential. In some other fields, the question whether services are "essential" is evaluated on a case-by-case basis.

Quebec is the only province with an administrative tribunal devoted exclusively to essential services. The Essential Services Council (*Conseil des services essentiels*) was created in 1982. Key portions of the legislation state:

> s. 111.10. In the event of a strike in an institution, the percentage of employees to be maintained per work shift from among the employees who would usually be on duty during that period shall be at least
> (1) 90% in the case of an institution operating a residential and long-term care centre, a rehabilitation centre, a psychiatric hospital, a hospital providing specialized care in neurology or cardiology or a hospital centre having a department of clinical psychiatry or a community health department, in the case of an institution to which a regional board entrusts functions relating to public health, or in the case of ... hospital centres for long-term care or a reception centre;
> (2) 80% in the case of institutions operating a hospital centre other than those contemplated in subparagraph 1 or in the case of an institution designated as a health care centre;[68]

This is a consensual approach to resolving disputes: the union files a list of essential services with the employer and the Council, and the Council encourages mediation to resolve any disputes. Mediation is conducted by

---

[64] *Labour Relations Code*, S.A. 1988, c. L-1.2, s. 94(2) [am. 1998, c. 22, s. 16].
[65] For example, see *An Act respecting Temporary Provisions for Labour-Management Disputes*, ss. 1981-82, c. L-0.1.
[66] *Labour Relations Code*, R.S.B.C. 1996, c. 224, s. 72.
[67] R.S.O. 1990, c. H-14.
[68] *Labour Code*, R.S.Q. 1977, c. C-27, ss. 111.0.1-111.20.

the Council, and the goal is for the parties to take responsibility for the decision. The assumption is that if the parties make the decisions themselves, the services are more likely to be provided without interruption. However, the Council has the power to decide whether the services agreed to by the parties are sufficient. The Council must see that the statutory levels are met, and it may decide that services must be increased beyond those levels if it considers them insufficient.

In Newfoundland, the determination of who is an "essential employee" is made upon certification of a union or afterward, when the employer supplies the labour board and the union with a written statement of the number of employees in the unit that the employer considers essential. The union may object to this assessment, and ultimately the labour board will decide whether to accept this number as correct. "Essential employee"(under s. 10(13)) means:

> One of a number of employees whose duties consist in whole or in part of duties the performance of which at a particular time or during a specified period of time is or may be necessary for the health, safety or security of the public.[69]

Essential employees cannot strike or participate in a strike. Further, employees of health service institutions cannot strike until seven days have elapsed since the union gave written notice to the minister of labour that a majority of the employees have voted in favour of a strike, and advised the minister of the day the strike will start.[70] Rotating strikes or any other forms of strike than one continuous strike period are not permitted.[71]

As stated earlier, the hospital sector in Ontario is prohibited from striking. Therefore, when parties engaged in collective bargaining cannot reach a resolution, they proceed to arbitration as mandated by the *Hospital Labour Dispute Arbitration Act*. This legislation has recently been amended by the *Public Sector Dispute Resolution Act, 1997*,[72] and was proclaimed at the same time as the *Public Sector Labour Relations Transition Act, 1997*.[73] The Ontario government has made significant changes to the delivery of public services in the province, and these two acts were designed to enable the transitions. The *Public Sector Dispute Resolution Act* applies to firefighters, the police, public services and hospital services. It provides for similar procedures for all of these services and models them after the procedure in the *Hospital Labour Disputes Arbitration Act*. The procedure of dispute resolution under the HLDAA has not changed sig-

---

[69] R.S.N. 1990, c. P-42, s. 28. See definition of "essential employee", s. 10(13).
[70] *Ibid.*, s. 27.
[71] *Ibid.*, s. 27(4).
[72] S.O. 1997, c. 21, Sch. A.
[73] S.O. 1997, c. 21, Sch. B.

nificantly, however, there is more emphasis on negotiated settlements than arbitrated contracts, and there are time lines to ensure that disputes are resolved in a timely fashion.[74]

In Ontario and in other provinces where the legislation prohibiting striking applies to hospital (or other health care facility) employees, nurses who are not hospital employees may have a right to strike.[75] Most of the time, however, there will be too few of these employees to make up a collective bargaining unit of their own.

PROFESSIONAL RESPONSIBILITY

One element of nursing that makes nurses different from most other workers is the nurses' professional responsibility to provide good quality health care to patients. Nurses are directly accountable to their professional associations which require them to practise nursing in a competent and professional manner. In *Re Mount Sinai Hospital and Ontario Nurses' Association*,[76] three nurses were suspended without pay as a result of insubordination resulting from their failure to provide nursing care to a patient who was ordered to be admitted to the I.C.U.. The nurses had refused to care for the patient on the basis that the I.C.U. was already filled to capacity and their professional judgment dictated that an additional patient could not be safely accommodated. The nurses argued that they were entitled to consider the condition of the patients already under their care and the potential legal liability and professional discipline to which they might be subject if they abandoned those patients. They argued that their refusal to provide nursing care was justifiable. They submitted that a nurse is a:

> "[s]elf-starter", one who does not require detailed and close supervision but who, because of his/her professional skills and expertise, exercises to an extent some independent judgment as to what is required. Secondly, in the hospital environment, many of the work instructions are issued by persons who strictly speaking have no

[74] J. Sack, C.M. Mitchell and S. Price, *Ontario Labour Relations Board: Law and Practice*, 3rd ed. (Markham: Butterworths, 1997), at para. 9.187.1.
[75] Note, however, that "hospital" for the purposes of the HLDAA has been interpreted quite broadly and whether a particular institution will be considered a hospital will be based "not only [on] the nature and extent of the care provided, but also [on] the extent too which the health and safety of those in receipt of the care would be endangered by a withdrawal of that care" and has been interpreted to include "a retirement home, an organization providing services to persons with developmental disabilities, and an organization providing attendant care to physically disabled adults in a group home", see Sack, *ibid.*, at para. 9.191
[76] (1978), 17 L.A.C. (2d) 242 (Ont.).

"supervisory" authority over the nurses, in the labour relations context the medical staff at Mount Sinai Hospital have no such authority over the nurses. The employment relationship which carries such authority is between the hospital and the nurses and it is the nursing office, in the person of the nursing supervisor, which "directs" the nurses in what they do.[77]

However, the majority of the board of arbitration ruled that the nurses' conduct was unacceptable. It concluded:

[A]s compared to the medical staff, the grievors lacked the ability to make an informed judgment as to the capacity of the unit as a whole to accept another patient, they should not be permitted to argue that provision of care for patient R. would have jeopardized the care of other patients in the unit. The fact of the matter is that no one nurse was in a position to know that to be the case.[78]

In the result, the three-day suspension meted out by the hospital was upheld.

In *Re Foothills Provincial General Hospital and U.N.A., Local 115,*[79] the union grieved the employer's refusal to accept a professional responsibility form from its nurses. The union argued that the right to refuse to carry out instructions and the right to issue a disclaimer were part of the nurses' patient advocacy role and a function of their professional responsibility. However, the board of arbitration held that the form was the "antithesis of professionalism"[80] and that conflicting perceptions of unsafe conditions were not justified as an exception to the nurses' obligation to obey and grieve later, especially where there was a committee procedure designed to resolve such conflicts. The arbitration board held that the attempt to absolve the nurse from responsibility was offensive to hospital management, and that the hospital was justified in not giving any status to a form that disclaimed responsibility for patient care.

EQUAL TREATMENT

Employers may trigger a grievance under the collective agreement, a complaint pursuant to relevant human rights legislation or other legal remedies if they discriminate on the basis of a person's race, colour, sex, sexual orientation, religion, physical or mental disability or place of origin. An employer is prohibited from discriminating in the recruitment

---

[77] *Ibid.,* at p. 246.
[78] *Ibid.,* at p. 256.
[79] (1989), 7 L.A.C. (4th) 359 (Alta.).
[80] *Ibid.,* at p. 370.

process, in employment application forms or in remuneration to employees. It is also not permissible to engage employment agencies that discriminate.

A rule or policy purporting to treat everyone equally may be ruled, nonetheless, discriminatory. Discrimination can occur where there is no intent to discriminate on the part of the employer. A rule which requires part-time employees to work on Saturdays, even though applied uniformly, is discriminatory if it causes undue hardship to an employee who is precluded from working on Saturdays because of a genuine religious belief.[81] A rule or standard adopted for sound business or economic reasons and applied equally may still be discriminatory. Employers must make an effort to avoid undue hardship to those employees who are affected by the rule where it is reasonable to do so.

If an employee requests that he or she not be given Friday evening or Saturday shifts because of a genuine religious belief, the health facility cannot arbitrarily dismiss the request. An effort should be made to identify alternatives, such as adjusting the schedule or transferring the employee to another area, department or service. If, in the end, there is no feasible alternative, the employer may be justified in refusing the request. Similarly, if a nurse is physically incapacitated and cannot perform all of the required duties, the health facility should attempt to accommodate him or her by assigning some of the duties to others or by transferring the nurse to another position.

An employer may be entitled to "discriminate" where the rule or policy is a *bona fide* occupational requirement. The rule or policy must be imposed honestly, in good faith, and in the sincerely held belief that it is necessary for the adequate performance of the work. It must be reasonably necessary to ensure the efficient and economical performance of the job without endangering the employee, his or her fellow employees, or the general public.[82]

Whether a person's gender can be a valid consideration in formulating management policies has arisen in the health-care context. In *Sunnyside Home for the Aged v. London and District Service Workers' Union*,[83] a nursing home had a policy prohibiting male nursing attendants from caring for female residents. Female attendants, however, were permitted to care for male residents unless the resident objected. Although the arbitrator found that the policy in the nursing home was motivated by what he termed "morality and decency", he nonetheless held that the policy was

[81] *Ontario Human Rights Commission v. Simpsons-Sears Ltd.*, [1985] 2 S.C.R. 536, 23 D.L.R. (4th) 321.
[82] *Ontario Human Rights Commission v. Etobicoke (Borough)*, [1982] 1 S.C.R. 202, 132 D.L.R. (3d) 14, at 19-20.
[83] (1985), 21 L.A.C. (3d) 85 (Ont.).

discriminatory as it treated male attendants differently from female attendants. It was held that there was no legitimate business or professional justification for the distinction. [84]

WORKERS' COMPENSATION

All provinces and territories have enacted workers' compensation legislation to provide compensation, on a no-fault basis, to employees who are injured on the job. The administrative agency that deals with workers' compensation is generally called the Workers' Compensation Board, the Worker's Compensation Commission, the Worker's Safety and Insurance Board, the Commission de la Santé et de la Sécurité du Travail, or some similar appelation. These agencies or boards are statutory corporations having responsibility for the administration of the legislation and the adjudication of claims.

Workers' compensation is an industrial system based upon the principle of collective liability for employee injuries. Health facilities, such as hospitals and nursing homes, are collectively responsible for the costs of work-related accidents involving their employees. Employers pay a rate or premium based upon total employee remuneration. Rates are adjusted according to an employer's accident record.

ELIGIBILITY FOR BENEFITS

In Canada, compensation coverage is generally compulsory. Only a few excluded industries or workers remain. Doctors, for example, are likely to be ineligible for compensation as they are not "employees" of the hospital. They may sue a hospital for injuries that result from an accident in the hospital if the hospital is at fault. Nurses and other health-care workers are likely to be protected by workers' compensation legislation, regardless of whether they are full-time, part-time or casual employees and regardless of fault. Compensation is generally payable where:

1. A worker has coverage under the provincial or territorial workers' compensation legislation.
2. The worker has a disability or condition that is compensable under the legislation.

---

[84] *Ibid.* at 104; but see *McKale v. Lamont Auxiliary Hospital* (1986), 8 C.H.R.R. D/3659 (Alta. Bd. of Inquiry); affd. [1987] 3 W.W.R. 748, 51 Alta. L.R. (2d) 1 (Q.B.) and *Huronia District Hospital v. S.E.U., Local 204* (1980), 25 L.A.C. (2d) 183 (Ont.).

3.   The disability, condition, loss or death probably resulted from the employment.

To qualify for benefits, an employee must demonstrate that a "personal injury by accident arising out of and in the course of employment was caused to the worker." If a hospital worker falls on the slippery floor of a ward, the injury can be described as arising out of employment. The employer's premises include the parking lot, cafeteria, outdoor eating areas and any other area over which the employer has some measure of control.

As a rule, a worker is "in the course of employment" from the time of reporting to work until the end of the shift. This generally includes accidents in the parking lot or while travelling, if the travel is work-related. Although ordinary commuting to and from work is not usually compensable, if an employee, such as a nurse on call, is telephoned by the employer and told to come in, he or she would be eligible for compensation if injured in transit. Some activities, like eating lunch, may be considered incidental to work, although other exclusively personal activities will not be deemed to occur "in the course of employment."

A claim may be denied if the employee does not promptly report the injury or condition or does not obtain immediate medical attention. A claim is not barred if it is the result of multiple causes, some of which are not related to the employment: the test is: "would the worker be suffering from the disability but for the employment event, exposure or circumstance?"[85]

CLAIMS BY NURSES

In recent years, claims for worker compensation in the health-care field have grown significantly.[86] Some of this increase is attributable to claims advanced for conditions or diseases that do not arise from an accident or a similar traumatic event. Health-care workers may be exposed to chemicals, drugs, radiation, and bacterial and viral agents. Researchers have found that hospital pharmacists and nurses are exposed to levels of antineoplastic agents in certain drugs that are potentially carcinogenic and hazardous to workers' reproductive systems.[87]

[85]   T.G. Ison, *Workers' Compensation in Canada*, 2nd ed. (Toronto: Butterworths, 1989), p. 58.
[86]   Between 1982 and 1992, workers' compensation claims by Ontario health-care employees rose by 40 per cent, *Workers' Compensation Annual Report* (Ont. W.C.B., 1993), p. 18.
[87]   J. J. McDervitt, et al., "Exposure of Hospital Pharmacists and Nurses to Antineoplastic Agents" (1993), 35 J. of Occupational Medicine 57.

The coverage of disease in workers' compensation is generally more restrictive than the coverage of injuries. Diseases are more difficult to trace back to a single source. There may be multiple causes. It is harder to distinguish between industrial diseases and illnesses for which the general sick pay scheme, not workers' compensation, is appropriate. Several provincial statutes contain lists of diseases that will be considered for compensation: infections, hearing loss due to exposure to noise over time, osteoarthritis, contagious diseases, allergic reactions and disabilities caused by the gradual absorption of a chemical through the skin or by inhalation are all examples of compensable diseases. Generally, a disease is compensable if it can be shown that the disease resulted from exposure to a substance relating to a particular process, a trade or occupation in an industry or if it is a disease peculiar to or characteristic of a particular occupation.

Examples of disorders that have been classified as injuries include wounds, fractures, sprains, strains, dislocations, burns and any other disorder caused by trauma. Although controversial, stress has also been considered a compensable injury in some jurisdictions. "Injury" can include a disability resulting from activity over time or from a specific incident. Mental disorders with an undiagnosed organic cause are also compensable. Degenerative disc disease has been recognized as a compensable occupational disease. The disease may be caused by substantial periods of heavy lifting, and thereby directly affects nurses, nurses' aides and orderlies who lift and handle patients on a daily basis.

Stress has also been considered an occupational disease. This is a particularly contentious claim, perhaps because it is often impossible to distinguish between personal and occupational stress, both of which lead to stress-related disorders, such as heart attack, exhaustion or nervous breakdown. Where not precluded by legislation, compensation for stress may be possible.

VIOLENCE IN THE WORKPLACE

Violence toward nurses and other health-care workers is becoming a significant occupational hazard.[88] According to the British Columbia Workers' Compensation Board, acts of violence and force were the second-highest cause of injuries to nurses, orderlies and nursing assistants

---

[88] Health and Safety Commission, *Violence to Staff in the Health Services* (London: HMSO, 1987); G.M. Liss. *Examination of Workers' Compensation Claims Among Nurses in Ontario for Injuries Due to Violence* (Ont. Ministry of Labour, March, 1993).

in that province for the five-year period ending in 1992.[89] According to the same survey, occupational violence accounts for more compensation claims for health-care workers than for all other occupations combined. Violent acts against nurses doubled between 1984 and 1988. Acts range from kicks and punches, to sexual assault, severe beatings and assault with weapons or sharp objects. In 1989 the Manitoba Association of Registered Nurses made a study on occupational violence and discovered that half of Manitoba's nurses are physically attacked by patients at some point during their careers. In Ontario, almost six out of 10 nurses say they have been physically assaulted during their nursing careers, and 17 per cent say they have been sexually assaulted at work.[90]

British Columbia has implemented workers' compensation regulations regarding workplace violence. According to the British Columbia regulations, violence means "the attempted or actual exercise by a person, other than a worker, of any physical force so as to cause injury to a worker, and includes any threatening statement or behaviour".[91] The regulations direct employers to perform a risk assessment of the workplace and where a risk of injury is identified, the employer shall:

(a)   establish procedures, policies and work environment arrangements to eliminate the risk to workers from violence,

(b)   where elimination of the risk to workers is not possible, establish procedures, policies and work environment arrangements to minimize the risk to workers, and

(c)   establish procedures for reporting, investigating and documenting incidents of violence in accordance with the requirements of section 6.[92]

In addition, employers have a duty to inform employees of the risk of violence from persons (patients, for instance) who have a history of violent behaviour, and a duty to train staff members to recognize the potential for violence and how to respond appropriately.

OCCUPATIONAL HEALTH AND SAFETY

Occupational health and safety legislation provides for the imposition of rights, duties and obligations on workers, employers and supervisors.

---

[89] *Trend in Types of Accident by Occupation, 1988-1992*, British Columbia, Workers' Compensation Board of British Columbia, Statistical Services Department (July 1993), Table 4.

[90] *Supra*, note 88, p. 1.

[91] Workers' Compensation Regulations, B.C. Reg. 269/93, s. 8.88.

[92] *Ibid.*, s. 8.92.

Duties that are not fulfilled may lead to substantial penalties. Employers in particular have the obligation to take "every precaution reasonable in the circumstances for the protection of a worker."[93]

Since employers have much more power and control over the way work is organized and performed, it follows that they should hold the greatest responsibilities. In addition to self-regulation, government inspectors may enter the workplace to conduct inspections, order compliance, carry out investigations and lay charges. Fines and jail terms may be imposed for non-compliance in certain jurisdictions. In Ontario, a non-corporate employer may be fined up to $25,000 and/or 12 months in jail; the penalty for a corporation could be as high as $500,000. Although the maximum penalty is imposed only in the most egregious of cases, the elevated ceiling for penalties has sent a signal to the courts that the legislatures intend much heavier penalties to be meted out as a specific and general deterrent. The amount of any fine imposed will depend upon a variety of factors:

- the extent of the actual or potential harm to the public and to employees;
- the size of the hospital or health facility and the perceived ability to pay;
- the maximum penalty prescribed by statute; and
- the need to enforce regulatory statutes by general deterrence.[94]

In general, "[w]ithout being harsh, the fine must be substantial enough to warn others that the offence will not be tolerated. It must not appear to be a mere license fee for illegal activity."[95]

EMPLOYERS' DUTIES

Employers' general duties are enumerated in the governing statutes, with more detailed measures specific to a particular industry outlined in health and safety regulations.[96] General duties include:

---

[93] See for example, the Ontario *Occupational Health and Safety Act*, R.S.O. 1990, c. O.1, s. 25(2)(h).

[94] *R. v. Cotton Felts Ltd.* (1982), 2 C.C.C. (3d) 287 (Ont. C.A.).

[95] *Ibid.*, at 295.

[96] Although a number of industries are covered by specific safety regulations, such as mining and construction, in most provinces hospitals are not and are ordinarily expected to conform to the standards set out in the O. Reg. for Industrial Establishments and other regulations that can reasonably be applied to their operations as guides to safe work practices. Ontario, however, passed O.Reg. 67/93, "Health Care and Residential Facilities", under the *Occupational Health and Safety Act*, addressing such issues

- providing and maintaining a workplace, equipment, tools and systems that are safe;
- training, instructing and supervising workers to ensure their safety;
- notifying workers of potential hazards;
- ensuring that all employees are familiar with the proper use of all devices and equipment; and
- providing all prescribed protective equipment, devices and materials.[97]

Health-care workers may be exposed to chemicals and drugs that may cause serious illnesses and injuries if handled or administered improperly. Housekeeping staff must handle soaps, detergents and disinfectants. Laboratory technicians work with alkalis that have been held responsible for various illnesses, including hemorrhagic cystitis and bladder tumours.[98] Pathologists and technologists working in the autopsy room are exposed to formalin, which can result in irritation of the mucous membranes, especially of the nose and respiratory tract. Formaldehyde is also considered a suspect human carcinogen. Nurses and doctors are at risk of inhaling fumes and gases in many different situations; for instance, it has been reported that female health-care workers exposed to waste anaesthetic gases may have a greater risk of spontaneous abortion.[99] Less extreme side-effects of exposure to anaesthetic gases are also common, including headache, fatigue, irritability and sleep disturbances.[100]

Many jurisdictions have detailed provisions regarding the use and identification of hazardous materials incorporated into their respective occupational health and safety legislation. An employer is required to keep inventories of hazardous chemicals, their ingredients, methods of proper use, dangers and location in the workplace.[101] Employers may be obligated to post data sheets with this safety information in a conspicuous place and must provide instruction to workers exposed or likely to be exposed to a hazardous material.

At least one province has also responded to the particular dangers associated with drugs. Ontario's *Health Care and Residential Facilities Regu-*

---

as the disposal of syringes and hazardous liquids, the handling of antineoplastic drugs and protective clothing of x-ray technicians.

[97] See, for example Ontario: *Occupational Health and Safety Act*, R.S.O. 1990, c. O.1, s. 25; Nova Scotia: *Occupational Health and Safety Act*, S.N.S. 1996, c. 7, s. 9; Manitoba: *Workplace Safety and Health Act*, R.S.M. 1987, c. W210, s. 4(2).

[98] R. Frith and A. Strickler, "Occupational Health Hazards in Hospitals: An Overview" (1991), 12 Occupational Health in Ontario 89 at 93.

[99] *Ibid.*, at 94.

[100] It is interesting to note that Ontario's Health Care and Residential Facilities Regulation, O. Reg. 67/93, has a specific provision (s. 96) on anaesthetic gases. This provision requires that hospitals install "effective scavenging systems to collect, remove and dispose of waste gases" and to perform a regular monthly inspection for leakage.

[101] See for example Ontario's *Occupational Health and Safety Act*, R.S.O. 1990, c. O.1, Part IV.

lation under the *Occupational Health and Safety Act* addresses the hazards associated with antineoplastic drugs most often used in cancer treatment.[102] The regulation states that hospitals "shall, in consultation with the joint health and safety committee ... develop, establish and put into effect written measures and procedures to protect workers who may be exposed to antineoplastic agents or to material or equipment contaminated with antineoplastic agents".[103] There follows a more detailed list of measures to be addressed by the committee and administration, as well as a requirement that the administration provide training and instruction to workers. The explicit mention of the need for management to consult with the joint health and safety committee points to the need for a flexible, progressive policy-making regime that will respond to the dangers associated with these drugs.[104]

A breach of occupational health and safety legislation by an employer, supervisor or worker will not result in a conviction if the defendant can demonstrate that it exercised "due diligence" in its health and safety activities. In essence, where the court finds on the evidence that a defendant has established a "proper system to prevent the commission of the offence" and that "reasonable steps have been taken to ensure the effective operation of the system",[105] no conviction will follow. A "proper system" will follow the guidelines established in the governing legislation; particularly important are proper training and monitoring systems that function well.

REFUSAL TO WORK

Generally, occupational health and safety legislation gives workers a right to refuse to work when continuing to work poses a danger to themselves or to others. In some provinces, special provisions apply to health-care workers. In Ontario, for example, a right to refuse or stop work is not extended to health-care workers where a perceived danger or hazard is "inherent" or a "normal condition" of the worker's employment. Further, a health-care worker cannot refuse to work where to do so would "directly endanger the life, health or safety of another person".[106] Arguably, the restricted right of health-care workers to refuse to work in condi-

---

[102] O. Reg. 67/93, s. 97.

[103] *Ibid.*, s. 97(1).

[104] For example, a recent study has found that the common use of biological safety cabinets in hospitals may not be enough to control inhalation exposures: J. J. McDevitt et al., "Exposure of Hospital Pharmacists and Nurses to Antineoplastic Agents" (1993), 1 J. of Occupational Medicine 57.

[105] *R. v. Sault Ste. Marie (City)*, [1978] 2 S.C.R. 1299, 85 D.L.R. (3d) 161.

[106] *Occupational Health and Safety Act*, R.S.O, 1990, c. O.1, s. 43(1)(b).

tions that may be potentially unsafe or hazardous places an extra burden on the employer to ensure that all reasonable precautions are taken to protect workers from harm.

CURRENT ISSUES: OCCUPATIONAL HEALTH AND SAFETY

It is one of the ironies of employment in health care that occupational health and safety is one of the most frequently overlooked aspects of working life. The same people who help solve the health problems of patients are frequently working in situations that compromise their own health. Disease transmission is the obvious hazard of working with sick people, but other hazards in the health care environment include back injuries from lifting patients, cuts or punctures from "sharps" (and the attending dangers of HIV or hepatitis transmission), attacks by mentally disturbed patients, the potential exposure to radiation used in treatments, and a host of others. In Ontario, the recently-formed Health Care Health and Safety Association has a mandate to monitor health and safety issues and to recommend legislative changes that might make the situation better.

One aspect of occupational health and safety that is deeply troubling to nurses in particular is the issue of nurse abuse by patients. While violence against women in non-work situations is becoming increasingly well understood and is the subject of moral outrage, violence against nurses (who are frequently women) is still frequently dismissed as "part of the job" or, worse, as something that nurses could have prevented if they had not provoked the situation. Yet the parallels are shocking: in a Toronto study,[107] nurses who had been assaulted by their patients reported feelings that closely mirror the reactions of abused wives. Minimizing, denying and forgetting were strategies they used to cope with their assault. One nurse reported that after the assault, she tried to become "the quintessential nurse": "I bought the whitest pair of stockings and the whitest pair of shoes". Any nurse, or other person, who has spent time counselling women who have been raped will recognize that urge to "purify" oneself, and to deflect the inner voice that insists that "you brought it upon yourself". Such studies raise the question whether popular understanding of violence against women has gone far enough. Perhaps a step in the right direction is British Columbia's workers' compensation regulation, which addresses workplace violence and places a duty on employers to inform employees about potentially violent patients and a duty to train staff members to recognize potential violence and how to respond to it.

---

[107] Shirley Roberts, "Nurse Abuse: A Taboo Topic", *Canadian Nurse*, March 1991, p. 23.

Relevant Legislation

CANADA

Canada Labour Code, R.S.C. 1985, c. L-2

ALBERTA

Employment Standards Code, S.A. 1996, c. E-10.3.

Labour Relations Code, S.A. 1988, c. L-1.2

Occupational Health and Safety Act, R.S.A. 1980, c. O-2

BRITISH COLUMBIA

Employment Standards Act, R.S.B.C. 1996, c. 113

Labour Relations Code, R.S.B.C. 1996, c. 244

Workers Compensation Act, R.S.B.C. 1996, c. 492.

Occupational Health and Safety Regulation, B.C. Reg. 296/97

Workers' Compensation (Occupational Health and Safety) Amendment Act, 1998, S.B.C. 1998, c. 50

MANITOBA

Employment Standards Act, R.S.M. 1987, c. E110

Labour Relations Act, R.S.M. 1987, c. L10

Workplace Safety and Health Act, R.S.M. 1987, c. W210

NEW BRUNSWICK

Employment Standards Act, S.N.B. 1982, c. E-7.2

Industrial Relations Act, R.S.N.B. 1973, c. I-4

Occupational Health and Safety Act, S.N.B. 1983, c. O-0.2

NEWFOUNDLAND

The Labour Relations Act, R.S.N. 1990, c. L-1

The Labour Standards Act, R.S.N. 1990, c. L-2

Occupational Health and Safety Act, R.S.N. 1990, c. O-3

Public Service Collective Bargaining Act, R.S.N. 1990, c. P-42

NORTHWEST TERRITORIES

Labour Standards Act, R.S.N.W.T. 1988, c. L-1

Safety Act, R.S.N.W.T. 1988, c. S-1

NOVA SCOTIA

Labour Standards Code, R.S.N.S. 1989, c. 246

Occupational Health and Safety Act, S.N.S. 1996, c. 7

Trade Union Act, R.S.N.S. 1989, c. 475

ONTARIO

Employment Standards Act, R.S.O. 1990, c. E.14

Labour Relations Act, S.O. 1995, c. 1, Sch. A

Hospital Labour Disputes Arbitration Act, R.S.O. 1990, c. H.14 (HLDAA)

Occupational Health and Safety Act, R.S.O. 1990, c. O.1

PRINCE EDWARD ISLAND

Labour Act, R.S.P.E.I. 1988, c. L-1

Occupational Health and Safety Act, R.S.P.E.I. 1988, c. O-1

Youth Employment Act, S.P.E.I. 1990, c. 66

QUEBEC

An act respecting labour standards, R.S.Q. 1977, c. N-1.1

An act respecting occupational health and safety, R.S.Q. 1977, c. S-2.1

Labour Code, R.S.Q. 1977, c. C-27

SASKATCHEWAN

Labour Standards Act, R.S.S. 1978, c. L-1

Occupational Health and Safety Act, 1993, S.S. 1993, c. O-1.1

Trade Union Act, R.S.S. 1978, c. T-17

YUKON

Employment Standards Act, R.S.Y. 1986, c. 54

Occupational Health and Safety Act, R.S.Y.T. 1986, c. 123

CHAPTER 12

Canadian Charter of Rights and Freedoms

SYNOPSIS

This chapter sets out the important components of the *Canadian Charter of Rights and Freedoms*[1] for the consideration of nurses. Although a lengthy treatise is not possible within the context of this publication, this overview discusses fundamental freedoms, as well as democratic, mobility, legal and minority rights. It also explains the purpose of the "override" power, which places limits on *Charter* rights.

INTRODUCTION

Since it became law in 1982, the *Charter* has had an enormous impact on the Canadian legal system. While Canadian law prior to the *Charter* had been interpreted by the courts to guarantee Canadian citizens certain rights and freedoms based on common and natural law,[2] there was no clear codification of these rights and freedoms.

The *Canadian Bill of Rights*[3] was passed in 1960. It set out certain rights and freedoms similar in scope to those contained in the *Charter*. However, the *Bill of Rights* was an ordinary statute passed by the federal parliament. It was not a constitutional document. It applied only to federal legislation and not to the provinces. As an ordinary federal statute, it had no higher standing than other federal statutes, and accordingly, courts interpreted restrictively its impact on legislation or activities of government. The *Charter*, however, is a part of the Canadian Constitution and can only be altered by constitutional amendment. Because it is a part of the Constitution, the *Charter* supersedes any inconsistent statutes.

---

[1] Part I of the *Constitution Act, 1982*, being Schedule B to the *Canada Act*, 1982 (U.K.), 1982, c. 11 [hereafter "the *Charter*"].

[2] *Switzman v. Elbling and Quebec (A.G.)*, [1957] S.C.R. 285, 7 D.L.R. (2d) 337, 117 C.C.C. 129; *Saumur v. Quebec (City)*, [1953] 2 S.C.R. 299, [1953] 4 D.L.R. 641, 106 C.C.C. 289.

[3] S.C. 1960, c. 44 (R.S.C. 1970, App. III).

The *Charter* applies to both federal and provincial levels of government. Government laws or activities which contravene the *Charter* are invalid.[4] It does not, however, apply to or invalidate the acts of private individuals or entities unless they have become, as a result of their conduct or activity, agents of the government. Therefore, the release of confidential information by a nurse or another health care provider, though perhaps in breach of the common law or the code of conduct that applies to the profession, is not a breach of the *Charter* if the health care provider is acting in the capacity of a private individual.[5]

The rights and freedoms entrenched in Canadian law by the *Charter* are not absolute. Section 1 of the *Charter* provides that the rights and freedoms are "guaranteed", subject only "to such reasonable limits prescribed by law as can be demonstrably justified in a free and democratic society". In interpreting the effect of the *Charter*, the courts must balance competing interests. Certain rights will be inhibited by others by necessity. The right to associate freely, or to form a bargaining group or union, does not allow citizens to participate in a riot. The right to express oneself freely does not permit one to make obscene telephone calls to an unwilling recipient. Consequently, even if a particular right or freedom has been abridged, the court must then inquire under s. 1 of the *Charter* whether or not the abridgement is justified.

1. Fundamental Freedoms

Section 2 of the *Charter* lists certain "fundamental" freedoms. The first of these is "freedom of conscience and religion".[6] The Supreme Court of Canada has stated that this provision of the *Charter* protects "profound personal beliefs that govern one's perception of oneself, humankind, nature, and, in some cases, a higher or different order of being."[7] As such, protection goes beyond traditional religious denominations and may extend to less mainstream, even bizarre, religious practices if it can be demonstrated that a conduct or practice stems from strong moral or ethical convictions. Despite a reference in the preamble of the *Charter* to the "supremacy of God",[8] it is not necessary that the religious conviction be rooted in the belief in a supreme being. In fact, the *Charter*'s guarantee of

---

4   *R. v. Big M Drug Mart*, [1985] 1 S.C.R. 295, [1985] 3 W.W.R. 481, 37 Alta. L.R. (2d) 97, 60 A.R. 161, 58 N.R. 81, 18 D.L.R. (4th) 321, 13 C.R.R. 64, 18 C.C.C. (3d) 385, 85 C.L.L.C. 14,023.

5   *R. v. Dersch*, [1993] 3 S.C.R. 768, 25 C.R. (4th) 88.

6   The *Charter*, s. 2(a).

7   *Edwards Books & Art Ltd. v. R.*, [1986] 2 S.C.R. 713, at 759.

8   "Whereas Canada is founded upon principles that recognize the supremacy of God and the rule of law ..."

freedom of "conscience and religion" guarantees to Canadian citizens the right *not* to believe and to exercise atheistic or agnostic practices.[9]

Canadian courts have held that federal legislation entitled the *Lord's Day Act* is invalid because it is too closely associated with certain religious sects and not with others.[10] They have also declared certain employment practices discriminatory under provincial human rights legislation such as a Seventh Day Adventist employee unable to work on Saturdays,[11] and have held legislation restricting Sunday shopping to be invalid.[12]

The second fundamental freedom listed in the *Charter* is that of "freedom of thought, belief, opinion and expression, including freedom of the press and other media of communication".[13] As with all other rights and freedoms contained in the *Charter*, freedom of expression is not absolute. Judicial consideration has involved the difficult balancing of that right with others. It has been held, for example, that freedom of expression is not infringed by s. 177 of the *Criminal Code*,[14] which prohibits wilful publication of false statements, tales or news,[15] that a professional code of ethics overrode the right of one teacher to express certain views about another teacher at a parents' meeting,[16] and that a prohibition against the publication of the names of juveniles involved in juvenile delinquency proceedings was a reasonable restriction on freedom of expression.[17] The obligation that prevents health practitioners from releasing information about the identity or treatment of patients, except in limited circumstances, is the result of similar constraints.

While recognizing an expanding role for freedom of expression in our society, the courts have held that freedom of expression must be balanced against the need for privacy in certain administrative proceedings. In *Hirt v. College of Physicians & Surgeons of British Columbia*,[18] the court held that the names and identities of complainants who gave evidence before

---

9   *R. v. Big M Drug Mart, supra*, note 4.
10   *Ibid.*
11   *Ontario Human Rights Commission v. Simpsons-Sears Ltd.* [1985] 2 S.C.R. 536.
12   *Peel (Regional Municipality) and Ontario (Attorney General) v. Great Atlantic & Pacific Co. of Canada Ltd.* (1990), 73 O.R. (2d) 289 (H.C.).
13   The *Charter*, s. 2(b).
14   R.S.C. 1970, c. C-34 [now R.S.C. 1985, c. C-46, s. 181].
15   *R. v. Zundel* (1986), 58 O.R. (2d) 129, 18 O.A.C. 161, 35 D.L.R. (4th) 338, 31 C.C.C. (3d) 97, 56 C.R. (3d) 1, 29 C.R.R. 349 (C.A.); leave to appeal to S.C.C. refused (1987), 23 O.A.C. 317n, 61 O.R. (2d) 588n, 56 C.R. (3d) xxviii.
16   *Cromer v. British Columbia Teachers' Federation*, [1986] 5 W.W.R. 638, 4 B.C.L.R. (2d) 273, 29 D.L.R. (4th) 641 (C.A.).
17   *Southam Inc. v. R.* (1986), 53 O.R. (2d) 663, 50 C.R. (3d) 241, 12 O.A.C. 394, 25 C.C.C. (3d) 119, 26 D.L.R. (4th) 479, 20 C.R.R. 7 (C.A.); leave to appeal to S.C.C. refused (1986), 26 D.L.R. (4th) 479n.
18   [1985] 3 W.W.R. 350, 60 B.C.L.R. 273, 17 D.L.R. (4th) 472 (C.A.).

a confidential inquiry could be kept secret when the proceedings were published. The court concluded that although this constituted an infringement of freedom of expression in preventing access by the press for publication of the complainants' identities, it was nonetheless justified on the basis that an absence of confidentiality would deter patients from coming forward with complaints. Conversely, a court has refused to prohibit publication of the names of men charged with gross indecency on the ground that public access to information about criminal proceedings is a vital component of the process.[19]

The last two fundamental freedoms protected by s. 2 of the *Charter* are freedom of peaceful assembly and freedom of association.[20] These two freedoms are most commonly associated with the right to engage in labour activities such as forming a union or collective bargaining unit, or engaging in a strike. Picketing is a common activity, engaged in by unions and others, for the purpose of communicating a particular message or position.

The right of anti-abortion activists to protest and picket is subject to reasonable limits and must be balanced against other fundamental rights. In *Ontario (Attorney General) v. Dieleman*,[22] the Attorney General of Ontario sought to prohibit anti-abortion protest activity within 500 feet of locations that included the homes and offices of physicians who provided abortion services at hospitals, and three clinics where abortion services were provided. The picketers were on public property and sometimes tried to speak to women entering a facility offering abortions. Sometimes, the posters identified the doctors by name. Some contained graphic statements and pictures protesting abortion. One protestor engaged in silent prayer vigils on public property near some of the locations, but did not carry signs or talk to patients. The application by the government stated that the protest activities had a negative psychological impact upon patients seeking abortions. While concluding that the protestors' right to express their opinion was, for the most part, protected by the *Charter*, the court also recognized the physiological, psychological and privacy interests of women about to go an abortion as sufficiently important to warrant overriding a constitutionally protected right or freedom. The privacy interests of physicians and their families who were targeted by residential picketing were also seen as pressing and substantial considerations for the court. A request for an injunction protecting the hospitals from picketing was refused as it was not demonstrated that the protest activities constituted an unreasonable interference with the operation of the hospitals or the appropriate interests of the patients and

---

[19]   *R. v. Several Unnamed Persons* (1983), 44 O.R. (2d) 81 (H.C.).
[20/21] The *Charter*, s. 2(c) and (d).
[22]   (1994), 117 D.L.R. (4th) 449 (Ont. Ct. Gen. Div.).

physicians, especially given the multiplicity of entrances and services at these locations. Limits, however, were placed upon the protesting activities at the office and residence locations of the physicians and at the abortion clinics. The limits were in relation to the location, size, nature and time of the protest activities. The picketers were barred from approaching within 10 feet of a person who made it clear that he or she did not wish to receive communications from the protestors. The picketing of homes and families was barred completely as the court concluded that the repetitive presence of the picketers went beyond the purpose of communicating anti-abortion views and constituted an attempt to harass physicians, their families and their neighbourhoods by impairing their ability to enjoy and occupy their homes and neighbourhoods.

2. Democratic Rights

The *Charter* contains provisions that guarantee those rights associated with a democracy: the right to vote, the right to stand for election and the right to an accountable government.[23] Under the *Charter*, every Canadian citizen is guaranteed the right to vote in federal and provincial elections. Every citizen has the right to be elected as a member of the federal parliament or of a provincial legislative assembly. This right may be balanced, to some extent, by certain special requirements which are justified in a democratic society; for example, one must register to vote, or one may be required to make a modest deposit with the chief electoral officer in order to stand for election. The registration of voters is an acceptable qualification as it is designed to ensure that only qualified citizens vote and that each citizen has only one vote. The deposit of a sum of money by an electoral candidate may be necessary to ensure that candidates who run for election are serious-minded and that the process will not be trivialized. On the other hand, to establish an onerous registration procedure or to require a monetary deposit which could be afforded only by the rich would be considered an unjustified restriction on basic democratic rights, and thereby, unconstitutional.

The *Charter* entrenches the concept of an accountable, duly elected government by requiring an election of the House of Commons or of any legislative assembly every five years, subject to an extension only in time of "real or apprehended war, invasion or insurrection".[24] The House of Commons and every legislature must sit at least once a year. Although nothing is said in the *Charter* about how long such a sitting must last, a court would probably rule that it must be sufficiently long to conduct the proceedings of a democratic government and not of a token duration.

---

[23] The *Charter*, ss. 3, 4 and 5.
[24] *Ibid.*, s. 4(2).

3. Mobility Rights

Section 6 of the *Charter* guarantees every citizen of Canada the right to enter, remain in and leave Canada. Furthermore, it guarantees every Canadian citizen and every person who has permanent residence in Canada the right to move and take up residence in any province, and the right to pursue the gaining of a livelihood in any province. In effect, the *Charter* prevents any government from enacting legislation or engaging in practices which prevent individuals from travelling to and from, or working in, certain parts of Canada. Again, mobility rights are not absolute. They may be restricted by laws or practices that do not discriminate "on the basis of province of present or previous residence,"[25] or by "reasonable residency requirements as a qualification for the receipt of publicly provided social services".[26] Mobility rights may also be restricted, justifiably, by programmes or activities which are aimed at amelioration of conditions of individuals in a province who are socially or economically disadvantaged where the rate of employment in that province is below the rate of employment in Canada.[27]

4. Legal Rights

Sections 7 to 14 of the *Charter* contain "legal rights". Section 7 guarantees the right to life, liberty and security of the person and the right not to be deprived of these rights except in accordance with the principles of fundamental justice. The meaning of the term "right to life" has been scrutinized closely by the Supreme Court of Canada in a series of cases involving abortion.[28] In those decisions, the Supreme Court refused to engage in a philosophical debate over when life begins or ends, but rather, restricted the application of the "right to life" to those individuals who, traditionally, have been interpreted to be "persons" by the courts.[29]

In *R. v. Morgentaler* the Supreme Court of Canada has held that liberty includes the right of an individual to a degree of autonomy in making decisions of fundamental personal importance.[30] The majority of the court spoke of a woman's right of autonomy in terms which balanced the right of abortion, in certain circumstances, against protection of the fetus by the state. In that case, the Supreme Court of Canada held that the legal procedure by which the state afforded protection to the fetus was an un-

---

25   *Ibid.*, s. 6(3)(a).
26   *Ibid.*, s. 6(3)(b).
27   *Ibid.*, s. 6(4).
28   See "Abortion", below.
29   *Tremblay v. Daigle*, [1989] 2 S.C.R. 530, 69 D.L.R. (4th) 634, 102 N.R. 81.
30   [1988] 1 S.C.R. 30, 44 D.L.R. (4th) 385, 37 C.C.C. (3d) 449, 62 C.R. (3d) 1.

acceptable restriction on the woman's right to have access to abortion in certain situations.

It has been held that the right to "liberty" does not protect members of the medical profession from a mandatory retirement scheme established by a government-funded hospital.[31] It has been held, however, that denial to a qualified physician by a provincial statutory authority of a "billing number" under the provincial medicare scheme amounted to a denial of the physician's "right to liberty".[32] The concept of "security of the person" has been linked to an individual's right to "complete physical, mental, and social well-being".[33] A court has ruled that the transfer of an inmate with a heart condition to a location with restricted access to adequate medical services was a breach of the inmate's right to security of the person.[34] Although reversed on appeal[35] because there was no demonstrated jeopardy to the inmate, the appeal court left intact a suggestion in the lower court ruling that restrictive access to medical services infringed an individual's right to security of the person.

A number of cases in the health-care context have raised questions about the right of patients to be protected from illegal search or seizure. In Saskatchewan, a court ruled that "security of the person":

> [I]ncludes a right to personal dignity and a right to an area of privacy or individual sovereignty into which the State must not make arbitrary or unjustified intrusions. These considerations also underlie the privilege against self-incrimination.[36]

The Supreme Court of Canada has stated that even if a sample has been obtained with the consent of the patient, use of the sample is restricted to medical purposes.[37] The patient had a reasonable expectation that his privacy interests in the sample would continue into the future. In his reasons for judgment, LaForest J. commented:

---

31   *Staffman v. Vancouver General Hospital*, [1986] 6 W.W.R. 23, 30 D.L.R. (4th) 700, 25 C.R.R. 16, 14 C.C.E.L. 146, 87 C.L.L.C. 17,004; affd. on other grounds, [1988] 2 W.W.R. 708, 21 B.C.L.R. (2d) 165, 49 D.L.R. (4th) 727 (C.A.); revd. [1990] 3 S.C.R. 483, 76 D.L.R. (4th) 700.

32   *Mia v. Medical Services Comm. of B.C.* (1985), 61 B.C.L.R. 273, 15 Admin. L.R. 265, 17 D.L.R. (4th) 385, 16 C.R.R. 233 (S.C.).

33   See P. Garant, "Fundamental Rights and Fundamental Justice", in Beaudoin and Ratushny, eds., *The Canadian Charter of Rights and Freedoms* 2nd ed. (Toronto: Carswell, 1989), p. 345.

34   *Collin v. Lussier*, [1983] 1 F.C. 2187 (T.D.).

35   *Lussier v. Collin*, [1985] 1 F.C. 124 (C.A.).

36   *R. L. Crain Inc. v. Couture* (1983), 30 Sask. R. 191, 6 D.L.R. (4th) 478, 10 C.C.C. (3d) 119, 9 C.R.R. 287 (Q.B.), at p. 502 D.L.R.

37   *R. v. Dyment*, [1988] 2 S.C.R. 417, 73 Nfld. & P.E.I.R. 13, 229 A.P.R. 13, 55 D.L.R. (4th) 503, 89 N.R. 249, 45 C.C.C. (3d) 244, 66 C.R. (3d) 348, 10 M.V.R. (2d) 1.

The dignity of the human being is equally seriously violated when use is made of bodily substances taken by others for medical purposes in a manner that does not respect that limitation. In my view, the trust and confidence of the public in the administration of medical facilities would be seriously taxed if an easy and informal flow of information, and particularly of bodily substances from hospitals to the police, were allowed.[38]

It has been held that where a physician takes a blood sample illegally at the request of the police the physician is acting as an agent of the government and, therefore, his or her actions are subject to the *Charter*.[39] In *R. v. Dersch*,[40] the Supreme Court of Canada confirmed that although misconduct by health practitioners in providing samples of bodily fluids to police without the consent of the patient does not, strictly speaking, violate the *Charter* where the health practitioners are not acting as agents of government, it is nonetheless clear that such conduct is wrong as it violates the practitioner's common-law duty of confidentiality to the patient. Where blood samples or records showing evidence of impairment are obtained as a result of lawfully authorized search warrants, however, the evidence will be admitted at trial.[41]

Nurses, especially those working in emergency departments, may frequently come into contact with law enforcement authorities. Patients may be brought to the hospital who have been involved in accidents or injured while engaged in criminal activity. Police officers who accompany the patient may be in the course of conducting a criminal investigation. They may seek the assistance and cooperation of nurses and doctors in the collection of evidence and the detention of the patient.

In *R. v. Dyment*,[42] the Supreme Court of Canada considered the conduct of a doctor who supplied a blood sample to a police officer who had brought a patient to the emergency department after the patient was involved in a car accident. The blood sample had been obtained by the physician for medical purposes. When the sample was turned over to the police officer at his request, it was analyzed and disclosed a blood-alcohol level exceeding the legal limit for driving. The patient was not aware that the blood specimen had been obtained. The court ruled that the taking of the specimen without the patient's consent, where not required by law and not part of a medical procedure, violates the right to security of the person under the *Charter*.

---

38 *Ibid.*, at 439 [S.C.R.].
39 *R. v. Pohoretsky*, [1987] 1 S.C.R. 945, 39 D.L.R. (4th) 699.
40 [1993] 3 S.C.R. 768, 25 C.R. (4th) 88.
41 *R. v. Erickson* (1992), 125 A.R. 68, 72 C.C.C. (3d) 75, 38 M.V.R. (2d) 260, 14 W.A.C. 68 (C.A.).
42 *Supra*, note 37.

Nurses and other hospital staff do not have any legal obligation to as-sist the police in the investigation of a crime. A test should not be carried out without the patient's consent simply because it will assist the police investigation. Where tests are carried out for a medical purpose, with the patient's consent, that consent is limited to use of the specimen or sample for the medical treatment and not to incriminate the patient in any crimi-nal proceeding. If a police officer obtains a warrant or subpoena, hospital staff will be obliged, as a matter of law, to provide to the police anything covered by the subpoena or search warrant.

There is, however, no legal requirement for a nurse to assist in investi-gative activity against his or her will. There is no requirement in the *Criminal Code* that a citizen actively assist in a criminal investigation. There is a provision authorizing health-care personnel to assist in an in-vestigation in good faith, without legal recourse by the patient. As a practical matter, those involved in health care may wish to co-operate as a matter of civic duty, but this cannot be done in a manner that violates the patient's fundamental rights.

In *Reynen v. Antonenko*,[43] a case decided before the *Charter* was enacted, a resident physician agreed, at the request of police, to carry out a sig-moidoscopy of a patient who was suspected of having hidden illegal nar-cotics in his rectum. The physician told the patient that he would have to perform a rectal examination and that it might be uncomfortable. The patient did not resist and positioned himself for the examination. Heroin was found. The patient sued the physician for assault and battery. The patient's claim was dismissed on the basis that the sigmoidoscopy could not have been conducted without the patient's full co-operation. The court did not accept the patient's contention that he believed, at the time, that he had no other recourse but to submit to the procedure.

There may be some question with the advent of the *Charter* whether the physician's conduct in the *Reynen* case would sustain a challenge under the *Charter*. A patient who is under arrest and is brought to the hospital by police may be under considerable duress and the "consent" may be given in circumstances which render the consent involuntary. If a health practitioner concludes that the test or examination requested as a part of the police investigation cannot be conducted without the free and voluntary consent of the patient, there should be no compli-ance with the police request.

It has been suggested that any procedure involving a significant risk to the health or physical integrity of the person, such as a surgical opera-tion, would be unreasonable under the *Charter*, but that procedures such as enemas, intubations, rectal or vaginal searches would be acceptable if

---

[43] (1975), 54 D.L.R. (3d) 124, [1975] 5 W.W.R. 10, 20 C.C.C. (2d) 342, 30 C.R.N.S. 135 (Alta. S.C.).

performed by medical personnel on reasonable grounds.[44] On the other hand, a court has refused to issue a search warrant to permit a doctor, at the request of the police, to remove a bullet from the shoulder of an accused.[45] Communications to police about the condition of the patient by hospital personnel may be a violation of the patient's right to privacy. Patient records and the information contained in them are confidential. Police officers have no right of access to a patient's chart in the absence of a subpoena or search warrant.

The activities of police officers in health-care facilities may also raise questions. Do police officers have any right to question patients who are ill and in need of emergency medical treatment? It would not seem that police officers have any higher right to visit patients than any other visitor. The overriding concern ought to be the welfare of the patient. Can a police officer attend in the operating room to observe an operation and apprehend the bullet removed from a patient for the purpose of maintaining continuity of evidence? Again, if the police officer's activity will in any way compromise patient care (for example, breaking the sterile seal or distracting operating room personnel), this may result in harm to the patient and is not authorized by law. In the absence of a court order, a police officer has no right to be in the operating room. A nurse or physician can testify in court that the particular bullet was removed from the particular patient.

The *Charter* has been a factor in numerous reported decisions concerning the rights of patients who have a mental disability or are psychiatric patients. The British Columbia Court of Appeal has ruled that medical treatment without the consent of a patient with mental disability, where it is in the patient's best interest, is not an infringement of the right to life, liberty and security of the person. In such a case, a girl with a mental disability had a pronounced fear at the sight of blood. Her parents sought to give a substitute consent for a hysterectomy. The girl's official guardian objected on the ground that an elective treatment of this nature ought not to be carried out without the consent of the patient and that it violated s. 7 of the *Charter*. The court held, however, that in all the circumstances it was in the best interests of the child to have the hysterectomy performed and that the treatment was not inconsistent with the *Charter*.[46]

---

[44] F. Chevrette, "Protection Upon Arrest or Detention and against Retroactive Penal Law" in Beaudoin and Ratushny, *supra*, note 33, p. 387, at 406.

[45] *Laporte v. Langaniere* (1972), 29 D.L.R. (3d) 651, 8 C.C.C. (2d) 343 (*sub nom. Re Laporte and R.*), 18 C.R.N.S. 357 (Que. Q.B.).

[46] *Re K.* (1985), 63 B.C.L.R. 145, 19 D.L.R. (4th) 255 (*sub nom K. v. Public Trustee*), [1985] 4 W.W.R. 725 (C.A.); leave to appeal to S.C.C. dismissed on jurisdictional grounds, [1985] 4 W.W.R. 757. But see *Re Eve*, [1986] 2 S.C.R. 388, 61 Nfld. & P.E.I.R. 273, 31 D.L.R. (4th) 1, where it was held that a disabled child's parents could not authorize a hysterectomy for contraceptive as opposed to therapeutic purposes.

It has been held that provincial mental health legislation permitting the involuntary admission and detention of psychiatric patients is valid under the *Charter* as long as admission and detention occur in accordance with the principles of natural justice and in a way that strikes a balance between the rights of the individual and the general rights and obligations of society.[47] The continued detention of a patient diagnosed as a pedophile was not a violation of the patient's right to liberty where the evidence disclosed that his release into the community posed a serious risk of bodily harm to others.[48] A psychiatric facility is not required to prove beyond a reasonable doubt that a patient who has been found not guilty by reason of mental disorder is not a significant risk to society if released.[49] Nor is the admission of hearsay evidence at a review board hearing a violation of the *Charter*.[50] Government activity imposing care upon mentally ill, incompetent adults, is in violation of the *Charter* if it does so in a way that is "intrusive and devoid of…essential safeguards and procedures to ensure that the adult's rights to privacy and independent living are not violated."[51]

It has been suggested that access to medical care is a component of the right to "security of the person".[52] It has been argued that the "right to life" must be balanced against the right to a natural death.[53] The Law Reform Commission of Canada has suggested that in the absence of reasons to the contrary, medical authorities ought to assume that a patient would prefer life to death, even when the patient is not able to express a preference.[54] It has been held that a patient's right to refuse treatment, even where the refusal will result in death, is a fundamental right protected under Quebec's human rights legislation,[55] but that there is no right protected under the *Charter* that will allow a terminally ill patient to have others assist in his or her death.[56]

---

[47] *McCorkell v. Riverview Hospital*, [1993] 8 W.W.R. 169, 81 B.C.L.R. (2d) 273, 104 D.L.R. (4th) 391 (S.C.).

[48] *Penetanguishene Mental Health Centre v. Stock* (1994), 116 D.L.R. (4th) 550 (Ont. Gen. Div.).

[49] *Davidson v. British Columbia (Attorney General)* (1993), 87 C.C.C. (3d) 269 (B.C.C.A.).

[50] *Dayday v. MacEwan* (1987), 62 O.R. (2d) 588 (Dist. Ct.).

[51] *Nova Scotia (Minister of Community Services) v. Keeble* (1991), 290 A.P.R. 377, 107 N.S.R. (2d) 377 (N.S. Fam. Ct.); additional reasons at (1992), 11 N.S.R. (2d) 36, 303 A.P.R. 36 (N.S. Fam. Ct.).

[52] P. Garant, *supra*, note 33, p. 354.

[53] B.M. Dickens, "The Right to Natural Death" (1981), 26 *McGill L.J.* 847.

[54] Law Reform Commission of Canada, "Euthanasia, assisting suicide and interrupting treatment" (Report No. 20) (Ottawa: Supply and Services, 1983), p. 11.

[55] *Nancy B. v. Hôtel-Dieu de Quebec*, [1992] R.J.Q. 361 (C.S.).

[56] *Rodriguez v. British Columbia (Attorney General)*, [1993] 3 S.C.R. 519, 82 B.C.L.R. (2d) 273, 107 D.L.R. (4th) 342, [1993] 7 W.W.R. 641, 85 C.C.C. (3d) 15.

Section 8 of the *Charter* provides that everyone has the right to be secure against unreasonable search or seizure. Section 9 provides that everyone has the right not to be arbitrarily detained or imprisoned. An individual cannot be detained under adult protection legislation simply because the individual engages in conduct that seems unusual or even risky. In *Ministry of Community Services v. Perry*,[57] an adult absconded from a psychiatric facility where she had been a patient for 16 years. An order was sought under Nova Scotia's adult protection legislation for a declaration that she was in need of protection and could be returned involuntarily to the facility. The evidence disclosed that she had been evicted from the hotel where she had been staying, lacked any plans for shelter or food and was at risk because of her history of failing to take medication. The application was refused on the ground that the evidence did not disclose a danger or risk significant enough to override the individual's right to make decisions about her own status and treatment.

Section 10 provides every individual with the right, on arrest or detention, to be informed promptly of the reasons for the arrest or detention, to be permitted to retain and instruct counsel without delay, to be informed of that right, to have the validity of any detention determined quickly, and to obtain a release if the detention is not lawful.

The right not to be arbitrarily detained or imprisoned may also have implications for health care personnel. Generally speaking, patients are free to come and go as they please. This would apply to health care facilities such as hospitals, nursing homes and psychiatric facilities. However, patients who have been confined involuntarily to psychiatric facilities pursuant to a province's mental health legislation must still be afforded certain procedural protections. In Prince Edward Island, the Court of Appeal has held that the *Charter* prohibits unreasonable detention and that the patient's rights under the *Charter* are in addition to any protection provided by the provincial mental health legislation.[58]

Section 11 of the *Charter* contains rights that are to be afforded to any person charged with a criminal offence. Such rights include the right to be informed without unreasonable delay of the specific offence, to be tried within a reasonable time, not to be required to testify against oneself, to be presumed innocent until proven guilty and not to be tried more than once for the same offence. Justice Wilson of the Supreme Court of Canada specifically distinguished criminal offences from offences arising out of domestic or disciplinary matters which are "regulatory, protective or corrective and which are primarily intended to maintain discipline, professional integrity and professional standards or to regulate conduct

---

[57] (1990), 98 C.L.R. (2d) 263 (N.S. Prov. Ct.).
[58] *Re Jenkins* (1984), 45 Nfld. & P.E.I.R. 131, 132 A.P.R. 131, 5 D.L.R. (4th) 577 (*sub nom. Ref. re Mental Health Act*), 8 C.R.R. 142 (P.E.I.S.C.).

within a limited private sphere of activity".[59] Consequently, nurses charged with misconduct in professional disciplinary proceedings will not be afforded the same level of protection under the *Charter* as they would if they were charged with a criminal offence.

The *Charter* provide certain rights to witnesses in respect of self-incrimination and, to any party or witness, the right to language interpretation.[60]

5. Cruel and Unusual Treatment or Punishment

Section 12 of the *Charter* provides that "[e]veryone has the right not to be subjected to any cruel and unusual treatment or punishment". The word "treatment" has obvious implications for health care. Certain types of treatment, such as a lobotomy or castration, are by their very nature cruel and unusual.[61] For example, electric shock therapy, involuntary administration of hormonal medication to reduce sexual drive, confinement of patients in solitary settings and the use of physical restraints are all areas of treatment that, in certain circumstances, may raise *Charter* concerns.[62] Treatment may be cruel and unusual insofar as it is disproportionate to the anticipated benefit of the treatment.

It has been questioned how the death penalty, if re-established by parliament, can be said not to offend this provision by its very nature.[63] The Saskatchewan Court of Appeal ruled, however, that a mandatory 10-year sentence for second degree murder, even where the killing was carried out as an act of mercy by the father of a severely disabled child, did not constitute cruel and unusual punishment.[64]

6. Equality Rights

Section 15 of the *Charter* provides that "[e]very individual is equal before and under the law" and prohibits discrimination, including discrimination "based on race, national or ethnic origin, colour, religion, sex, age or mental or physical disability". It has been suggested that mental health

---

[59] In *R. v. Wigglesworth*, [1987] 2 S.C.R. 541, [1988] 1 W.W.R. 193, 61 Sask. R. 105, 60 C.R. (3d) 193, 81 N.R. 161, 28 Admin. L.R. 294, 24 O.A.C. 321, 45 D.L.R. (4th) 235, 32 C.R.R. 219, 37 C.C.C. (3d) 385 (*sub nom. Wigglesworth v. R.*).

[60] The *Charter*, ss. 13 and 14.

[61] See *Sexual Sterilization Act*, S.A. 1928, c. 37 (later R.S.A. 1970, c. 341; repealed R.S.A. 1972, c. 87).

[62] See H. Savage and C. McKague, *Mental Health Law in Canada* (Toronto: Butterworths, 1987), pp. 127-8.

[63] A. Morel, "Certain Guarantees of Criminal Procedure," in Beaudoin and Ratushny, eds., *The Canadian Charter of Rights and Freedoms*, 2nd ed. (Toronto: Carswell, 1989), p. 550.

[64] *R. v. Latimer*, [1995] 8 W.W.R. 609 (Sask. C.A.); revd on appeal on other grounds (1997), 142 D.L.R. (4th) 577 (S.C.C.).

legislation discriminates against psychiatric and non-psychiatric patients and between informal and involuntary patients.[65] The Alberta government has established the office of Patient Advocate. However, the Alberta Patient Advocate is empowered only to investigate complaints from or relating to formal patients and not informal patients. One may question what rational basis there is for distinguishing between the two. Arguably, an informal patient who is threatened with involuntary confinement for refusing to take prescribed medication is equally, if not more, entitled to advocacy assistance than a formal patient who is being compelled to take medication. Mandatory retirement rules have been pronounced non-discriminatory under the *Charter* where they do not establish an arbitrary and unfair system of retirement for physicians whose medical skills may be declining.[66]

It has been argued that every citizen in a province must have, within a reasonable distance from his or her residence, equal availability of medical services. In *Ponteix (Town) v. Saskatchewan*,[67] an application was brought for an interlocutory injunction to prevent what was perceived as reduced emergency nursing services at a local hospital. The court found that changes had arisen as a result of the government's conclusion, in 1993, that significant alterations were necessary in the delivery of health services in Saskatchewan. The court rejected the applicants' position that all people in Saskatchewan are entitled to the same standard of medical care regardless of where they choose to reside.

> This, of course, is a physical and economic impossibility for any government. It is surely incongruous in the extreme to expect that people who choose to reside, for example, on the north shore of Lake Athabaska, should be entitled to the same standard of health care on that north shore as is readily available to the people who live in Regina or Saskatoon. I cannot hold that the *Charter* requires the government to do that which is physically or economically impossible and patently unreasonable.[68]

In *Fernandes v. Manitoba (Director of Social Services Winnipeg Central)*,[69] the Court of Appeal was asked to rule whether a refusal to fund a hospital patient's request for a personal attendant infringed s. 15 of the *Charter*. The patient suffered from a muscular disease that caused progressive respiratory failure. He was mobile in an electric wheelchair, and with appropriate care, which involved an attendant for 16 hours per day,

---

[65] *Ibid.*

[66] *Staffman v. Vancouver General Hospital, supra,* note 31.

[67] [1995] 1 W.W.R. 400, (1994) 124 Sask. R. 165 (Sask. Q.B.).

[68] *Ibid.*, at p. 179 Sask. R.

[69] (1992), 78 Man. R. (2d) 172, 7 Admin. L.R. (2d) 153 (Man. C.A.), leave to appeal to S.C.C. denied, [1993] 2 S.C.R. vii.

would be able to live in his own apartment. The court ruled that the patient was required to demonstrate that he had received unequal treatment before and under the law and that the treatment was discriminatory. The court found that he was not receiving unequal treatment under the law and the fact that he was not being housed in a community-based residence, as opposed to a hospital, was not discriminatory.

> Fernandes remains as an in-patient for many reasons. He has a physical handicap which requires an attendant on hand sixteen hours per day. He has no independent means to cover the costs of that attendant. He lost his primary caregiver in the fall of 1990 and has no family member or other person who can perform that function on his behalf. There are no other facilities with vacancies that can accommodate his needs. The hospital is available at no additional costs to the program under the Act. It was not his illness that led to his social admission to hospital. It was the loss of his caregiver coupled with the limited resources available in the community to provide the care he requires. The director's decision denying the request for an additional allowance did not amount to discrimination under the *Charter*.[70]

In *Ontario Nursing Home Assn. v. Ontario*,[71] a judge accepted that a difference in government funding between nursing homes and homes for the aged was "illogical and unfair", but nonetheless concluded that a patient receiving care at a lesser level of funding was not denied any equality right under the *Charter*. He held that any discrimination was based upon the type of residence occupied by the nursing home patient and that this was not one of the enumerated grounds (*i.e.*, race, national or ethnic origin, colour, religion, sex, age, or mental or physical disability") in section 15 (1). In effect, the "place of residence is not a personal characteristic".

7. Minority Rights

The *Charter* also contains revisions which entrench certain linguistic and cultural rights in the Constitution. French and English are given constitutional status at certain levels of government, in the courts, in the receipt of government services and in language education. Section 25 of the *Charter* preserves existing aboriginal rights and freedoms. Section 27 provides that the *Charter* is to be "interpreted in a manner consistent with the preservation and enhancement of the multicultural heritage of Canadians".

---

[70] *Ibid.*, at 167.
[71] (1990), 74 O.R. (2d) 365, 72 D.L.R. (4th) 166 (H.C.J.).

8. Override Power

The *Charter* is a legal mechanism designed to prevent the enactment or operation of statutes that contradict basic human rights. However, s. 33 permits Parliament or the legislatures to enact legislation that would otherwise violate s. 2 or ss. 15 to 17 of the *Charter*. In one sense, s. 33 provides an escape hatch by which government can override the *Charter* in circumstances where it considers it to be expedient to do so. On the other hand, the very fact that such legislation would violate fundamental freedoms and legal rights ought to ensure that its use is very restrictive.

It has been suggested that the formal requirements of s. 33, which require an express declaration of the specific provision of the *Charter* which the legislation wishes to override, are designed to ensure that the decision to employ s. 33 is carried out with full knowledge of the facts and to encourage public discussion of the issues raised by the use of it.[72] Outside of Quebec, the power has been used on only one occasion.[73] In Quebec, the Parti Québecois enacted a statute in 1982 which purported to override the relevant provisions of the *Charter* in respect of all provincial legislation. The constitutionality of this statute itself was contested and ruled invalid by the Quebec Court of Appeal.[74] However, s. 33 provides that any declaration which overrides the *Charter* ceases to have effect five years after it comes into force, although it may be re-enacted. In Quebec, there was no re-enactment in 1987 and the general override legislation, even if constitutional, expired. The Liberal government in Quebec has enacted specific legislation on three occasions which overrides the application of s. 15 of the *Charter*.[75]

PROVINCIAL HUMAN RIGHTS LEGISLATION

As noted above, the *Charter* applies to both federal and provincial levels of government but not to acts of private individuals or entities, unless they have become agents of the government. Although the *Charter* is often not applicable in a health-care setting, all jurisdictions in Canada

---

[72] R. Tasse, "Application of the Canadian Charter of Rights and Freedoms," Beaudoin and Ratushny, *supra*, note 33, p. 105.

[73] *The SGEU Dispute Settlement Act*, S.S. 1984-85-86, c. 111.

[74] *Alliance des professeurs de Montréal v. Quebec (A.G.)* (1985), 21 D.L.R. (4th) 354, 18 C.R.R. 195, [1985] R.D.J. 376, 21 C.C.C. (3d) 273 (Que. C.A.); leave to appeal to S.C.C. granted (1985), 1 C.R.R. 195n (Settled out of court, January 16, 1990.)

[75] *An Act to amend the Act to promote the development of agricultural operations*, S.Q. 1986, c. 54, s. 16; *Act to again amend the Education Act and the Act respecting the Conseil Supérieur de l'Éducation and to amend the Act respecting the Ministère de l'Éducation*, S.Q. 1986, c. 101, ss. 10, 11 and 12; *An Act to amend various legislation respecting the Pension Plans of the Public and Parapublic Sectors*, S.Q. 1987, c. 47, s. 157.

have enacted some form of legislation that prohibits discrimination based on race, colour, religion, creed, marital status, physical or mental disability, sex, or national origin, ethnic origin or place of origin. Individuals are also expressly protected from discrimination based on sexual orientation in most jurisdictions. It has been added to the list of protected grounds by court decisions in instances where legislatures have declined to make a formal addition.[76]

For example, the Ontario *Human Rights Code*[77] accords individuals a right to equal treatment with respect to services, accommodation, contracts and in other areas.[78] Provision of health-care services would thus be governed by the *Code*. Individuals are accorded equal treatment "without discrimination because of race, ancestry, place of origin, colour, ethnic origin, citizenship, creed, sex, sexual orientation, age, marital status, family status or handicap".[79] Note that even where the *Code* and not the *Charter* applies, the principles courts have used to apply the *Charter* are also useful to determine whether human rights violations under the *Code* have occurred.

---

[76] See, for instance, *Vriend v. Alberta*, (1998) 156 D.L.R. (4th) 385.

[77] R.S.O. 1990, c. H.19.

[78] For example, a physician who owned the building in which his practice was based was ordered by the Ontario Human Rights Commission to provide wheelchair access by a ramp to the first floor, to make necessary renovations in the interior of the building to accommodate wheelchairs and to pay $500 in damages. This principle could be extended to hospitals to properly accommodate physically challenged people. J. Sack and V. Payne, "The Duty to Accommodate Disabled Patients" (1995), Vol. 62, No. 6, Ont. Med. Rev. 52.

[79] *Ibid.* In *Korn v. Potter* (1996), 134 D.L.R. (4th) 437 (B.C.S.C.). A decision of the British Columbia Council of Human Rights finding a physician guilty of discrimination for refusing to offer artificial insemination to a lesbian couple was upheld by the British Columbia Supreme Court. He was ordered to pay damages to the couple and to stop discriminating against lesbians in offering his services.

CHAPTER 13

Current Legal Issues in Canadian Health Care

SYNOPSIS

This chapter examines a number of topical issues that arise in modern health care settings. Termination of treatment, right to die, HIV/AIDS, abortion, and the Canadian blood supply are known to most of us. The emerging areas of telemedicine and telehealth may also change the scope of nursing practice. An overview of these topics highlights their relevance to nurses wanting to be informed about the latest trends in health care.

TERMINATION OF TREATMENT AND THE RIGHT TO DIE

Death is a common event in hospitals and other health facilities. The best efforts of health-care providers will not always succeed. In most cases, death comes naturally and results in the termination of the patient's treatment. Death is pronounced by a physician, a death certificate is issued and arrangements are made for the disposition of the body.

In some instances, however, the occurrence of death and the termination of treatment is not so straightforward. Health professionals may be asked to terminate treatment while the patient is still alive.[1] This may accelerate, or even cause, the patient's death. When the patient is unconscious, caregivers may be met with advance directives, signed by the patient or communicated by family members, that place limitations on treatment and compromise effective care.

When patients are in pain and death is inevitable, requests may be made for proactive steps to be taken that will accelerate or cause death.

---

[1]   In an American survey of 852 nurses working in critical care units, 141 reported that they had received requests from patients or family members to perform euthanasia or to assist in suicide. 129 reported that they had engaged in such activity and an addition 35 reported that they had hastened death by pretending to provide life-sustaining treatment ordered by a physician. A. Asch, "The Role of Critical Care Nurses in Euthanasia and Assisted Suicide" (1996), vol. 334, No. 21, New England J. of Med. 1374.

This type of activity may be more typical than society generally recognizes; many physicians privately admit to helping patients with incurable diseases to accelerate death or to commit suicide by medical means.[2] The legal and medical issues are fraught with controversy, so much so that the concept of euthanasia has been called "the abortion debate of the next century".[3]

In recent years there has been a small flood of Canadian legislation and judicial pronouncements affecting this area of the law. Although there is still significant confusion, these developments provide some guidance to health practitioners. And though it may not be possible (or even advisable) for health facilities to institute formal policies or protocols for assisted death, some understanding of the legal principles involved will permit nurses and other health professionals to understand the implications of their decisions.

1. Criminal Code

In an environment where do-not-resuscitate (DNR) orders and the withdrawal of life support systems are almost routine, the considerations of criminal liability seem counter-intuitive. Yet, recent court decisions in this area have focused on provisions of the *Criminal Code* as the basic instrument of legal analysis. Where a patient sought an injunction to prevent the further administration of treatment without her consent and to compel the removal of a ventilator, the court considered whether the request would constitute a criminal act by those carrying out her request.[4] In another case, the court was asked to consider whether a woman suffering from amyotrophic lateral sclerosis had a right to assistance in bringing about her own death.[5]

The *Criminal Code* provides that "a person commits culpable homicide when he [or she] causes the death of a human being by means of an unlawful act."[6] It is also a crime to cause the death of another person by "criminal negligence".[7] Criminal negligence is defined as doing or omitting to do anything in "wanton or reckless disregard for the lives or safety of other persons".[8]

---

[2] L. K. Altman, "More Physicians Broach Forbidden Subject of Euthanasia", *New York Times*, March 12, 1991, as cited in "Physician-Assisted Suicide and the Right to Die with Assistance" (1992), 105 Harv. L. Rev. 2021.

[3] A. Solomon, "A Death of One's Own", *New Yorker*, May 22, 1995, p. 67.

[4] *Nancy B. v. Hôtel-Dieu de Québec* (1992), 86 D.L.R. (4th) 385 (Que. S.C.).

[5] *Rodriguez v. British Columbia (Attorney General)*, [1993] 3 S.C.R. 519, 82 B.C.L.R. (2d) 273, 103 D.L.R. (4th) 242, [1993] 7 W.W.R. 641, 85 C.C.C. (3d) 15.

[6] R.S.C. 1985, c. C-46, s. 222(5)(a).

[7] *Ibid.*, s. 222(5)(b).

[8] *Ibid.*, s. 219.

It is generally recognized that the duty of health care professionals is to preserve and protect the lives of their patients. *The International Code of Ethics* advises doctors to:

> [B]ear in mind the importance of preserving human life from the time of conception until death.[9]

Guidelines for ethical behaviour published by the College of Nurses of Ontario provide:

> Sanctity of life ... means that human life is precious, needs to be respected, protected, and treated with consideration .... Sanctity of life also includes considerations of the quality of life. It is difficult sometimes to identify what is human life and what society wants, values, and protects in relation to human life. It is even more difficult for health professionals, including nurses, to identify their own beliefs in relation to human life.[10]

Health professionals have made every reasonable effort to preserve human life. Technology now allows life to be preserved indefinitely. Many health professionals and clients believe that some treatments that preserve life at all costs are unacceptable when the quality of life is questionable.

Activities of health professionals, which result in the death of patients by commission or omission, may constitute offences under the *Criminal Code*. Where an order is made not to resuscitate a patient in the event of further organ failure, does the order allow a death to occur that would not occur otherwise? When a dose of medication is given to a terminally ill patient in order to relieve pain and it is known that the administration of such medication is also likely to cause or accelerate the patient's death, does such comfort care constitute an offence?

One may argue that where such treatment is condoned, or indeed requested, by the patient or the patient's legal guardian, the treatment is carried out with the consent of the patient, and is, therefore, acceptable. However, the *Criminal Code* also provides that anyone who "counsels [or procures] a person to commit suicide, or who "aids or abets a person to commit suicide", is guilty of an offence.[11] Moreover, the *Criminal Code* states that "no person is entitled to consent to have death inflicted on him [or her]."

The term "suicide" is not defined in the *Code* but, generally speaking, it means the willing cessation of one's own life. Consequently, even if a

---

[9] International Code of Ethics of the World Medical Association, cited in D. A. Frenkel, "Human Experimentation: Codes of Ethics" (1977), 1 L. Med. Q. *Quarterly* 7, at p. 13.

[10] College of Nurse of Ontario, *Guidelines for Professional Behaviour* (Toronto: College of Nurses, 1995), p. 10.

[11] R.S.C. 1985, c. C-46, s. 241 [am. 1985, c. 27 (1st Supp.), s. 7].

patient executes a written consent specifically authorizing treatment, or the withholding of treatment, and is likely to result in death, does this relieve the health care professional of criminal liability?

One may argue that where death is imminent and measures are taken to alleviate pain, which, as a side effect accelerate death, such measures are consistent with humane health care and offer dignity to the patient. However, the *Criminal Code* provides:

> [W]here a person causes to a human being a bodily injury that results in death, he [or she] causes the death of that human being notwithstanding that the effect of the bodily injury is only to accelerate his [or her] death from a disease or disorder arising from some other cause.[12]

Does treatment that alleviates pain, but impairs physiological functions and hastens death, constitute criminal conduct?

If an accused is able to demonstrate that his or her conduct did not cause the death of the patient, this may constitute a defence. In *R. v. Adams*[13] a physician was accused of murdering a patient who had died of an overdose of morphine. He argued that his intention was to relieve the patient's pain and that the cause of death was the patient's illness and not the morphine. The trial judge instructed the jury that while the motive of relieving pain was not in itself a defence to the charge of murder, an acquittal should be registered if the jury found that the physician's conduct had not caused the death, and further, that a marginal shortening of life by administration of the medication could not be described meaningfully as having caused the death.

It has been suggested that the defence of "necessity" may be available in certain situations.[14] It might be argued that the employment of prolonged resuscitative measures to restore a patient momentarily may constitute treatment which is cruel and ultimately useless.[15] Health care personnel may feel justified in withholding further treatment. However, there is, at present, no legal precedent or statute to justify or support such conduct.

In fact, recent case law suggests that a defence of necessity is unlikely to be available in such circumstances. In *R. v. Latimer*,[16] the father of a 12-year-old girl suffering from severe cerebral palsy took his daughter's life

---

[12] *Ibid.*, s. 226.
[13] Unreported decision referred to in P. MacKinnon "Euthanasia and Homicide" (1984), 26 *Criminal Law Quarterly* 483, at p. 502.
[14] *Ibid.*, at p. 504.
[15] See "Charter of Rights and Freedoms", above.
[16] [1995] 8 W.W.R. 609 (Sask. C.A.); revd. on other grounds (1997), 142 D.L.R. (4th) 577 (S.C.C.). A second trial resulted in a conviction: (1997), 121 C.C.C. (3d) 326, 12 C.R. (5th) 112 (Sask. Q.B.); appeal dismissed and sentence vard. (unreported), Nov. 23, 1998, Regina C.A. 7413 and 7416, Cameron, Vancise and Wakeling JJ.A. (C.A.).

by administering carbon monoxide. He and the rest of the family had actively cared for her at home throughout her life, but the father decided that, because of her suffering, the quality of his daughter's life had diminished to the point that it was no longer worth enduring. He was charged and convicted of second degree murder, and the conviction was upheld by the Saskatchewan Court of Appeal.

In ruling out a defence of necessity, the court held that the defence of necessity is available only in circumstances where the accused's illegal action or conduct is taken "in urgent situations of clear and imminent peril when compliance with the law is demonstrably impossible". It stated:

> This is not a case of withholding potentially life-prolonging treatment to a seriously disabled person. It deals with the deliberate decision to terminate another's life rather than continue with the scheduled medical treatment and care. In such circumstances it is no defence for a parent to say because of a severe handicap, a child's life has such diminished value that the child should not live any longer. It does not advance the interest of the state or society to treat such a person as a person of lesser status or dignity than others.[17]

Latimer is distinguishable, perhaps, from the health care context in that the death occurred outside of any health facility, death was not imminent, the cause of death was poisonous gas, which had no other purpose than to terminate the daughter's life (as opposed to medication which may relieve suffering, and, at the same time, cause death) and the person causing the death was a family member and not a health practitioner acting in a professional capacity. Nonetheless, it is doubtful that there are many "urgent situations of clear and imminent peril" that would authorize a physician or nurse to act in contravention of the *Criminal Code*. A court may not accept that there is a substantive difference between administering a noxious substance that causes death and administering a narcotic, which in a high dosage, causes death. Heath practitioners who administer medication or any other form of treatment for the purpose of accelerating or causing the death of a patient may be crossing the line and engaging in criminal conduct.

In several recent cases, health practitioners have pleaded guilty to a charge under the *Criminal Code* of administering a noxious substance (the Crown having withdrawn, at the same time, a charge in relation to murder). In *R. v. Mataya*,[18] a nurse was charged with first degree murder and, ultimately, convicted of administering a noxious substance when, during the withdrawal of life support as requested by a patient's family, he ad-

---

[17] *Ibid.*, at 642.
[18] Unreported, August 24, 1992, Weir J. (Ont. Gen. Div.).

ministered a lethal dose of potassium chloride to the patient when complications developed. In that case, no prison term was imposed by the court, though a conviction was registered and sentence suspended. Subsequently, the nurse's registration with the Ontario College of Nurses was revoked on the ground that his conduct would reasonably be regarded as disgraceful, dishonourable or unprofessional.[19]

In *R. v. De La Rocha*,[20] a physician was charged with second-degree murder and administering a noxious substance. He pleaded guilty to the second count and the murder count was withdrawn. In that case, a patient who had tumours on her tongue and in her bronchial area had asked to be extubated. Subsequently, large doses of morphine were administered. At a point when the patient had stopped breathing and the heart rate had dropped to the low 50s, the physician asked a nurse to obtain potassium chloride for him. She refused. The doctor proceeded to obtain the potassium chloride and administered it himself. Once the potassium chloride was administered, the patient's death followed rapidly with an episode of ventricular fibrillation. In the circumstances, the conduct of the doctor was accepted by the court, as well as by the family members of the patient, as being an act of compassion for the patient. The judge, in imposing sentence, reasoned that the heavy doses of morphine were not lethal, or intended to be lethal, to the patient. The judge concluded that the potassium chloride "was administered to a patient who had already stopped breathing". A conviction was entered, but sentence was suspended and the physician was put on probation for three years.

In most instances, however, the decision to cease or withhold treatment is made without the assistance of a court. One of the most difficult areas is in the care and treatment of newborn infants. Newborns that would have died several decades ago are now saved as a result of modern neonatal treatment. However, this sophisticated care poses difficult questions for parents and health care practitioners. As one writer comments,

> [n]eonatal intensive care also generates grossly deformed survivors, many of whom require permanent institutional care. Some survivors never achieve a cognitive existence. Others are monsters. Many doctors think that because of this not all seriously ill children should be treated actively. All of the neonatal intensive care units practice selective treatment and management of seriously ill children. In many cases, beyond feeding and keeping the child warm, care is simply

---

[19]　Discipline decision reported at (1993), 18:2 *College Communique* 26.
[20]　Unreported, April 2, 1993, Loukidelis J. (Ont. Gen. Div.).

withheld. The child is allowed to die. This practice of selective treatment raises intractable problems of ethics and of law.[21]

Moreover, the decision to withhold treatment from newborn infants is most often taken without any legal authority. The decision may be the result of a variety of pressures within the hospital.

Interaction between doctors and parents is the main locus for making decisions ... However, other hospital personnel participate actively, particularly nurses and residents. It is not uncommon for differences of views to erupt, especially in the case of nurses. Nurses are responsible for day to day care of the children. The pediatrician and parents may see the children infrequently, or not at all . . . In one case, pressure from nursing staff forced a doctor to operate after active treatment had been withheld for six weeks ... [In another] case a nurse who disagreed with the medical/parental decision informed the Children's Aid Society.[22]

While the best interests of the infant would appear to be the focus of any decision, it is difficult to ignore other factors which may affect a decision to treat or not to treat. Treatment of badly damaged neonates is very costly and reduces the availability of health care resources for other patients. Treatment may be withheld for economic reasons outside the health care economy. It has been suggested that where an infant is born to a young, single, unwed mother, physicians are more likely to withhold treatment.[23]

The perceived ability of the parents to care for a defective child, the presence or absence of siblings, the likelihood or unlikelihood of the parents' being able to produce another child, the parents' own personal preference as to whether or not they wish the child to survive, become factors which affect the ultimate decision.

Nurses may be asked to make, and possibly record, observations which may be instrumental in deciding whether or not an infant will live or die. Nurses are a prime source of information. A neonatal nurse, in describing her role, said that she is expected to develop information as to:

[h]ow the parents seem when they come; what kind of questions they ask; do they touch the baby; do they look at the baby; do they feel comfortable with the baby; will they hold it; will they not hold it ... It is not infrequent that neonatal nurses will be sent to the birth facility to speak with the parents ...[24]

---

[21] J. E. Magnet, "Withholding Treatment From Defective Newborns: A Description of Canadian Practices" (1980), 4 L. Med. Q. 271 at p. 272.

[22] *Ibid.*, at p. 274-5.

[23] *Ibid.*, at p. 279.

[24] *Ibid.*, at p. 280.

Responsibility for the actual administration of medication may lie with nursing staff.

Administration of increasing dosages of pain killers creates problems in the unit. Doctors are responsible for ordering the medication. Nurses are responsible for administering it. Because the doctor may have little contact with the baby in question, the consequences of the doctor's orders do not impact on his conscience with the same immediacy as occurs with the nurses. The doctor will not suffer from the same sense of anxiety or guilt. However, the orders may require nurses to administer painkillers to a child on a regular schedule, even if the child shows no sign of pain, or is sleeping. It will be crystal clear to the nurse that the medication given to the child is unwarranted.[25]

2. Withdrawal of Treatment Based Upon Patient Consent

The countervailing legal analysis to the *Criminal Code* is the law pertaining to informed consent. In *Nancy B. v. Hôtel Dieu de Québec*[26] and *R. Latimer*[27] a significant consideration in the court's ultimate disposition was the presence or absence of consent. Where the *withdrawal* of treatment is in compliance with the express wish or directive of the patient, the likelihood of criminal or legal liability is reduced significantly.

Canadian law not only authorizes but demands the withdrawal of treatment where its continuation is inconsistent with the expressed wish of a competent patient. In *Malette v. Shulman*,[28] a patient was awarded damages against a physician, where the physician had administered treatment contrary to the patient's expressed wish. The patient was a Jehovah's Witness who had been seriously injured in a car accident. When brought to the Emergency Department of the hospital, she was unconscious, but her personal effects contained a card stating that she did not wish to receive any blood transfusion (as it would be contrary to her religious beliefs). Believing that in the absence of a blood transfusion the patient was likely to die, the physician ignored the patient's wish and transfused blood. Although sympathetic to the physician and the altruistic principles that may have motivated his conduct, the Ontario Court of Appeal nonetheless upheld a trial judgment in which the physician was found to have committed a battery. The decision supports the principle that no treatment can be administered to any patient who refuses it, even if the decision is "foolhardy". Although the court of Appeal relied upon

---

[25] *Ibid.*, at p. 284.
[26] *Nancy B. v. Hôtel-Dieu de Québec* (1992), 86 D.L.R. (4th) 385 (Que. S.C.).
[27] *Supra*, note 16.
[28] (1990), 72 O.R.(2d) 417 (C.A.).

the rationale of individual religious freedom in supporting the patient's right to refuse treatment, the language in the decision means that there are few, if any, situations in which a health practitioner would be justified in administering treatment to a competent patient who is refusing it.[29]

In *Nancy B.*,[30] the Quebec Superior Court recognized the patient's right to refuse treatment even if the refusal is certain to result in death. Nancy was a 25-year-old woman suffering from an incurable neurological disorder who sought an injunction to have the use of a ventilator discontinued. Removal of the ventilator was likely to result in immediate death, but its removal was justified by the patient on the ground that her quality of life had so deteriorated that it was not worth living. Health personnel and the hospital did not directly oppose the patient's wish, but they were concerned that conduct compatible with the patient's wish might offend provisions in the *Criminal Code*. The physician who would be responsible for removing the respirator wished to be assured that she would not be engaged in a criminal act.

Issuing an order, which permitted the withdrawal of treatment pursuant to the patient's wish, the court concluded that a physician who "interrupts the respiratory support of a patient, at the patient's informed request, in order to let nature take its course" would not be engaged in criminal activity. The respirator was removed pursuant to the patient's request and she died shortly thereafter. It is questionable whether an order is necessary, or even appropriate, in the circumstances. The health professionals involved were seeking a form of advance ruling that their conduct would not, at some future point in time, be judged criminal. Arguably, recent decisions in this area make it clear that a patient's right to refuse treatment must lead to the withdrawal of treatment. Failure to comply expeditiously with the patient's expressed direction may, according to the *Malette* decision, constitute a battery.[31]

Our courts have drawn the line, however, at conduct that goes beyond the withholding or withdrawal of treatment which permits death to occur by natural causes. Compliance with a patient's express wish to have

---

[29]   See, however, *Procureur Général du Canada v. Hôpital Notre Dame et E.T. Niemiec*, [1984] C.S. 426, in which the Quebec Superior Court authorized a hospital to force-feed, if necessary, and to treat surgically a *competent* adult detained pending deportation. The patient had swallowed a piece of wire and was refusing medical treatment on the rationale that he preferred death to a return to his own country. Whether *Niemiec* remains good law is questionable in the face of the subsequent decision in *Nancy B.* and its subsequent citation, with approval, by the Supreme Court of Canada in *Rodriguez*.

[30]   *Supra*, note 26.

[31]   See also *Manoir de la Pointe Bleue (1978) Inc. v. Corbeil*, [1989] R.J.Q. 759, in which a Quebec Superior Court judge granted a declaration that a long-term care institution was not required to administer treatment nor to transfer a patient elsewhere without consent when the patient had executed a legal directive requesting that he be allowed to die by starvation.

treatment that will cause or accelerate death — even where continuation of the patient's life may seem cruel or useless — contravenes the *Criminal Code*.

In *Rodriguez*,[32] a 42-year-old woman suffering from amyotrophic lateral sclerosis sought to have the section of the *Criminal Code* prohibiting assisted suicide declared invalid under the *Charter of Rights and Freedoms*. Whereas there is no criminal prohibition against an individual taking his or her own life, Sue Rodriguez was concerned that her disease would leave her in such a disabled condition that she would not be able to terminate her own life without the assistance of others. Although a majority of the Supreme Court of Canada held that Rodriguez's rights to liberty and security of the person were violated by the provision of the *Criminal Code*, it nonetheless held that this violation was consistent with principles of fundamental justice in a democratic society, and was, therefore, justified. In examining the history of the common law in this area, as well as the law in other international jurisdictions, Sopinka J., speaking for the majority, held that the prohibition against assisted suicide was not "arbitrary or unfair". He held that there is a legal consensus that "human life must be respected and that we must be careful not to undermine the institutions that protect it". He found that the prohibition against assisted suicide served the purpose of discouraging those who consider that life is unbearable at a particular moment, or who perceive themselves to be a burden upon others, from committing suicide. To permit a physician to lawfully participate in taking life would send a signal that there are circumstances in which the state approves of suicide.[33]

The Supreme Court also referred to the difficulty of distinguishing between active and passive forms of treatment and whether the withdrawal of life support measures, knowing that death would result, is any different than taking steps in which death results directly from human intervention.

The administration of drugs designed for pain control in dosages that the physician knows will hasten death constitutes active contribution to death by any standard. However, the distinction drawn here is one based upon intention — in the case of palliative care the intention is to ease pain, which has the effect of hastening death, while in the case of assisted suicide, the intention is undeniably to cause death. The Law Reform Commission, although it recommended the continued criminal prohibition of both euthanasia and assisted suicide, stated, that a doctor should never refuse palliative care to a terminally ill patient only because it may

---

[32]   *Rodriguez v. British Columbia (Attorney General)*, [1993] 3 S.C.R. 519.
[33]   *Ibid.*, p. 608.

hasten death.[34] In the author's view, distinctions based upon intent are important, and in fact form the basis of our criminal law. While factually the distinction may be difficult to draw at times, legally it is clear. The fact that in some cases, the third party will, under the guise of palliative care, commit euthanasia or assist in suicide and go unsanctioned due to the difficulty of proof cannot be said to render the existence of the prohibition fundamentally unjust.[35]

In short, where a health practitioner engages in conduct that is intended to cause the death of a patient, such conduct, if this intention can be proved, will be judged criminal. On the other hand, where the intention is to administer treatment to relieve pain or in some other way assist the patient in coping with the disease, the conduct is not criminal.

3. Incompetent Patients

The legal analysis of informed consent is not available if the patient is not competent to give consent, unless the patient has, by means of an advanced directive or the appointment of a substitute decision maker, created a mechanism which allows a caregiver to obtain consent for the withdrawal of treatment. In *Malette*,[36] the patient was unconscious, but had completed a card that clearly directed that no blood transfusion be given. The current legal practice in Canada, which is supported by legislation in a number of provinces, allows patients to create advance directives that will be legally effective in circumstances in which the patient is not competent to communicate directly with caregivers. Similarly, Canadian law permits the patient to appoint a substitute decision maker who can make decisions about the patient's care and treatment consistent with what he or she considers to be the wishes of the patient.

In many cases, an advance directive will not be available, nor will there be a substitute decision maker to make decisions about the patient's treatment. The fact that family members or close friends may express views as to modes of treatment and whether treatment should continue may have some persuasive value to a caregiver, but that does not constitute a legal consent. The wishes of family and friends, in the absence of a formal appointment of a substitute decision maker or an attorney for personal care, do not constitute legal authority that is binding upon the physician or other health professional.[37] Moreover, where a physician is

---

[34] Law Reform Commission of Canada, "Biomedical Experimentation Involving Human Subjects," Working Paper 61 (Canada, 1989), p. 70.

[35] *Ibid.*, at p. 607.

[36] *Supra*, note 28.

[37] However, such legislation as the Ontario *Health Care Consent Act, 1996*, S.O. 1996, c. 2, Sch. A, authorizes the appointment of family members as substitute decision makers

concerned that a substitute decision maker or personal attorney is offering instructions for treatment that are inconsistent with the patient's best interests, this may be a basis upon which to question or challenge those instructions. However, care must be taken that a rejection of a patient's directive (or those of a substitute decision maker) is not made for irrelevant or otherwise prejudiced reasons.[38]

Generally, when a patient is not competent to direct his or her own treatment, and when there is no advance directive or authorized representative to direct treatment, it will be necessary to seek the approval of a court or appropriate administrative tribunal before withholding or withdrawing treatment that will result in the death of a patient. Although this issue has not come squarely before a court in Canada, it has been dealt with in other jurisdictions.

In *Cruzan v. Director, Missouri Department of Health*,[39] a patient had sustained brain damage that left her in a persistent vegetative state. There was no hope of recovery and she was not expected to live for more than several years. Her parents sought to have nutrition and hydration withdrawn, but the hospital refused to honour the request without a court order. The United States Supreme Court's analysis focused on whether there was clear and convincing evidence, in the absence of an advance directive, of what the incompetent patient's wishes would have been had she been in a position to make her own decisions about treatment. The court upheld state legislation preventing the withdrawal of treatment in the absence of clear and compelling evidence of the patient's wishes. The result is anomalous in that the absence of such evidence seems to dictate that a patient must be kept alive artificially for an indefinite period unless he or she happened to have expressed a wish, in a way that constitutes "clear and compelling evidence", to the opposite effect.

In England, the House of Lords took a somewhat different, and perhaps more practical approach, in a similar case. In *Airedale N.H. Trust v. Bland*,[40] a 21-year-old patient had been in a persistent vegetative state for three and one-half years following an accident. He was being fed artificially and there was no hope of recovery or improvement in his condition. It was proposed that the artificial feeding be discontinued and that any antibiotic treatment not be offered if an infection appeared. The health authority for the patient's care applied to the court for a declara-

provided the incompetent patient does not have a court-appointed guardian or an individual with power of attorney to fill this role. See Chapter 8, "Consent to Treatment".

[38]   Women's decisions, requests, and directives are more frequently rejected by the authorities than men's, according to the research of J. Downie and S. Sherwin, "A Feminist Exploration of Issues Around Assisted Death", 15 St. Louis U. Pub. L. Rev. 303. This raises serious questions about how societal perceptions of gender affect patients' rights "in real life".

[39]   58 U.S.L. Week 4916 (U.S. 1990).

[40]   [1993] 1 All E.R. 821.

tion that it and the responsible physicians could discontinue lawfully all life-sustaining treatment and medical support. This action was supported by the parents and family of the patient. The House of Lords, in granting the request, focused its consideration on the patient's "best interest". Although deferential to what the patient might have wanted had he been able to express his wish, the court concluded, in the absence of an advance directive, that it must consider what was best for the patient. Importantly, the court expressed the opinion that the decision was not one that could be made by the doctors alone, and that in cases of such gravity it was necessary to apply to the court for an order to discontinue treatment (although it was also suggested that as greater experience was gained in the area, the procedural requirements for obtaining court authorization might be relaxed).

See also Chapter 8, "Consent to Treatment".

4. Brain Death and Patients in a Persistent Vegetative State

Cases in which the courts have authorized the withholding or withdrawal of treatment, assume, by definition, that the patient is *alive*. In *Nancy B.*,[41] for example, there was no question that the patient was alive, competent, conscious and in full command of her faculties, despite severe and permanent physical incapacity. In *Airedale*,[42] however, the patient was incompetent and judged to be in a "persistent vegetative state". In those circumstances, a threshold question arises whether the patient is already, for all intents and purposes, dead, so that the withholding or withdrawal of treatment does not accelerate or cause death. The task of pronouncing death is within the domain of the medical profession. There is, however, no simple medical definition. The Canadian Medical Association has employed the term "brain death" as a basis for defining death.[43] Manitoba has expressly recognized brain death as an acceptable criterion for determination of death.[44] In several reported decisions, Canadian judges have considered, in the criminal law context, whether someone is already dead where there has been "brain death" or where some or all of the body's vital functions have ceased to perform.[45] In *R. v. Malcherek*,[46] an English court held that a physician's withdrawal of treat-

---

[41] *Nancy B. v. Hôtel Dieu, supra*, note 30.
[42] *Supra*, note 40.
[43] Canadian Medical Association, "A CMA Position – Guidelines for the Diagnosis of Brain Death" (1987), 136 Can. Med. Assoc. J. 200A-B.
[44] *Vital Statistics Act*, R.S.M. 1987, c. V-60
[45] See *R. v. Kitching and Adams*, [1976] 6 W.W.R. 697, 32 C.C.C. (2d) 159 (Man. C.A.); leave to appeal to S.C.C. refused (1977), 32 C.C.C. (2d) 159*n*, and *R. v. Green* (1988), 43 C.C.C. (3d) 413 (B.C.S.C.).
[46] [1981] 2 All E.R. 422.

ment did not cause the death of a patient who was already brain dead. One Canadian legal commentator has suggested:

> [T]he weight of legal and medical authority leads to no other sensible conclusion than that brain dead patients need not be maintained on life support mechanisms, and that no liability would attach as a result of a physician suspending life support from a patient determined to be brain dead in accordance with currently accepted medical practice.[47]

Professor Gilmour questions, however, whether a *persistent vegetative state* is sufficient for a court to conclude that life has ended. A cautious approach suggests that in the absence of direct legal authority in Canada, an application be made to the court of competent jurisdiction (or to the appropriate statutory tribunal) for a decision on whether a patient in a persistent vegetative state is an appropriate one for the cessation of treatment.

5. The Need for Legislation

The activities of Canadian lawmakers in this area have centered on legislation dealing with consent to treatment, advance directives and substitute decision making. There has not been any significant reform of the criminal law to take into account recent developments in medical technology, the ability of health-care practitioners to extend life through artificial means and health-care practices that may permit, or even accelerate, death. Recently, considerable momentum has developed in support of legislation to modify *Criminal Code* provisions that do not seem to contemplate current attitudes and practices in relation to the withdrawal of treatment and assisted death. In 1995, the Canadian Senate released a report on the subject of euthanasia and assisted suicide.[48] While it recommended that the offences of assisting suicide and non-voluntary and voluntary euthanasia remain in the *Criminal Code*, a majority of the committee recommended that a less severe penalty be attached to cases where there is the essential element of compassion and mercy.

In some jurisdictions,[49] practices (in some cases supported by legislation) have developed in which "end-of-life treatment" by physicians is tolerated and legally permitted.[50] In the Netherlands, although assisted

---

[47] Joan Gilmour, "Withholding and Withdrawing Life Support from Adults at Common Law" (1993), 31 Osgoode Hall L.J. 473, at 503.

[48] *Of Life and Death: Report of the Special Senate Committee on Euthanasia and Assisted Suicide*, published under the authority of the Senate of Canada, May 1995.

[49] See also the attempt at regulating this practice reflected in Measure No. 16, *The Oregon Death With Dignity Act*.

[50] For example, *The Rights of the Terminally Ill Act*, N. Terr. Austl. Laws, proclaimed in force July 1, 1996, was passed in the Northern Territory in Australia legalizing eutha-

suicide remains punishable by up to 12 years in prison, guidelines have been developed and approved by parliament to allow voluntary euthanasia under very specific circumstances.[51] The approved procedure requires a physician to provide a full written report and complete a lengthy questionnaire under the jurisdiction's *Burial Act* for submission to the municipal coroner who forwards it to the local public prosecutor. Where the physican's conduct complies with the substantive and procedural guidelines, a policy of non-prosecution is adopted. Nonetheless, concern has been expressed about whether the practice of euthanasia in the Netherlands is underreported and whether a large portion of euthanasia cases does not result from direct and persistent requests from patients.[52]

End of life treatment remains a controversial and difficult area for health practitioners in Canada. Of most concern is the fact that certain practices, including assisted suicide, are common in Canada despite clear criminal prohibitions and the absence of any legal basis for a court relieving against the consequences of such criminal action.[53] In his submission to the Senate Committee, Dr. Boadway, the Director of Health Policy for the Ontario Medical Association, advised the Committee that the practice of assisted suicide was "constant".[54] The Senate Committee, however, indicated that it was not possible for it to "gather accurate or complete information on the incidents of assisted suicide" and cited the submission of a chaplain from the New Brunswick health-care system who indicated that there was an absence of participation in the public hearings by those who were fearful of investigation and potential punitive action.[55] In

---

nasia in specified circumstances. The validity of this law was challenged in *Wake v. Northern Territory of Australia*, no. 112 of 1996, July 24, 1996 (S.C.N. Terr. Austl.). The appellants argued that the legislative assembly did not have the power to make a law of this nature. The majority decided that the legislature did have this power as it had the constitutional power to make laws for the "peace, order and good government of the Territory".

51 See *supra*, note 47 at A-127.

52 See H. Rigter et al., "Euthanasia in the Netherlands" (1989), 140 Can. Med. Assoc. J 788. The Royal Dutch Medical Association has shifted its policy on euthanasia, indicating that it would be better if candidates ended their own lives rather than have physicians do it for them. This is tacit recognition that many physicians struggle with euthanasia as they feel their primary responsibility is to heal patients. An official with the Medical Association indicated that the new policy is meant to alleviate the emotional stress that doctors experience when performing euthanasia. "Dutch Doctors Revise Policy on Mercy Killing," *The [Toronto] Globe and Mail*, August 26, 1995, p. A2.

53 See *R. v. Morrison* [1998] N.S.J. No. 75 (N.S. Prov. Ct.); affd. [1998] N.S.J. No. 441 (N.S.S.C.). In that case, a doctor was charged with second-degree murder in the death of a terminally ill cancer patient. Dr. Morrison was alleged to have administered potassium chloride to hasten the death of a patient who had been removed from a respirator. The appeal court held that the Preliminary Inquiry Judge was correct in discharging Dr. Morrison due to a lack of evidence to commit her to stand trial.

54 *Supra*, note 47 at p. 54.

55 *Ibid*.

effect, there appear to be health professionals who are engaged in what the legal system considers criminal conduct.

EXPERIMENTAL CARE AND TREATMENT

Innovation occurs through trial and error. Many health-care procedures are, in reality, experiments that have been demonstrated to work by repeated performance. Open heart surgery, although fraught with risk in its early development, has become almost routine with increased technology and expertise. Many treatments available to patients would not be available if they had not first attempted in a more high-risk setting to test the result. Even the most common medical procedures are experimental: a trial of labour is little more than a controlled experiment to determine if a woman can deliver naturally or will be compelled to undergo a caesarean section.

Many patients have benefited from modern, innovative medical techniques. However, the benefits obtained also raise questions about how innovative practices become routine and to what extent it is ethical to put patients at risk in order to achieve a benefit which may only accrue to other patients once experimental techniques have been perfected. There is an unavoidable tension between pioneering new techniques and the right of patients not to be used as subjects for scientific experiments. The obligation of a physician to obtain informed consent places a high value on the patient's right to refuse treatment that may have risks that the patient is not prepared to accept.

In a well-known Canadian medical experiment which resulted in civil litigation,[56] a doctor involved a student in an experiment which involved the introduction of a catheter under general anaesthetic. The doctor failed to disclose to the student, who was paid $50 to participate in the experiment, that the catheter would reach as far as his heart. The student suffered a heart attack during the experiment and sued. Liability was found on the ground that a proper consent to an experimental procedure had not been obtained from the patient.

In *Cryderman v. Ringrose*,[57] a physician performed a tubal sterilization in his office by the introduction of silver nitrate into the fallopian tubes. The physician had learned about the technique from a medical article which was termed a preliminary report. The physician's sterilization of the patient using the technique was unsuccessful. The overwhelming

---

[56] *Halushka v. University of Saskatchewan* (1965), 52 W.W.R. 608, 53 D.L.R. (3d) 436 (Sask. C.A.).

[57] [1977] 3 W.W.R. 109, 6 A.R. 21, 89 D.L.R. (3d) 32; affd. [1978] 3 W.W.R. 481, 89 D.L.R. (3d) 32 (C.A.).

weight of expert evidence at trial indicated that the technique employed by the physician was experimental. The court found that the physician did not properly inform the patient about the procedure and the fact that it was of an experimental nature.

In *Coughlin v. Kuntz*,[58] an orthopaedic surgeon carried out an anterior cervical disectomy which required the insertion of a plastic spacer in the narrowed disc space in the neck area. The procedure was developed by the physician and was in an experimental stage. The procedure was in conflict with a recommendation of doctors from the Workers' Compensation Board who thought that shoulder surgery, instead of neck surgery, was appropriate. When complications ensued, the patient sued the physician. The court found that the physician failed to disclose to the patient the more conservative treatments that were available and that his use of an experimental surgical procedure unsupported by scientific clinical study constituted negligence.

The Law Reform Commission of Canada has made recommendations for the regulation of human experimental treatment in Canada.[59] The Commission has recommended that non-therapeutic biomedical experimentation should be considered legal where the subject's free and informed consent has been properly obtained and where there is an acceptable ratio between the risks incurred by the subject and the benefits expected to result from the experiment.

Procedures that are purely experimental are unlikely to have any direct benefit for the subject. Consequently, even the smallest risk for the subject in what is a pure experiment may be difficult to justify. Most types of biomedical experimentation will be carried out in circumstances in which the patient stands to benefit if the innovative treatment being administered is successful. For example, patients who face certain death without organ replacement may volunteer to undergo risky surgery. Patients who are threatened with a terminal illness may be prepared to experiment with forms of treatment which have severe side effects, but may offer a chance of survival. In those instances, a greater risk may be justified by an anticipated benefit to the patient. In *Halushka*[60] the experiment conducted by the physician was purely experimental; there was no anticipated benefit to the student. The student was only a means to test the form of catheterization, which once clinically demonstrated, would be used on patients requiring treatment. In *Coughlin*,[61] the patient required treatment of the cervical spine and shoulder, but there were more conser-

---

[58] (1987), 17 B.C.L.R. (2d) 365, 42 C.C.L.T. 142 (S.C.).

[59] Law Reform Commission of Canada, *Biomedical Experimentation Involving Human Subjects*, Working Paper 61 (Canada, 1989).

[60] *Ibid.*, at note 100.

[61] *Ibid.*, at note 109.

vative forms of treatment available. The patient was experiencing pain, but there was no urgency. The selection by the doctor of an experimental form of treatment, with a significant risk of complications, was not justified when balanced against the likely benefit to the patient.

Some forms of scientific experimentation, in order to be clinically sound, involve deception of the subject. One group of subjects may be given the medication being tested and another group may be given a placebo. The experiment will not be valid if patients know which group they are in. Even the individual administering the experiment may not be aware of the purpose of the experiment or into which group the subjects fall. This is to ensure that the results are objective and not distorted, even inadvertently, by the participants. Such deception or non-disclosure may be necessary as a means of achieving research goals. The Law Reform Commission has recommended that in circumstances where participants must be kept in the dark, any deception or non-disclosure ought not to involve the non-disclosure of risk to the patient, the research must be of major scientific value and subjects should be debriefed following the experimentation to inform them why deception was thought to be necessary.

The Law Reform Commission has recommended that non-therapeutic biomedical experimentation be considered legal where the subject's free and informed consent is obtained and the risks incurred are not disproportionate to expected benefits.[62] The term "risk" includes the nature of the risk, the potential gravity of the consequences and the likelihood that the risk will materialize. Even though the risk itself may not be serious in terms of the potential harm to the patient if it occurs (*e.g.*, a skin rash from medication), the risk may nonetheless be disproportionate to the expected benefit of the innovative therapy if it is likely that all subjects will contract a rash. The experimentor must advise the subject, even though the side effect is minimal, that a rash is likely to occur to allow the patient to make a free and informed decision about whether or not he or she wishes to engage in the experiment.

The development of innovative therapies for children is highly problematic. It may not be possible to speak in terms of a free and informed consent when one is speaking of a child. The Law Reform Commission has recommended, however, that experimentation of a therapeutic nature, which offers a reasonable hope of benefiting the child, be considered legal where its ultimate aim is to provide an individual benefit of the child.[63] Therefore, the introduction of a new medication in the treatment of adolescent leukemia, the use of innovative surgical techniques and the resort to organ transplantation may be justified if the risk involved in the procedure is proportionate to the anticipated benefit to the

---

[62]   *Ibid.,* at note 98, p. 61 of Working Paper 61.
[63]   *Ibid.,* p. 62 of Working Paper 61.

child. The Law Reform Commission has recommended that non-therapeutic experimentation should only occur when the research is of major scientific importance, where the research cannot proceed using competent adult subjects, or where the research is in relation to infant conditions and does not involve any serious risks for the child and a substitute consent is obtained from an independent third party.[64]

Non-therapeutic experimentation may be carried out on tissue removed from patients during surgical procedures. Does the patient have any right to give or refuse consent to such activity? It has been suggested that where tissue or fluid has been removed from a patient, consent to its experimental use in the institution possessing it is not required.[65] However, in some circumstances, testing fluid or tissue may produce results which have implications for the patient. If randomized testing of body fluid for the AIDS virus produces a positive result, should the patient from whom the body fluid was removed be informed? Should the local health authority be notified pursuant to provincial legislation requiring disclosure? If testing of tissue for a particular genetic strain reveals that offspring of the patient may be affected, should the patient be informed? Can failure to disclose result in liability should the patient bear a child who is handicapped and whose birth or condition might have been prevented had the patient been aware of the genetic condition?

Canadian researchers have transplanted brain tissue from aborted fetuses to treat patients with Parkinson's disease.[66] The informed consent of the women having the abortions was obtained. The Law Reform Commission deals specifically with experimentation on embryos and fetuses. It recommends that any non-therapeutic biomedical experimentation on embryos and fetuses take place only after the experimentation has received a prior approval of a multi-disciplinary ethics committee, only if the research is carried out in centres or hospitals recognized by public authorities, and only where the consent of both parents of the embryo or fetus has been obtained.[67] The Commission has also recommended that the creation of embryos solely for the purpose of scientific research should be prohibited, that the re-implantation of embryos used for experimental purposes should be prohibited and that certain types of experimentation on embryos (such as cloning, ectogenesis, parthenogenesis and the crossing of human and animal gametes) should be prohibited.[68] The Commission has recommended that experimentation on embryos

---

[64] *Ibid.*, p. 62.
[65] B.M. Dickens, "Information for Consent in Human Experimentation," (1974), 24 U.T.L.J. 381, at p. 405.
[66] "Canadians plan transplants of tissue from aborted fetuses", *The Globe and Mail*, Toronto, July 14, 1988, p. 1.
[67] *Supra*, note 59, p. 62.
[68] *Ibid.*

should be prohibited after Day 14 of embryonic development and that the freezing of embryos should be allowed, but not prolonged for more than five years, and that standards should be developed for the creation, expansion and management of sperm and embryo banks.[69]

Advances in the area of reproductive technology resulted in the federal government appointing a Royal Commission on New Reproductive Technologies.[70] The mandate of the Commission was to examine how new reproductive technologies should be handled in Canada and to identify those technologies that may result in, or arise from, misuse. In 1996 the federal government adopted many recommendations of the Commission in an Act that imposes criminal sanctions for carrying out, offering to carry out or offering compensation to carry out any of the prohibited activities. These include: researching cloning of animal/human hybrids; altering genetic structure of an ovum, sperm, zygote or embryo, if these changes are capable of being transmitted to a subsequent generation; fertilization of eggs from female fetuses for implantation; using any medical procedures to ensure or increase the likelihood of having a child of a particular sex; using any diagnostic procedures to determine the sex of the zygote or embryo, except for reasons relating to its health; maintaining the embryo outside of the human body and fertilizing an ovum outside the human body for research; commercializing birth surrogacy arrangements and selling eggs, sperm, zygotes or fetal tissues.

No person may use ova, sperm, zygotes or embryos for research, donation, maturation, fertilization, or implantation in a woman without express consent. This prohibition does not apply in respect of sperm for the purposes of identification or prosecution in relation to an offence under the *Criminal Code*. The Canadian government has introduced proposals[71] for the creation of a government agency that would report to the Ministry of Health to implement the regulatory regime recommended by the Commission. The function of the agency would be to develop standards for the use of reproductive materials in medical research and practice, issue licenses to permit such activities and ensure compliance with the standards. The proposals suggest there should be licensing of the following: in vitro fertilization; donor insemination; use of fetal tissue; storage, handling and donation of human eggs, sperm and embryos; embryo research; pre-implantation diagnosis and post-menopausal pregnancy.

---

[69]   *Ibid.*, p. 63.
[70]   Canada, Royal Commission on New Reproductive Technologies, *Proceed with Care: Final Report of the Royal* Commission *on New Reproductive Technologies* (Ottawa: Canada Communications Group, 1993).
[71]   Canada, Ministry of Health, *New Reproductive and Genetic Technologies: Setting Boundaries, Enhancing Health* (Minister of Supply and Services Canada, 1996).

Many hospitals have established research or ethics committees in their own facilities or in conjunction with an affiliated teaching institution. The role of these committees is increasingly important as technology continues to present new challenges to health practitioners.

ABORTION

There is an intricate link between abortion, health care and the Canadian legal system. In the early 1980s, more than 60,000 abortions were being performed in Canada every year.[72] Presently, many abortions are performed in hospitals, some in physicians' offices, some in the type of abortion clinic established by Dr. Henry Morgentaler, and others in less safe, more covert, locations. Abortion interacts with a number of corollary issues: women's rights, fetal status, reproductive technology, eugenics and others.

Until 1988,[73] performance of an abortion, except in circumstances provided by statute, constituted a criminal act. Section 287 of the *Criminal Code*,[74] enacted in 1969 by the federal government, preserved abortion as a criminal offence, liable to imprisonment, but not if performed by a qualified medical practitioner who performed the abortion in an approved or accredited hospital with the prior written consent of the hospital's therapeutic abortion committee once the committee had issued a certificate stating that the pregnancy would or would be likely to endanger the women's life or health.

Section 287 of the *Criminal Code* was the result of the government's stated policy of reducing government intrusion in the "bedrooms of the nation". Liberalization of abortion permitted legal access to abortions performed by competent medical practitioners at public health facilities, but at the same time, did not go so far as to permit pregnant women to have abortions "on demand". The thrust of the legislation was that abortions would only be legal in circumstances in which the woman's life or health was endangered.[75]

In 1973, Dr. Morgentaler advised a pro-abortion rally that he had performed more than 5,000 abortions since 1968. In May of the same year he performed an abortion on national television. His clinic was raided on August 15, 1973 after he had performed an abortion on a 26-year old graduate student. Morgentaler was charged with numerous criminal of-

---

[72] "Basic Facts on Therapeutic Abortions", *Statistics Canada*, 1983, Catalogue A2-211.
[73] *R. v. Morgentaler*, [1988] 1 S.C.R. 30, 44 D.L.R. (4th) 385, 37 C.C.C. (3d) 449, 62 C.R. (3d) 1.
[74] R.S.C. 1985, c. C-46.
[75] J.P. Maksymiuk, "The Abortion Law: A Study of *R. v. Morgentaler*" (1974), 39 Sask. L. Rev. 259.

fences.[76] It was alleged that Morgentaler had engaged in criminal activity by performing abortions without a certificate from a therapeutic abortion committee.

Morgentaler testified at trial that his initial discussions with the patient referred to her country of origin, her vocation, her marital status and why an abortion was necessary. He said that he assessed the necessity of an abortion by reference to her state of anxiety, her inability to eat or sleep properly and the consequent adverse effect upon her health. He considered that her determination to have an abortion might lead her to do something foolish. He was aware that his patient had approached a number of hospitals without success (although he did not know that she had been offered an appointment at a hospital in Montreal which would allow her case to be considered by that hospital's Therapeutic Abortion Committee in August, 1973, when she would be eight to 10 weeks pregnant). Morgentaler's counsel argued that he was entitled to rely upon the defence of necessity. Further, that a defence was provided by s. 45 of the *Criminal Code*, protecting a physician from criminal responsibility for a surgical operation if performed with reasonable care and skill, and it is reasonable to perform the operation, "having regard to the state of health of the person at the time the operation is performed and to all the circumstances of the case".[77] The jury accepted this defence and Morgentaler was acquitted. However, the Crown appealed to the Quebec Court of Appeal which ruled that the defences relied upon by Morgentaler at trial were not, as a matter of law, available to him and substituted a conviction. The decision of the Quebec Court of Appeal was upheld by the Supreme Court of Canada.[78]

Subsequently, another Quebec jury in another case acquitted Morgentaler based upon the defence of necessity. In that case, the Court of Appeal for Quebec upheld the decision[79] and leave to appeal to the Supreme Court of Canada was refused. In effect, despite the earlier decision of the Supreme Court, it was not prepared to hear a further appeal of a charge in which Morgentaler had been acquitted by a jury.

In 1983, Dr. Morgentaler and his associates were prosecuted again as a result of abortions performed at a Morgentaler clinic in Toronto. Again, Morgentaler was acquittted on the defence of necessity which led to an appeal to the Court of Appeal of Ontario, and subsequently, to the Supreme Court of Canada. In that case, the Ontario Court of Appeal had set aside the jury verdict on the ground that the defence of necessity was not

---

[76] *Ibid.*, at p. 269.

[77] *Criminal Code*, s. 45.

[78] *Morgentaler v. R.*, [1976] 1 S.C.R. 616, 53 D.L.R. (3d) 161, 4 N.R. 277, 30 C.R.N.S. 209, 20 C.C.C. (2d) 449.

[79] *R. v. Morgentaler* (1976), 64 D.L.R. (3d) 718, 33 C.R.N.S. 244, 27 C.C.C. (2d) 81 (Que. C.A.); leave to appeal to S.C.C. refd. 64 D.L.R. (3d) 718*n*.

available to Morgentaler on the facts of that case. The main thrust of Morgentaler's appeal to the Supreme Court of Canada was that the provisions of the *Criminal Code* which made non-therapeutic abortions illegal, were unconstitutional because they infringed the *Charter of Rights and Freedoms*. These provisions were said to violate s. 7 of the *Charter* which provides:

> Everyone has the right to life, liberty and security of the person and the right not to be deprived thereof except in accordance with the principles of fundamental justice.[80]

A majority of the court accepted this argument and ruled that s. 251 was inoperable. Some judges concluded that procedural requirements set out in s. 251 created a structure that was:

> . . . [m]anifestly unfair. It contains so many potential barriers to its own operation that the defence it creates will in many circumstances be practically unavailable . . .[81]

The court balanced the procedural obstacles contained in s. 251 against a woman's security of the person:

> Forcing a woman, by threat of criminal sanction, to carry a fetus to term unless she meets certain criteria unrelated to her own priorities and aspirations, is a profound interference with a woman's body and thus an infringement of security of the person.[82]

The court found that the legal mechanism chosen by the federal government to balance the rights of the pregnant woman with the "protection of the fetus" was disproportional, and therefore, inconsistent with the principles of fundamental justice.[83] The court found that the administrative *procedure* created by s. 287 operated in a way that was unfair, arbitrary and impaired more of the protected right than necessary.[84]

Justice Wilson wrote a separate judgment placing less emphasis on the procedural obstacles in s. 287, and more on what she perceived to be the substantive interference of s. 287 with a woman's right to liberty in the form of control over her own body. According to Wilson J., s. 287 of the *Criminal Code* resulted in the woman:

---

[80] The *Charter*, s. 7.
[81] *Supra*, note 73, at 72 S.C.R.
[82] *Ibid.*, at 56.
[83] *Ibid.* at 32 (headnote).
[84] M.L. McConnell, "Even by Commonsense Morality': *Morgentaler, Borowsky* and the Constitution of Canada" (1989), *Can. Bar Rev.* 766, at p. 774.

[b]eing treated as a means — a means to an end which she does not desire but over which she has no control. She is the passive recipient of a decision made by others ...

Justice Wilson also suggested:

[I]t is probably impossible for a man to respond, even imaginatively, to such a dilemma not just because it is outside the realm of his personal experience ... but because he can relate to it only by objectifying it, thereby eliminating the subjective elements of the female psyche which are at the heart of the dilemma.[85]

While Wilson J. expressed the view that the primary purpose of s. 287, protection of the fetus, was a "perfectly valid legislative objective",[86] she concluded that the framework was an unreasonable restriction on the woman's *Charter* rights. In the result s. 251 of the *Criminal Code* was ruled invalid.

Since the *Morgentaler* decision in 1988 there has been no legislation in Canada governing abortions. The activities of the therapeutic abortion committees no longer have any legal or statutory foundation.

The absence of legislation under the *Criminal Code* dealing directly with abortion did not prevent further litigation. In the summer of 1989, a male applicant brought an application for an injunction in a Quebec court to prevent a woman from having an abortion.[87] The man and woman had lived together as a couple for five months. There had been a break-up. The woman was pregnant and decided to obtain an abortion. The male applicant argued that the rights of the fetus were protected under the Quebec *Charter of Human Rights and Freedoms* which stated:

1.   Every human being has a right to life, and to personal security inviolability and freedom. He [or she] also possesses juridical personality.
2.   Every human being whose life is in peril has a right to assistance.
3.   Every person must come to the aid of anyone whose life is in peril, either personally or calling for aid, by giving him [or her] the necessary and immediate physical assistance, unless it involves danger to himself [herself] or a third person, or he [or she] has another valid reason.[88]

The application for the injunction was denied initially, but then granted on appeal by the Quebec Court of Appeal. This led to an expedited

[85]   *Supra*, note 73, 171 S.C.R.
[86]   *Supra*, note 73 at p. 181.
[87]   *Tremblay v. Daigle*, [1989] 2 S.C.R. 530, 62 D.L.R. (4th) 634, 102 N.R. 81.
[88]   R.S.Q. 1977, c. C-12, ss. 1 [am. 1982, c. 61, s. 1] and 2.

hearing before the Supreme Court of Canada. The Supreme Court of Canada, in overturning the Quebec Court of Appeal and ruling in favour of the female respondent, made it clear that the issue of whether or not the fetus was a "human being" under the legislation was, from the court's point of view, a legal question:

> The Court is not required to enter the philosophical and theological debates about whether or not a foetus is a person, but, rather, to answer the legal question of whether the Quebec legislature has accorded the foetus personhood. Metaphysical arguments may be relevant but they are not the primary focus of inquiry. Nor are scientific arguments about the biological status of a foetus determinative in our inquiry. The task of properly classifying a foetus in law and in science are different pursuits. Ascribing personhood to a foetus in law is a fundamentally normative task. It results in the recognition of rights and duties — a matter which falls outside the concerns of scientific classification. In short, this Court's task is a legal one. Decisions based upon broad social, political, moral and economic choices are more appropriately left to the legislature.[89]

In the end, the court was not persuaded that the Quebec legislature, in enacting the Quebec *Charter of Human Rights and Freedoms*, had *intended* the term "human being" to include a fetus. It concluded that it would be wrong to "interpret the vague provisions of the Quebec *Charter* as conferring legal personhood upon the foetus".[90]

The male applicant had also raised the argument of "fathers' rights" as a basis for the injunction. It was argued that his contribution to the act of conception gave him an equal say in what happened to the fetus. The Supreme Court responded:

> [T]here does not appear to be any jurisprudential basis for this argument. No court in Quebec or elsewhere has ever accepted the argument that a father's interest in a foetus which he helped to create could support a right to veto a woman's decisions in respect of the foetus she is carrying. A number of cases in various jurisdictions outside of Quebec have considered this argument and explicitly rejected it . . . We have been unable to find a single decision in Quebec or elsewhere which would support the allegation of a "father's rights" necessary to support this injunction. There is nothing in the *Civil Code* or any legislation in Quebec which could be used to support the argument. This lack of a legal basis is fatal to the argument about "father's rights".[91]

In the absence of any regulation of abortion at the federal level, the province of Nova Scotia passed, in 1989, a *Medical Services Act* which

---

[89] *Supra*, note 87 at 552-53 S.C.R.
[90] *Ibid.*, at 570 S.C.R.
[91] *Ibid.*, at 572 S.C.R.

prohibited the privatization of certain medical services in the province for the stated purpose of maintaining "a single high-quality health-care delivery system for all Nova Scotians."[92] The Act prohibited the performance or assistance in the performance of a designated medical act other than in an approved hospital. A number of medical services were designated by regulation, one of which is:

> Abortion, including a therapeutic abortion, but not including emergency services related to a spontaneous abortion or related to complications arising from a previously performed abortion.[93]

In other words, the Nova Scotia provincial government attempted to regulate abortion as a matter of public health law. However, in yet another case involving Henry Morgentaler, it has been held that the Nova Scotia legislation is *ultra vires* the provincial government, and therefore invalid, in that it attempts to regulate criminal law, an area of federal jurisdiction.[94]

Since then, legislation and corresponding litigation in this area has concentrated on abortion funding. In *Lexogest Inc. v. Manitoba (Attorney General)*,[95] a therapeutic abortion clinic challenged a regulation passed under that province's *Health Services Insurance Act*,[96] that excluded payment for therapeutic abortions unless they were performed by a medical practitioner in a hospital. The majority rejected arguments that the legislation contravened the *Charter* or that it was inconsistent with the *Canada Health Act*.[97] The court did rule, however, that the regulation was invalid as it was inconsistent with the intention of the *Health Services Insurance Act*, which did not authorize a regulation composing an increase in the cost of abortions for the tax paying public. Since such a regulation was not authorized by the statute, it was struck down. A subsequent case in Prince Edward Island had a similar result at trial but was reversed on appeal.[98]

HIV AND AIDS

Acquired immunodeficiency syndrome (AIDS), unrecognized by conventional medicine until a little over a decade ago, has provoked intense

---

[92] R.S.N.S. 1989, c. 281, s. 2.
[93] *Medical Services Designation Regulation*, N.S. Reg. 152/89, Sch. "A", (d).
[94] *Nova Scotia (A.G.) v. Morgentaler*, unreported [1990] N.S.J. No. 77 (S.C.).
[95] (1993), 85 Man. R. (2d) 8 (C.A.).
[96] R.S.M. 1987, c. H-35.
[97] R.S.C. 1985, c. C-6.
[98] *Morgentaler v. Prince Edward Island (Minister of Health & Social Services)* (1995), 126 Nfld. & P.E.I.R. 240 (P.E.I.T.D.), revd. (1996) 139 D.L.R. (4th) 603 (P.E.I. App. Div.).

scrutiny of patient rights and the obligations of health-care providers to patients who have been, or may become, victims of AIDS and other infectious diseases. AIDS has resulted in legislation in the area of infectious disease, protracted litigation, and a government condition to inquire into the safety of the blood system in Canada.[99]

1. Health Protection and Promotion Legislation

AIDS is reportable to public health authorities in all provinces and HIV infection is reportable in all provinces except Quebec, Alberta and British Columbia.[100] Failure to meet the legislative requirements may result in civil liability for the institution as well as its health practitioners. In Ontario, for example, the reporting of communicable diseases is governed by the *Health Protection and Promotion Act*.[101] AIDS, in the Ontario legislation, is both a communicable and a reportable disease. HIV, as an agent of AIDS, therefore, is also reportable. The report required must contain the name, address, date of birth, sex and date of onset of symptoms of the patient. Any person who fails to make a report as required by the legislation is guilty of an offence.[102]

It has been held that the protection of the public is more important than keeping the identity of HIV-infected blood donors secret.[103] The Canadian AIDS Society had sought an injunction to prevent public health officials from obtaining the names of 13 donors who had unknowingly donated contaminated blood. It was argued that disclosure would breach the donors' privacy rights and their rights under the *Charter*. However, the court ruled that the donors should be notified of their HIV status and their names reported to the Ministry of Health, pursuant to that province's health protection and promotion legislation.

2. Workplace Identification and Testing

The possible transmission of the HIV virus in the health-care setting has become a significant area of controversy as health facilities attempt to balance competing risks and obligations. The right of an AIDS patient to high quality, non-discriminatory treatment must be balanced against the risks to health practitioners and other patients. Similarly, a patient may wish to know whether he or she is being treated by an infected health-

---

[99] Commission of Inquiry on the Blood System in Canada, appointed by Order in Council P.C. 1993-1879.

[100] J. Hamblin and M.A. Somerville, "Surveillance and Reporting of HIV infection and AIDS in Canada: Ethics and Law" (1991), 41 U.T.L.J. 224.

[101] R.S.O. 1990, c. H.7.

[102] *Ibid.*, s. 100.

[103] *Canadian AIDS Society v. Ontario*, unreported August 4, 1995 (Ont. Gen. Div.).

care worker and whether that person's treatment puts the patient at risk. The Canadian Medical Association has recommended that health-care workers who are at risk of having contracted the HIV virus voluntarily seek counselling and HIV-antibody testing. Where a health-care worker has been infected, the health-care worker is encouraged to

> ...seek medical advice regarding the management of his or her condition, which should include a discussion of the current knowledge of risk of transmission in personal and professional life. Advice regarding occupational transmission risks could be sought from knowledgeable people such as staff responsible for Occupational Health and infectious disease epidemiology, or the Medical Officer of Health.[104]

The Center for Disease Control in Atlanta, Georgia has issued guidelines for HIV-infected health care workers:

> All HCWs [health care workers] should adhere to universal precautions in the health care setting, including use of protective barriers and the disinfection and sterilization of reusable devices used in invasive procedures.

> Currently available data provide no basis to restrict the practice of HCWs infected with HIV "who perform basic procedures not identified as exposure-prone".

> "Exposure-prone procedures should be identified by medical/surgical/dental organizations and institutions at which the procedures are performed".

> HCWs who perform exposure-prone procedures should know their HIV status.

> HIV-infected HCWs should not perform exposure-prone procedures "unless they have sought counsel from an expert review panel and have been advised under what circumstances, if any, they may continue to perform these procedures. Such circumstances would include notifying prospective patients of the HCWs seropositivity before they undergo exposure-prone invasive procedures".

> Mandatory testing of HCWs for HIV infection is not recommended. "The current assessment of the risk that infected health care workers will transmit HIV or HBV to patients during exposure-prone procedures does not support the diversion of resources that would be required to implement mandatory testing programs. Compliance by

---

[104] Canadian Medical Association, "CMA Draft Position Paper—HIV Infection in the Workplace", February 13, 1992, as cited in W. F. Flanagan, "AIDS-Related Risks in the Health Care Setting: HIV Testing of Health Care Workers and Patients" (1993), 18 Queen's L.J. 71, at 119-120.

health care workers with recommendations can be increased through education, training, and appropriate confidentiality safeguards".[105]

3. Liability for Transmission of the Aids Virus

The possibility of transmission of the HIV virus to patients and family members has given rise to intense and complex litigation. There are several reported cases in Canada in which health facilities and practioners have been required to defend allegations of negligence in apprising patients of the risk of AIDS transmission.

In *ter Neuzen v. Korn*,[106] a patient entered into an artificial insemination programme operated by a Vancouver obstetrician and gynecologist. She underwent 33 to 35 insemination procedures and became HIV-positive as a result of the last insemination procedure in 1985. The Supreme Court of Canada upheld the finding of the British Columbia Court of Appeal, which found that the risk of HIV infection from the artificial insemination technique employed by the physician in 1989 was not well-known in the medical community and that the physician's own practice complied with the general standards of his colleagues. The Supreme Court held that the conduct of physicians must be judged in the light of the knowledge that ought to have been reasonably possessed at the time of the alleged act of negligence. There was no basis to support the argument that, in Vancouver in 1985, a reasonably competent medical practitioner would have ceased to practice artificial insemination or would have warned patients of the danger of HIV transmission. The matter was sent back to be retried on the issue of whether the physician had failed to take reasonable steps to protect his patients against sexually transmitted diseases in the screening of donors.

In *Pittman v. Bain*,[107] the patient was infected with HIV by her husband, who was unaware that he had contracted the AIDS virus through a blood transfusion. Five years after the surgery, as part of a look-back programme at the hospital where the surgery took place, it was discovered that Mr. Pittman had received blood that was contaminated with HIV. The hospital notified Mr. Pittman's family physician. Because the family physician was concerned about Mr. Pittman's heart condition and mental health, he did not advise Mr. Pittman of his possible infection. When Mr. Pittman died approximately one year later, it was discovered that he had been HIV-positive. Several months later his wife tested positive for the AIDS virus.

---

[105] "Recommendations for Preventing Transmission of Human Immunodeficiency Virus and Hepatitis B Virus to Patients During Exposure-Prone Invasive Procedures" (1991), 40 N.M.W.R. RR-8, as cited in W. F. Flanagan, *ibid.* at 111.
[106] [1995] 10 W.W.R. 1 (S.C.C.).
[107] (1994), 112 D.L.R. (4th) 257 (Ont. Gen. Div.).

At trial, liability was found against the Canadian Red Cross Society, the hospital and the family physician. The trial judge found that the hospital and the Canadian Red Cross Society breached their duty to conduct an appropriate look-back programme. She concluded that the hospital was negligent in the implementation and design of its look-back programme. When it became apparent that it was going to take an unreasonably long time to achieve a need that was urgent, the hospital should have sought alternatives. Its failure to do so, and its failure to appreciate the serious threat caused by its delay, constituted negligence. The trial judge also concluded that both the Canadian Red Cross Society and the hospital were negligent in not ensuring that the family physician had sufficient information to enable him to give an adequate warning to Mr. Pittman. The family physician was also held negligent in withholding from Mr. Pittman the information that he had been transfused, in 1984, with a potentially HIV-contaminated blood component. Mrs. Pittman, her family and her husband's estate were awarded over $500,000 in damages.

4. The Future of Canada's Blood Supply

It is well known that thousands of Canadian have contracted HIV and hepatitis through tainted blood. The *Commission of Inquiry on the Blood System in Canada* ("Krever Commission") tabled its final report in the House of Commons on November 26, 1997. Based on the recommendations of the Krever Commission, the Canadian Blood Services assumed responsibility for the administration of the blood supply on September 28, 1998. Blood is viewed as a public resource, and the Canadian Blood Services acts as its trustee. The Canadian Blood Services' website address (www.bloodsystems.ca) provides a wealth of information on the current status of the blood system.

Given the unresolved debates over compensation for tainted blood, and the deaths that have occurred due to the public's reliance on a flawed system, it is no surprise that an alternative strategy has been devised to monitor the current blood supply.

TELEMEDICINE AND TELEHEALTH

This is a topic that could easily find its home in the chapters on professional status, professional discipline, malpractice, or employment law. Many Canadian provinces have developed, or are in the process of developing, systems of telehealth and telemedicine. The legal implications of providing these services (which may range from telephone advice to tele-triage) to recipients in one jurisdiction when they are licensed in another have not been resolved. It is not yet clear whether the same standard of care is created when a patient and provider do not meet face to face. Negligence and malpractice issues have not been tested in Canadian courts. It is simply the case that in most jurisdictions, the regulatory framework has not caught up to the new technology and realities of modern health care.

In the absence of absolute guidelines, nurses who engage in telemedicine and telehealth can expect that this area of health care will grow over the next years. There is no doubt that further directives from the federal and provincial governments, and professional licensing organizations, will be developed to assist health care providers practising in this relatively new area.

OTHER ISSUES

Canadian health practitioners are increasingly faced with complex challenges to their professional and ethical skills. Nurses work in increasingly computerized and technologically advanced settings where standard procedures may have to be radically adjusted. They are increasingly performing their duties in non-traditional settings, and the system that pays for many facets of health care is in a state of flux and reformation. It can only be hoped that an understanding of the legal implications of today's situation can be used to address tomorrow's issues.

Websites of Interest to Canadian Nurses

The Internet and the World Wide Web (WWW) hold a wealth of information for nurses. That information is constantly changing and developing, so please consider the following websites, listed in alphabetical order, as interesting starting points for your own searches. The following sites are Canadian, but a wide array of international sites can be found using any search engine (such as Yahoo!, Alta Vista, and Lycos).

Aboriginal Nurses Association of Canada:
    http://www.anac.on.ca

Alberta Association of Registered Nurses:
    http://www.nurses.ab.ca

British Columbia Nurses' Union:
    http://www.bcnu.org

Canadian Intravenous Nurses' Association:
    http://web.idirect.com/~csotcina/cina.html

Canadian Association of Critical Care Nurses:
    http://www.execulink.com/~caccn/

Canadian Association of Nurses in Independent Practice:
    http://www.websmart.com/canip/

Canadian Nurses' Association:
    http://www.cna-nurses.ca

Canadian Nurses' Foundation:
    http://www.can-nurses.ca/cnf

Canadian Nurses Protective Society:
    http://www.nanb.nb.ca/english/liabilit.html

Canadian Nurses' Respiratory Society:
    http://www.lung.ca/resp/info/news.html

Canadian Nursing Students' Association:
    http://www.cnsa.ca/

College of Nurses of Ontario:
    http://www.cno.org

Fédération des infirmières et infirmiers du Québec:
    http://www.fiiq.qc.ca

Health Canada:
    http://www.hc-sc.gc.ca

L'Ordre des infirmières et infirmiers du Québec:
    http://www.oiiq.org

Manitoba Association of Registered Nurses:
    http://www.marn.mb.ca

Manitoba Nurses' Union:
    http://www.nursesunion.mb.ca

New Brunswick Nurses' Union:
    http://www.nbnurses.nb.ca

Northern Nursing Network:
    http://www.geocities.com/Athens/Forum/5350

Northwest Territories Registered Nurses' Association:
    http://users.internorth.com/~nwtrna/

Nova Scotia Nurses' Union:
    http://fox.nstn.ca/~nsnu

NurseActive [Nova Scotia]:
    http://www3.ns.sympatico.ca/nurse.active/

Nursecom [British Columbia]:
    http://www.nursecom.com

Nurses Association of New Brunswick:
    http://www.nanb.ca

Nurses' Association of New Brunswick:
    http://www.nanb.nb.ca/
Ontario Nurses' Association:
    http://www.ona.org/

Organisation nationale des syndicats d'infirmiers libéraux:
    http://www.mygale.org/08/onsil

Registered Nurses' Association of British Columbia:
    http://www.rnabc.bc.ca/

Registered Nurses' Association of Nova Scotia:
    http://www.rnans.ns.ca/

Registered Nurses' Association of Ontario:
    http://www.rnao.org

Registered Psychiatric Nurses' Association of Manitoba:
    http://www.psychiatricnurses.mb.ca/rpnam/index.html

Saskatchewan Registered Nurses' Association:
    http://www.srna.org

Syndicat des infirmières et infirmiers de l'Est du Québec:
    http://www.fortune1000.ca/siieq/

United Nurses of Alberta:
    http://www.una.ab.ca

Urology Nurses of Canada:
    http://www.unc.org/

Victorian Order of Nurses:
    http://www.von.ca

Index

A

Abortion, 289-294
Accreditation. *See* Canadian Council on Health Services Accreditation (CCHA)
Advanced nursing practice
  clinical nurse specialist (CNS), 50
  midwives. *See* Midwifery
  nurse practitioner (NP), 50
  regulated health professions, 51
AIDS, 294-298
Alternative dispute resolution (ADR). *See* Malpractice
Alternative therapies, 74

B

Battery. *See* Consent to treatment
Blood supply, 298
Board of directors. *See* Health facilities, board of directors
Brain death, 281-282

C

Canadian Bill of Rights, 251
Canadian Blood Services, 298
Canadian Charter of Rights and Freedoms
  abortion laws, challenges *re*, 256, 289-294
  application of, 252
  cruel and unusual punishment
    death penalty, 263
    treatment of patients, 263
  democratic rights, 255
  equality rights, 263-265
  fundamental freedoms
    conscience and religion, 252
    expression, 253
    peaceful assembly/freedom of association
      anti-abortion picketing, 254
      privacy interest of physicians, 254-255
  legal rights
    arbitrary detention or imprisonment, 262
    blood samples, illegal taking of, 257-260
    liberty, 256
    mandatory retirement, 257
    mentally handicapped/psychiatric patients, 260-261
    police operations, 257-260
    right to counsel, 262
    right to life, 256
    right to medical care, extent of, 264-265
    right to refuse treatment, 261
    rights on being charged with offence, 262-263
    search and seizure, illegal, 262
    security of the person, 256-257
  minority rights, 265
  mobility rights, 256
  override power, use by Quebec, 266
  protection of fetus, 289-294
  reasonable limits on rights, 264-265
  residency requirements, 256
  substitute decision-making provisions 143
Canadian Council on Health Services Accreditation (CCHA)
  composition, 10
  standards for accreditation, 10-11
Charter. *See* Canadian Charter of Rights and Freedoms
Children. *See* Consent to Treatment
Collective bargaining. *See* Labour relations
Competency. *See* Consent to treatment; Mental health
Complaints. *See* Discipline
Computerization. *See* Health records; Websites
  health reform, 12
  telemedicine/telehealth, 12, 298-299
Confidentiality. *See* Health Records
Consent to treatment
  advance instructions/directives, 140-141, 144
  battery
    consent obtained through intimidation/duress, 136-137
    damages, 136-137
    described, 136
  capacity/competence to consent
    common law presumption, 142
    Health Care Consent Act, 1996 (Ont.), 135-136, 142
  children, 142-145
  consent forms
    performer of procedure, identity of, 146-147
    statutory requirements *re*, 146
    witnessing, 147
  delegation of consent, 146
  emergency care